A LANDMARK IN SEX RESEARCH, WHERE EVEN FREUD AND KINSEY HAVE NOT VENTURED. . . .

Ruth and Edward Brecher, the outstanding husband-and-wife science writers, give the inside story of the entire Masters-Johnson research operation. They describe in concrete terms just how it was carried out, who volunteered and why, how these ordinary citizens, including 274 married couples engaged in sexual intercourse as part of one of the boldest laboratory studies in human history.

The Brechers interpret the extraordinary facts discovered by recording for the first time the responses of 382 women and 312 men during sexual activity.

They describe findings of enormous importance to the understanding of

- *male and female orgasm*
- *frigidity and impotence*
- *contraception*
- *sterility*
- *sex during pregnancy*
- *sex in the later years*

They report on evidence that explodes many long-held fallacies and fantasies about human sexual response.

Leading experts in the field of sexual research report on their own work, with comment on this monumental project that reveals its impact on psychiatry, its practical application in marriage counseling and sex education, its cultural significance.

The result is an explicit, easily understood description of the Masters-Johnson work and an important roundup of related research rarely available outside the closed circuit of medical journals.

Other SIGNET Marriage Manuals

An Analysis of

HUMAN SEXUAL RESPONSE

Edited by
RUTH AND EDWARD BRECHER

A SIGNET BOOK from
NEW AMERICAN LIBRARY
TIMES MIRROR

ACKNOWLEDGMENTS AND COPYRIGHT NOTICES

The editors wish to thank the following for permission to reprint, in whole or part, the articles listed:

Basic Books, Inc., New York, for "I'm Sorry, Dear," from *The Ways of the Will,* by Leslie H. Farber. Copyright © 1966 by Leslie H. Farber, Basic Books, Inc., Publishers.

Emerson Books, Inc., New York, for "Sex Problems in Marriage Counseling," by Emily H. Mudd and Katherine von Minckwitz. Copyright © 1966 by Emerson Books, Inc.

The New York Times, New York, for "Current Sexual Behavior and Attitudes," by John Corry. Copyright © 1966 by The New York Times Company.

John Wiley & Sons, Inc., New York, for "Sexual Patterns in a Southwest Pacific Society," from *Sex & Behavior,* edited by Frank A. Beach. Copyright © 1965 by John Wiley & Sons.

The Williams & Wilkins Company, Baltimore, Maryland, for "Counseling with Sexually Incompatible Marriage Partners," by William H. Masters and Virginia E. Johnson, from *Counseling in Marital and Sexual Problems,* edited by Richard H. Klemer, M.D. Copyright © 1965, The Williams & Wilkins Company.

This book will state many things that would otherwise remain unsaid. Therefore it will have many unpleasant results for me. I know this, for I have gradually attained to some knowledge of my fellow human beings and of their habit of condemning what is unusual and unconventional. . . .

But . . . I must write down what I have learned to be true and right; I could not face the evening of my life with a quiet conscience if I omitted to do so. There is need of this knowledge; there is too much suffering endured which might well be avoided, too much joy untasted which could enhance life's worth.

Theodoor Hendrik Van de Velde
"Personal Introductory Statement"
Ideal Marriage (1930)

Contents

Contents

Contents

INTRODUCTION

This book is designed to bring to lay readers, in convenient form and in nontechnical language, the latest sex research findings from the physiological laboratory and from other sources.

Part I of this book presents the laboratory observations of human sexual responses by Dr. William H. Masters and Mrs. Virginia E. Johnson of the Reproductive Biology Research Foundation in St. Louis.

Part II presents other recent and current sex research projects.

In Part III, a panel of outstanding experts considers the practical applications of sex research in the treatment of patients by psychiatrists and other physicians, in marriage counseling, in sex education, and in other fields. Part III includes a chapter by Masters and Johnson on their own therapeutic work with patients suffering from sexual inadequacies, and on their counseling of sexually incompatible marriage partners—as well as an important chapter on "Sex After Forty—And After Seventy."

Finally, Part IV contains two essays selected by the staff of The New American Library—one of them concerned with the cultural implications of the Masters-Johnson findings, and the other reporting on current American sexual attitudes and behavior.

The U.S. Census Bureau reports nearly ninety million married men and women in the United States. In addition, of course, a large but unknown number are participating in liaisons—permanent or temporary, premarital, extramarital, or postmarital. The relevance of this book, and of the sex research it describes, will no doubt vary widely from couple to couple.

Some couples have no need for the findings of sex research. They just seem to click. They love one another. They find fulfillment in their sexual relations, and mutual delight in their children, their careers, their friends, their possessions, and other aspects of their lives together. Unburdened by feelings of guilt from the past, current anxieties, or fears for the future, they experience no conflicts between their sexual activities and their other human enjoyments or their "higher" aspirations; indeed, they make no sharp distinctions between them. Their blissful state may endure throughout their lives or may terminate earlier. While it lasts, let us call them, as does Professor Abraham Maslow, "the happy ones."

This book is not primarily addressed to them.

A second group might be called "the resigned ones." These couples may face frustrations and disappointments in their relationships, including their sexual relationships, but they have settled for what they have. If sex is unsatisfactory they may abandon it altogether or may engage in it without joy on rare occasions. In the nonsexual aspects of their lives, too, they may choose to accept their lot with resignation. Their lives are characterized, in Van de Velde's phrase, by "too much joy untasted which could enhance life's worth."

Their interest in sex research may be limited, yet this book, with the insights it can provide, may have much to offer them.

Finally, there are "the troubled ones"—the couples whose relationship is weighed down by woes. Physical illness, financial pressures, disparate tastes and clashing temperaments, unwanted pregnancies or pregnancies longed for but unattained —these are examples of what can and often does go wrong. Guilt, anxiety, and fear—along with recriminations and jealousies—may enter to make matters worse.

These troubled couples are legion, and their situation is often desperate. The number of American divorces and annulments each year is about one quarter the number of marriages; many other marriages end in psychological and sexual estrangement though the façade of the marriage is maintained. And the blight rate for nonmarital liaisons, though never adequately studied, is no doubt at least equally high.

In some of these cases, perhaps, sexual incompatibilities and inadequacies play no role whatever. For such couples, this book and the sex research it describes have little relevance. In the vast majority of cases, however, sexual concerns do either play the major role in marital discontent or contribute substantially to it. At the very least, sex fails to play a potentially constructive role that might favorably alter the marital balance sheet.

It is with these couples that much sex research, and this book, are primarily concerned.

A sexual relationship between a man and a woman can have deep psychological overtones. Poets and novelists have portrayed these emotional factors in all their richness, so that almost all of us are aware of the psychological interplay of love and affection, ego satisfaction, the need for security and the fascination of novelty, the pleasures of mutual esteem, the delights of mutual play, the joy of giving and receiving. The thesis of this book is that there are also rich *physiological* overtones; and that an awareness of bodily responses can contribute much to human sexual satisfactions. Both the psychological and physiological have their role in human relationships. Both are essential to mature sexuality. This book, however, is for the most part concerned with the physiological aspect of sexual response.

Substantial portions are concerned with sexual orgasm—especially female orgasm. Unsophisticated readers may therefore leap to the mistaken conclusion that orgasm is the be-all and end-all of sexual response. This is not our personal view, nor is it the view of Dr. Masters or Mrs. Johnson, nor of the other contributors to this book. Rather, we see orgasm, for women as for men, as an essential physiological phase of human response to sexual stimulation. Without it, the experience is impoverished. With it, the entire experience from the first stirrings of desire to ultimate satisfaction and resolution can be enjoyed in all its richness. Emphasis on female orgasm is warranted by the fact that its absence so frequently sets a limit to human experience. Once that limit is overcome, the whole transcendent experience with all of its psychological and physiological overtones can follow. For much the same reason, several of the chapters describe and discuss the occurrence of multiple orgasms in women—orgasms that follow one another in rapid succession during a single sexual encounter.

We have no doubt that some women can and do enjoy a sexual relationship without experiencing orgasm. But we are aware of no accounts of women who, once they have learned to experience it, prefer the sexual experience without its physiological climax.

No book, of course, can solve a couple's sexual problems. This book does not even try. Yet it is equally true that many books have had a transforming influence on the lives of their readers. Speaking for ourselves, as a married couple, we can recall at least four that have profoundly altered our own views on sexuality, and have thereby also altered the sexual aspects of our lives together. Our own marriage today is different from our marriage of a quarter of a century ago, primarily because of our experience in the interim; but the books we have read together are a significant part of that expanding mutual experience. This one is offered in the hope that it will play a similarly significant role in the experience of other couples.

We are most grateful to The Williams & Wilkins Company of Baltimore, Maryland, for permission to use two of the superb drawings of the late Robert L. Dickinson, M.D.[1] We wish also to thank Dr. John H. Talbott, editor of the *Journal of the American Medical Association*, for permission to quote from an editorial prepared by Dr. Charles G. Roland, which appeared in the issue of July 18, 1966.

We gratefully acknowledge the help of many people in bringing this book together, including Jean Read of The New American Library, our son Jeremy Brecher, and our secretary, Marion Burke; their working hours, like ours, have included nights and weekends. But our chief indebtedness is to Dr. William H. Masters and Mrs. Virginia E. Johnson, to the other contributors to this book listed in the table of contents, and to the 694 participants in the Masters-Johnson research project, whose names we do not know, but whose contributions to scientific knowledge and to human welfare should earn for them the gratitude of all who value human sexuality.

Ruth and Edward Brecher
West Cornwall, Connecticut

These drawings originally appeared in *Human Sex Anatomy* by Robert L. Dickinson. Baltimore: The Williams & Wilkins Company, 1949. Copyright © 1949 by The Williams & Wilkins Company.

Part I

THE WORK OF
MASTERS AND JOHNSON

Ruth and Edward Brecher

SEX IN THE LABORATORY

On April 10 and 11, 1959, a two-day "Conference on the Vagina" was held in New York City under the auspices of the venerable New York Academy of Sciences. Among the forty-four participants were many noted scientists; but by far the most astonishing paper was delivered in matter-of-fact tones by Dr. William H. Masters, associate professor of obstetrics and gynecology at the Washington University School of Medicine in St. Louis.

For several years, Dr. Masters told his fellow scientists, he had been studying in the laboratory the way in which the human body responds to effective sexual stimulation. Volunteers—most of them married couples—came to his laboratory at specified times, and engaged in specified sexual activities in specified ways while Dr. Masters and his research associate, Mrs. Virginia E. Johnson, observed and measured the physiological changes that occurred. Dr. Masters then proceeded to describe some of the changes occurring inside the human vagina during both masturbation and sexual intercourse.

The delivery of this paper, curiously enough, stirred up no interest whatever outside of strictly scientific circles; neither did its publication in the *Annals of the New York Academy of Sciences* for November 18, 1959.

During the next six years, from 1960 through 1965, a stream of additional papers emerged from the Masters-Johnson laboratory. These reported on the detailed physiological responses of 382 women and 312 men during more than ten thousand cycles of sexual excitation, orgasm, and return to an unexcited state. The papers were based on observations made not only during masturbation and sexual intercourse, but also during "artificial coition"—a laboratory procedure that makes accessible to direct vision, and to recording on motion-picture film, internal changes observable in no other way (see below, pages 69, 83, 97, 100–101). In some cases, too, female orgasms were observed following breast stimulation alone, without any genital contact.

Some of the papers describing the results of these observations were published in professional journals. Some appeared in medical textbooks and scientific symposium volumes (for a list, see page 311). Yet these papers, too, attracted very little attention outside of strictly medical and scientific circles.

Then, in April 1966, Dr. Masters and Mrs. Johnson published their first book-length report on their findings, entitled *Human Sexual Response*.[1] Despite the fact that it was a medical book, couched in highly technical language for physicians and other professionals, it promptly became a nationwide best-seller. It answered many questions lay readers wanted answered—but it left the answers to others in doubt.

In the pages that follow, we shall endeavor to answer as many as possible of these additional questions—and to present the Masters-Johnson findings in language as simple as the complex nature of human sexual response will permit.

WHAT THE LABORATORY STUDIES REVEALED: THE FOUR PHASES OF SEXUAL RESPONSE

The sexual responses of the human body, Dr. Masters' and Mrs. Johnson's observations indicate, begin in both men and women with some sexually arousing stimulus, proceed through orgasm, and end with a return of the body to a sexually unstimulated state. They describe the "response cycle" in terms of four phases: the *excitement* phase, the *plateau* phase, the *orgasmic* phase or orgasm, and the *resolution* or recovery phase.

The Excitement Phase

The very first sign of sexual arousal in men, of course, is erection of the penis—a marked increase in its size, and a rise in its angle of protrusion from the body. Erection may be triggered by stimulation of the penis itself or by a sexually

[1] Boston: Little, Brown and Company.

stimulating sight or by an erotic train of thought. It occurs within a few seconds, regardless of the nature of the stimulation.

During erection, Dr. Masters and Mrs. Johnson have found, a small penis may double or more than double in length. In a large penis, the lengthening is less marked. Thus there is less variation in length among erect than among flaccid penises.

Erection is due to the engorgement of the penis with blood; indeed, as we shall see, many of the most important sexual responses occurring in both men and women are the direct result of this kind of engorgement. More blood flows into an organ than flows out of it; the result is engorgement or *vasocongestion.* Dr. Masters and Mrs. Johnson call this change in blood supply, occurring not only in the penis but also in other male and female organs, "the primary reaction to sexual stimuli." The secondary reaction is a contraction of various muscle fibers, muscles, and groups of muscles.

The first sign of sexual response in women may seem to be different from either engorgement or muscular contraction; it is the moistening of the vagina with a lubricating fluid. This lubrication occurs quite promptly—within ten to thirty seconds of the onset of sexual stimulation. The lubrication appears with equal promptness whether the stimulus is direct stimulation of a woman's genital region, or of her breasts, or is an erotic train of thought.

"Identification of the vagina's lubricating mechanism has been one of the most interesting aspects of the anatomic study of the human female's sexual response cycle," Dr. Masters and Mrs. Johnson report. Some earlier investigators had believed that the fluid comes down into the vagina from the uterus, through the cervix. During many hundreds of observations inside the vagina, however, Dr. Masters and Mrs. Johnson observed a little fluid trickling down through the cervix on only one occasion—and this occurred late in the response cycle, after the vagina was already fully lubricated from some other source. They also observed full vaginal lubrication among women who had had complete hysterectomies, and who therefore possessed neither a uterus nor a cervix. Thus the uterus could be ruled out as a source of vaginal lubrication.

Another theory held prior to the Masters-Johnson research attributed vaginal lubrication to a pair of glands, known as Bartholin's glands, imbedded in the inner lips (minor labia) at the entrance to the vagina. This theory proved to be not entirely mistaken. Bartholin's glands, Dr. Masters and Mrs.

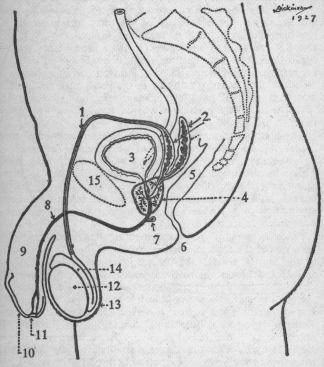

MALE PELVIS (Standing)

1. Vas deferens
2. Seminal vesicles
3. Urinary bladder
4. Prostate Gland
5. Rectum
6. Anus
7. Cowper's glands
8. Urethra
9. Penis
10. Foreskin
11. Entrance to urethra (meatus)
12. Testicle
13. Scrotum
14. Epididymis
15. Pubis

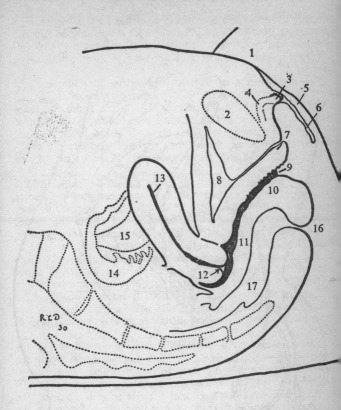

FEMALE PELVIS (Lying down)

1. Mons veneris
2. Pubis (bone)
3. Glans of clitoris
4. Shaft of clitoris
5. Outer lips (major labia)
6. Inner lips (minor labia)
7. Entrance to urethra
   (meatus)
8. Bladder
9. Entrance to vagina
10. Outer third of vagina
11. Inner two-thirds of
    vagina
12. Cervix
13. Uterus
14. Fallopian tube
15. Ovary
16. Anus

17. Rectum

Johnson observed, do sometimes contribute a few drops of a lubricating fluid to the vaginal entrance—but only late in the response cycle, following prolonged sexual activity and following copious lubrication of the vagina from some other source.

The true source of vaginal lubrication, Dr. Masters and Mrs. Johnson discovered, is a "sweating reaction" occurring on the walls of the vagina. Beads of moisture appear on these walls much as beads of sweat appear on the forehead—despite the fact that there are no sweat glands in the vagina. As sexual excitation continues, these drops coalesce to provide a lubricating film, readying the vagina for the entrance of the penis.

To lay readers, the increase in the size of the penis and the "sweating" of the vaginal walls may seem completely different responses; but Dr. Masters and Mrs. Johnson suggest that they may have a common cause. More blood enters the tissues around the vagina than can leave, producing vasocongestion. Both the walls of the smaller blood vessels and the walls of the vagina are "semipermeable membranes"; they hold fluids back under some conditions but let them seep through under others. The droplets of moisture that appear on the surface of the vagina during sexual excitation, it seems probable, have seeped out of the congested blood vessels. Thus engorgement with blood is the cause of both the male erection and vaginal lubrication.

The appearance of vaginal lubrication very early in the female response cycle is a point that deserves stress. Some sex manuals state, and some men no doubt believe, that the appearance of vaginal lubrication signals a woman's readiness to engage in sexual intercourse. This is true in a sense. The woman is *beginning* to respond, and lubrication does ready the vagina for the entrance of the penis. Entry prior to the appearance of adequate lubrication can be difficult and uncomfortable, or even painful. But, as we shall see, many more changes must follow before a woman is fully aroused erotically and ready for orgasm. Important changes occur, for example, in the clitoris.

This organ is located just above the entrance to the vagina. Like the penis, it is a shaft with a bulb or "glans" at the tip. Both the shaft and the glans vary in size from woman to woman. The shaft is sometimes described as being about as big around as a lead pencil and less than an inch long, with the glans at its tip a little smaller than a green pea—but in some women both glans and shaft are somewhat smaller, and in some they are two or three times that large. The size an location of the clitoris, Dr. Masters and Mrs. Johnson ha found, bear no relation whatever to a woman's sexual respon siveness or to her ability to achieve orgasm.

The glans of the clitoris is packed with sensitive nerve en ings. The stimulation of the glans thus contributes greatly heightening a woman's sexual response. Dr. Masters and Mr Johnson note, however, that direct contact with the clitoris *not* necessary in order to stimulate it. The glans is covere with a hood or prepuce; and this hood is attached to th inner lips (minor labia) of the vagina. Thus during ordinar sexual intercourse the rhythmic thrusting of the penis throug the inner lips produces a rhythmic friction between the clitor hood and the glans (see below, page 84).

In addition, the clitoris is responsive to purely psychologic stimuli, such as an erotic train of thought. In the labor tory, changes in the clitoris can be directly observed durin purely psychological stimulation, even though the clitor and other genital organs remain untouched. Changes in th clitoris can also be observed following stimulation of th breasts.

The first of these changes is the swelling of the clitor glans. In some women on some occasions, the glans ma actually double in size. In other women, the swelling may l so slight that it can only be observed with the help of th culdoscope, a device which enlarges the object viewed by for diameters or so. The amount of swelling, however—like th size and location of the clitoris—is not related to either sexu responsiveness or to ability to achieve orgasm. The swelli of the glans of the clitoris, like the swelling of the glans the penis, is no doubt the result of engorgement of the bloo vessels inside it.

Simultaneously with the swelling of the clitoral glans, th clitoral shaft also increases in diameter.

The time at which these changes occur depends upon th nature of the sexual stimulation to which the woman is r sponding. If her *mons veneris*—that is, the area surroundi her clitoris—is being stimulated directly, the engorgement the clitoral glans and shaft may occur quite promptly after th appearance of vaginal lubrication. If the stimulus is brea manipulation or an erotic train of thought, the clitoral r sponse generally takes somewhat longer.

A series of changes also occurs in the female breasts du ing this initial or "excitement phase" of erotic response. T first of these changes is an erection of the nipples. This ere tion is caused by contraction of muscle fibers. Often one nipple erects first and the other follows immediately, or after a considerable delay. In addition, the nipples increase both in length and in diameter as a result of blood-vessel engorgement similar to the engorgement of the penis and clitoris. The pattern of veins ordinarily visible on the surface of the breasts becomes more distinct, and veins previously invisible may make their appearance during this engorgement process.

The female breasts also increase in size late in the excitement phase; this is a sign of heightened sexual tension preliminary to the transition to the next phase of sexual response. The swelling of the breasts is more noticeable in women who have not breast-fed babies. Late in the excitement phase, too, the areolas—that is, the rings of darker skin surrounding the nipples—become engorged and swell.

Response of the male breast is less consistent. However, at least partial nipple erection was observed in three-fifths of the men participating in the Masters-Johnson studies. It generally occurred late in the excitement phase.

The outer lips (major labia) at the entrance to the vagina respond in several ways during the excitement phase. In an unexcited state, they generally meet in the midline of the vagina, protecting the inner lips and the other structures within. During excitation they open a bit, and may be displaced a bit upward, toward the clitoris. These changes are likely to occur quite late in the excitement phase. In women who have not had a baby, the outer lips also thin out and flatten themselves against the surrounding tissues.

In women who have had several babies, and especially in those who have developed varicose veins in their outer lips, the outer lips become noticeably distended and engorged with blood instead of flattening. In extreme cases there may be a twofold or even threefold increase in size, so that the outer lips come to resemble a sort of curtain surrounding the vaginal opening. In these cases, too, the lips tend to open outward toward the sides as erotic tension increases, so that they do not interfere with the entry of the penis.

The inner lips (minor labia) also tend to swell during the excitement phase; indeed, it may be the swelling of the inner lips that produces the opening-out of the outer lips, as an invitation for the entry of the penis.

The vagina, too, responds. It can be thought of as a cylinder or "barrel," which remains in a collapsed state in the absence of erotic stimulation. The Masters-Johnson studies have established that the outer third of this barrel reacts in one way and the inner two-thirds in a very different way during the successive phases of sexual response. As sexual tension mounts during the excitement phase, the inner two-thirds of the vaginal barrel begins to expand, and then relaxes again. "Slowly the demand to expand overcomes the tendency to relax, and the clinically distended vaginal barrel of the sexually responding woman is established," Dr. Masters and Mrs. Johnson report.

The cervix and uterus are pulled up and back at about this time, producing a "tenting" of the vaginal walls surrounding the cervix. The net result of these and other changes is a dramatic "ballooning" of the inner two-thirds of the vagina. The diameter at the widest point of the ballooning may be three times the diameter of the erotically unstimulated vagina; and the total length of the vaginal barrel may be increased as much as a full inch. (The swelling of the inner lips of the vagina also contributes to this lengthening.) The ballooning is accompanied by a change in the appearance of the vaginal walls; the wrinkles, or "rugae," are smoothed out and the color of the walls changes from a normal purplish red to a darker purple, indicating engorgement of the surrounding blood vessels.

In addition to these responses in the sex organs and breasts, there are many indications that the entire body, in both women and men, is participating in this gradual process of sexual arousal. In both women and men, the voluntary muscles tend to tense up, and there may also be some contraction of groups of involuntary muscles. The pulse rate speeds up, and the blood pressure rises. Most remarkable of all, perhaps, a "sex flush" often appears upon the skin.

This sex flush appears first on the upper portion of the abdomen, then spreads up over the breasts. It often takes the form of a measles-like rash. The time of appearance is variable. In most men, and in some women, it does not appear until later in the response cycle, and in some it does not appear at all. But about three-quarters of the women, and one-quarter of the men, exhibited the sex flush prior to orgasm on at least some occasions in the Masters-Johnson laboratory.

Changes are also noted in the male testes and scrotum during this first phase of sexual response. There is a tensing and thickening of the skin of the scrotum; and the whole scrotal sac is elevated and flattened toward the body. The spermatic cords, by which the testes are suspended, shorten, so that the testes are pulled farther up in the sac. Just as the nipple of one breast often becomes erected before the other, so one of the testes often rises before the other.

Such clues as these may later prove helpful in solving the physiological mystery of *why* these changes occur in the way they do, and at the times they do.

The Plateau Phase

Dr. Masters and Mrs. Johnson have made it clear that they divide human sexual responses into four phases—*excitement, plateau, orgasmic,* and *resolution*—for reasons of convenience. There is no sharply defined moment in time when one phase ends and the next begins—and this is particularly true of the relatively vague boundary which separates the excitement from the plateau phase.

In the male full erection of the penis is ordinarily completed during the excitement phase. The only additional changes in the penis during the plateau phase are a slight increase in diameter of the "coronal ridge" at the base of the glans of the penis; and in some men on some occasions, a deepening of the reddish-purple color of the glans.

The testes increase in diameter about 50 percent over their unstimulated size; and they are pulled up even higher into the scrotum by a further shortening of the spermatic cords. Indeed, the full elevation of the testes is a sign that a man has reached the "point of no return," and that his orgasm is imminent. If the man's nipples did not erect earlier, they may erect now.

In both men and women, the rate of breathing increases during the plateau phase, and there is a further increase in pulse rate and blood pressure. The sex flush may now appear, or may become more marked and widespread if it appeared earlier. The tension of both voluntary and involuntary muscles is heightened; and there may be almost spastic contractions of some sets of muscles in the face, ribs, and abdomen. The sphincter muscle, which holds the rectum closed, may tighten up; indeed, some men and women tighten up both this muscle and the muscles of the buttocks as a deliberate means of heightening tension.

In the female breasts, there is a further swelling of the areolas surrounding the nipples. This is often so marked as partially to mask the erection of the nipples; they may look shorter as a result. But in fact, there may be a further swelling of the nipples under the areolar mask.

If coitus is prolonged, a few drops of moisture may emerge from the Bartholin's glands imbedded in the woman's outer lips, as noted above. A few drops of moisture may also emerge from the male urethra. This fluid probably comes from Cowper's glands—the male equivalent of the female Bartholin's glands. The fluid is not semen; but it is important to know that large numbers of active sperm cells are sometimes found in it. Thus there is at least a possibility that a woman may become pregnant following the secretion of these preliminary droplets—even though the man withdraws his penis before semen is actively ejaculated. A man who does not ordinarily emit this preliminary fluid, moreover, may do so on some occasions.

The most dramatic change in women during the plateau phase is the appearance of what Dr. Masters and Mrs. Johnson call "the orgasmic platform." This is the engorgement and swelling of the tissues surrounding the outer third of the vagina. As a result of this swelling, the diameter of the outer third is reduced by as much as 50 percent. It thus actually grips the penis, and the erotic stimulus experienced by the man is notably increased. The appearance of the orgasmic platform, however, does not necessarily mean that a woman is ready for orgasm.

Accompanying the appearance of the orgasmic platform is a further elevation of the uterus, and a further ballooning of the inner two-thirds of the vagina.

The uterus also becomes enlarged during this phase; it may even double in size in women who have had babies. Among women who have not had babies, the size increase is less impressive, but it is noticeable in many cases.

Another dramatic change during the plateau phase is the elevation of the clitoris. In the process of elevation, the clitoris rises from its normal position overhanging the pubic bone, and seems to become retracted. It is drawn further away from the vaginal entrance. The clitoral shaft is shortened by as much as 50 percent following elevation, and it may seem to be lost altogether, or harder to find. It continues to respond to stimulation, however, either directly applied to the *mons veneris,* or indirectly through the thrusting of the penis into the vagina.

The outer lips of the vagina of women who have had babies may become even more engorged during the plateau phase than during the excitement phase; and even in women who have never had a child there may be some swelling of the outer lips if erotic stimulation has been prolonged.

The inner lips change color late in the plateau phase, from bright red to a deep wine color in women who have had children, and from pink to bright red in women who have not. This color change is important, for it is a sure sign that orgasm will occur—usually within a minute or a minute and a half—if effective erotic stimulation is continued. On occasions when a woman fails to reach orgasm despite prolonged stimulation, she also fails to show this telltale color change of the inner lips.

While these many changes, occurring in many parts of both male and female bodies, may seem complex and different from one another, all or almost all of them, as noted earlier, seem to fall into two main classes: the engorgement of blood vessels and other organs, and increases in muscle tension. Both the male and female achieve readiness for orgasm, it seems likely, when these two processes of increased engorgement with blood and increased muscular tension reach adequate peaks. As Dr. Masters and Mrs. Johnson once described it, the plateau phase is the period during which "the female gathers psychological and physiological strength from the stockpile of mounting sexual tension, until she can direct all her physical and mental forces toward a leap into the third, or orgasmic phase of sexual tension expression."

The Orgasm

The major observable feature of the female orgasm is a series of rhythmic contractions of the orgasmic platform— that is, of the outer third of the vaginal barrel and the engorged tissues surrounding it. These rhythmic contractions are muscular contractions.

The first few contractions occur at intervals of four-fifths of a second. Thereafter the intervals tend to become longer, and the intensity of the contractions tends to taper off.

A mild orgasm may be accompanied by only three to five contractions, an intense orgasm by eight to twelve. In an extreme case, actually recorded on an automatic recording drum in the laboratory, twenty-five rhythmically recurring contractions of the orgasmic platform followed one another over a period of forty-three seconds.

The onset of orgasm as experienced subjectively occurs simultaneously with an initial *spasm* of the orgasmic platform preceding the rhythmic train of contractions by a few seconds.

Along with this series of contractions of the orgasmic platform, the uterus also contracts rhythmically. Each contraction begins at the upper end of the uterus and moves like a wave through the midzone and down to the lower or cervical end. The more intense the orgasm, the more severe are these contractions of the uterus. Labor contractions prior to childbirth move similarly downward along the uterus in a wavelike progression, but are much stronger.

Other muscles, such as the anal sphincter muscle, may also undergo rhythmic contractions.

The male orgasm is rather similar in several respects. The central occurrence is a series of rhythmic contractions timed, as in the female, at intervals of four-fifths of a second. Following the first few contractions, in the man as in the woman, the intervals between contractions tend to become longer and the intensity of the contractions tapers off. As in the case of women, men may subjectively identify the onset of orgasm a few seconds before the occurrence of the first observable contraction.

The ejaculation of semen, which occurs during the male orgasm, is a complex process. Prior to orgasm, fluid containing millions of sperm cells from the testes has collected in the sacs known as seminal vesicles and in a pair of flasklike containers known as ampullae. These organs contract rhythmically, expelling their contents into the urethra. At the same time the prostate gland contracts rhythmically and expels prostatic fluid into the urethra. A bulb in the urethra near the base of the penis doubles or triples in size to receive the fluids. These changes constitute the first stage of ejaculation. The subjective *feeling* of orgasm occurs during this first stage.

During the second stage, a series of rhythmic contractions of the urethral bulb and of the penis itself projects the semen outward under great pressure, so that if it is not contained, the semen may shoot as much as two feet beyond the tip of of the penis. In older men, the contractions may be somewhat less vigorous, and the pressure of expulsion somewhat lessened. The urethra may undergo a series of minor contractions for several seconds after the contractions of the penis as a whole are no longer perceptible.

In both men and women, the events occurring in the genital organs during orgasm are accompanied by changes in the rest of the body. Pulse rate, blood pressure, and breathing rate reach a peak. The sex flush is most pronounced. And muscles throughout the body respond in various ways.

The face, for example, may be contorted into a grimace

through the tightening of muscle groups. The muscles of the neck and long muscles of the arms and legs usually contract in a spasm. The muscles of the abdomen and buttocks are also often contracted. Of special interest are the reactions of the hands and feet. Often a man or woman grasps his partner firmly during orgasm; the hand muscles then clench vigorously. If the hands are not being used in grasping, a spastic contraction of both hands and feet known as "carpopedal spasm" can be observed. Men and women are usually quite unaware of these extreme muscular exertions during orgasm; but it is not unusual for them to experience muscle aches in the back, thighs, or elsewhere the next day as a result.

The Resolution Phase

One major function of the orgasm becomes clearly visible in both men and women soon after it subsides. Orgasm initiates the release of muscular tensions throughout the body, and initiates the release of blood from the engorged blood vessels.

The first notable occurrence in women during the resolution phase that follows orgasm is the immediate return to normal of the areolas surrounding the nipples. Indeed, their rapid subsidence gives an observer the impression that the nipples are undergoing a further erection—though they are in fact only becoming more visible as the swelling around them subsides. The increased prominence of the nipples is a sign that the woman has in fact experienced orgasm. This sign appears so rapidly that it might almost be assigned to the end of the orgasmic phase rather than to the beginning of the resolution phase. Another sign of orgasm is the rapid disappearance of the sex flush in women who have had the flush during orgasm.

Accompanying the disappearance of the sex flush, a filmy sheen of perspiration appears on many women. In extreme cases it may cover a woman's entire body from shoulders to thighs. In other cases the perspiration may appear only on the soles of the feet and the palms of the hands, and there are other variations. About one-third of the women observed in the Masters-Johnson laboratory had this tendency to perspire following orgasm.

About one-third of the men also perspired at this time, but the reaction was more often limited to the soles and palms. Neither this perspiration nor the sex flush is related to the degree of muscular effort prior to or during orgasm. This lack of relationship was initially established by ordinary observation. It was later proved in the case of one woman who (for other reasons) was trained for four months to achieve orgasm with a minimum of muscular effort. Brainwave recordings made with the electroencephalograph confirmed the fact that her muscular activity was negligible. Yet this woman "repeatedly showed a marked flush phenomenon over the entire body during plateau and orgasm, and during resolution was completely covered by a filmy, fine perspiration."

Within five or ten seconds after a woman's orgasm subsides, several other changes can be noted. The clitoris promptly returns to its unstimulated position, overhanging the pubic bone; however, five or ten minutes may elapse, or in extreme cases half an hour, before it shrinks to normal size. Soon after this the orgasmic platform relaxes so that the outer third of the vaginal barrel increases in diameter. The ballooning of the vagina begins to diminish, and the uterus begins to shrink. The cervix descends into its normal position, and the passageway through the cervix enlarges—perhaps to make easier the ascent of the sperm cells into the uterus. These processes continue at various rates for various periods of time; as long as half an hour may elapse following orgasm before the entire female body is restored to its erotically unstimulated state.

If a woman who has reached the plateau phase does not experience orgasm, the resolution phase takes much longer—an hour or so in many cases (see below, pages 76–78).

In men the most obvious sign of the resolution phase is the prompt loss of erection of the penis and its shrinkage back to its unstimulated size. This shrinkage occurs in two stages. The first is quite rapid, but leaves the penis still noticeably enlarged. The remainder of the shrinkage is often a much slower process.

The male sex flush, like the female, rapidly disappears. The return of the scrotum and testes to their unstimulated state may be either rapid or slow. If the male nipples have erected, many minutes may elapse before they return to normal.

In both men and women, the pulse rate, blood pressure, and breathing rate gradually return to normal.

A significant feature of the male resolution phase is the "refractory period" that accompanies it. During this period, a man cannot again become sexually aroused or have another erection. In some men this period may be quite brief; one young man under laboratory conditions was able to achieve three orgasms in ten minutes, for example. But in most men it lasts for many minutes at least; and it tends to increase in duration as a man grows older.

Women do not have a similar refractory period. Indeed, if effective sexual stimulation is renewed immediately following orgasm, many women can promptly reach a second orgasm. A series of half a dozen or even a dozen orgasms without intervening resolution phases is not unusual for some women; during such a series, some women do not fall below the plateau level of arousal. This "multiorgasmic response" is described further below (pages 38, 84–89, 118, 136–138, 151, 187, 229).

The description of the four phases of sexual response we have presented does not, of course, exhaust the subject. Readers desiring additional detail may turn to the Masters-Johnson scientific papers and to their book, *Human Sexual Response*.

No single sexual experience, let us stress, proceeds in precisely the way described, just as no individual human being precisely matches the characteristics of the "usual," or "average," or "typical" human being. Thus the Masters-Johnson description should not be considered a model or norm toward which men and women should strive. On the contrary, it is simply a description of what often or usually happens. The sexual responses of any individual man or woman will almost certainly fail to show some of the characteristics described above, and will show features omitted from the description. It is usual and normal to vary from the norm. Individual variations are often in fact improvements rather than defects.

Note that the description we have presented above makes almost no distinction among sexual responses to masturbation, to sexual intercourse, or to other forms of stimulation including breast manipulation and artificial coition. The reason is quite straightforward. *The same responses occur, in very much the same order, regardless of the type of stimulation that evokes them.*

Some responses, it is true, may tend to occur a little more promptly, or to be a bit more intense, when evoked in one way rather than another. Some individuals no doubt respond more readily to one kind of stimulation than to another. *Psychologically*, the experiences may feel altogether different. But the basic pattern of *bodily* responses remains the same.

This physiological universality is among the most significant findings of the entire Masters-Johnson research program.

A number of reports have appeared concerning women able to achieve orgasm through erotic fantasy alone, without any direct stimulation of either the genitals or the breasts. Does the same series of events occur in the same order in such cases? There seems no sound reason to doubt it. Regretfully, however, Dr. Masters and Mrs. Johnson report that none of the 382 women in their sample was able to fantasy to orgasm.

WHY STUDY SEX?

The direct observations of sexual response reported above immediately give rise, of course, to a host of questions:

(1) What kinds of people are willing to engage in sexual intercourse and other forms of sexual activity in a laboratory, under observation?

(2) Even with willing participants, how could such detailed observations—including observations of the reactions of the interior of the vagina and of the cervix and uterus—be secured?

(3) What kind of a man was Dr. Masters to launch such a program? And what kind of woman was Mrs Johnson to help carry it out?

(4) What did they expect to learn that would justify such an intrusion into sexual privacy?

(5) What did they learn, in fact, in addition to the generalized pattern of sexual response presented above?

(6) Do their findings have any practical application to the lives of ordinary men and women, husbands, wives and lovers?

(7) Finally, what are the moral implications of this research? In the words of the title of an article in a popular woman's magazine, "Should This Sex Research Be Allowed To Go On?"

Let us state at once our personal answer to the last question

The importance of this work to the medical and behavioral sciences, to the health of human patients, and to the happiness of mankind is so great, and the problems with which this research is concerned are so pressing, that widespread support for a broad expansion of similar studies should be promptly forthcoming.

The ethical justification for intensive studies of human sexual behavior was eloquently set forth by the late Dr. Alan Gregg of the Rockefeller Foundation as far back as 1948:

> Certainly no aspect of human biology in our current civilization stands in more need of scientific knowledge and courageous humility than that of sex. The history of medicine proves that insofar as man seeks to know himself and face his whole nature, he has become free from bewildered fear, despondent shame, or arrant hypocrisy. As long as sex is dealt with in the current confusion of ignorance and sophistication, denial and indulgence, suppression and stimulation, punishment and exploitation, secrecy and display, it will be associated with a duplicity and indecency that lead neither to intellectual honesty nor human dignity.

The practical justification for the Masters-Johnson research has been similarly stated in a lead editorial in the *Journal of the American Medical Association* for July 18, 1966:

> Sexual incompatibility is a significant factor in many unhappy or broken marriages. It is not the only important factor. It may not be the most important factor. But sexual dissatisfaction is a problem which causes many couples to seek medical advice; physicians should receive assistance in managing such problems from the data of Masters and Johnson. . . .

Many scientists before Dr. Masters had acutely felt the need for direct scientific observations of sexual response. Among them was the late Dr. Alfred C. Kinsey of Indiana University. During the years from 1938 to 1953, Dr. Kinsey and his associates, Dr. Wardell B. Pomeroy, Dr. Clyde E. Martin, and Dr. Paul H. Gebhard, collected and analyzed the detailed sexual histories of 16,392 men and women. They asked these informants literally millions of questions, and recorded millions of replies. But when their findings were published, critics promptly pointed out one major shortcoming: *Almost all of the data was secondhand.*

Dr. Kinsey himself was acutely aware of this shortcoming. He regretted the need to rely on "secondhand reports which depend for their validity upon the capacity of the individual to observe his or her own activity." And he continued:

> In no other area have the physiologist and the student of behavior had to rely upon such secondhand sources, while having so little access to direct observation.
> This difficulty is particularly acute in the study of sexual behavior because the participant in a sexual relationship becomes physiologically incapacitated as an observer. Sexual arousal reduces one's capacity to see, to hear, to smell, to taste, or to feel with anything like normal acuity, and at the moment of orgasm one's sensory capacities may completely fail. . . . Persons who have tried to describe their experiences in orgasm may produce literary or artistic descriptions, but they rarely contribute to any understanding of the physiology which is involved.

To minimize this difficulty, the Kinsey group tried a number of techniques. One was to observe in detail, and to record on motion-picture film, the sexual responses of mammals other than man.

> Because of the extreme rapidity of sexual response [they explained] and because the responses may involve every part of the animal's body, it is exceedingly difficult and usually impossible to observe all that is taking place in the few seconds or minute or two which are usually involved in [animal] sexual activity. We have, therefore, found it necessary to supplement our direct observations with moving picture records which we, and several others collaborating with the research, have now made on the sexual activities of 14 species of mammals. With the photographic record, it is possible to examine and reexamine the identical performance any number of times and, if necessary, examine and measure the details on any single frame of the film. Thus we have been able to analyze the physiologic bases of the action in various parts of the animal body.

In addition, Dr. Kinsey and his associates noted that they had secured access to a limited amount of data collected by others "who have observed human sexual activities in which they themselves were not involved, and who have kept records of their observations." The usefulness of these data, they stressed, "depends in no small degree upon the fact that the observations were made in every instance by scientifically trained observers." Few of these observations, however, were of adult heterosexual activity.

Though Dr. Kinsey did not say so at the time, his account

of sexual physiology was also based in part on his own personal observations. "Dr. Kinsey probably observed directly more human sexual response than any scientist—except Dr. Masters and Mrs. Johnson," says Dr. Pomeroy, Dr. Kinsey's closest associate.

These observations of human sex activity, unfortunately, did not take place in the scientific laboratory, where appropriate equipment could be used to determine precisely and to record objectively the physiological reactions that were occurring. "The materials are still scant and additional physiologic studies will be needed," Dr. Kinsey wrote in 1953. He was planning to fill this gap in our knowledge of our own physiology at the time of his death (see page 118).

Dr. Masters picked up this scientific trail at the point where Dr. Kinsey and his associates left it.

No doubt one of Dr. Masters' motives was scientific curiosity —the same motive that may prompt other men to study earthquakes, or the orbits of comets, or the circulation of blood in whales. But as a practicing obstetrician and gynecologist, Dr. Masters also knew of many more practical reasons for launching the particular kind of laboratory study of human sex responses that he did.

To start with a simple example, pregnant patients frequently asked him whether they could safely have sexual intercourse during the months ahead. After the baby was born, they asked how soon they could resume sexual relations. Dr. Masters didn't know—*and neither did anyone else*. The effect of sexual intercourse, with or without orgasm, on the uterus shielding the unborn baby, or on the uterus and vagina following the birth of a baby was unknown. Some doctors forbade sexual intercourse during the last three months of pregnancy and the first three months after childbirth; others specified six weeks of abstinence before and six weeks after. Still others told their pregnant patients to continue "as long as you are comfortable and your husband is gentle." Pregnant women and their husbands have been included among the subjects engaging in sexual intercourse in the Masters-Johnson laboratory, and the physiological effects have been recorded in detail. (For the findings, see below, pages 88–96.)

Many patients also came to Dr. Masters, as to other gynecologists, complaining that despite years of trying, they had not succeeded in having a baby. This sad problem, infertility, is faced by several millions of unhappy American couples. In many cases, the most complete medical examination of both husband and wife fails to reveal anything wrong. Can the likelihood of achieving pregnancy in such cases be increased by changes in the technique of sexual intercourse, or in the environment inside the vagina—changes designed to assist the sperm cells on their journey from the place where the penis initially deposits them, through the cervix, and up into the Fallopian tubes where they can meet and fertilize a descending ovum? Rules-of-thumb for increasing the chances of pregnancy were oftentimes recommended; but no one really knew. No one had studied the interactions of penis, vagina, and cervix during and following the ejaculation of semen. (For the Masters-Johnson findings on infertility and ways of overcoming it, see below, pages 96–99.)

Another practical concern was contraceptive failure—the occurrence of an unwanted pregnancy despite the fact that a couple had used a recommended method of contraception. Why do contraceptive jellies, creams, foams, and diaphragms sometimes fail to accomplish their intended purpose? By observing the actual behavior of these contraceptives within the vagina during and following coitus, the products themselves might be improved—and ineffective new products might be ruled out without the tragic need to evaluate them by counting the number of unwanted babies born to women who use them. (For Masters-Johnson contraceptive findings, see pages 100–102.)

But the relevance of sex-response studies to pregnancy, in fertility, and contraception was almost an incidental concern as compared with their relevance to one of the major problems of our time and culture: the millions of husbands and wives suffering from sexual frustrations, sexual inadequacies, and sexual incompatibilities. An almost random selection of such cases will illustrate their variety and complexity:

A frantic wife reports to her physician that her husband of ten years' standing is threatening to divorce her. "He says I'm sexually frigid, and I guess he's right. But I love him and don't want to lose him. How can I become sexually responsive?"

Another woman complains that her husband is unable to arouse her sexually. "I love him, but somehow it never works out. After he's through, I suffer—or masturbate. Then I hate myself. Why can't I enjoy intercourse like other women?"

A bride of six weeks complains that sexual intercourse is physically painful to her—a condition known as *dyspareunia*.

An attractive young woman and her fiancé come to

gynecologist explaining that they are in love and want to marry. Though well formed in all other respects, and sexually very responsive, the young woman was born without a vagina. Her mother had told her years earlier that nothing could be done to correct this developmental defect, known as *vaginal agenesis*. Is there now any operation or treatment, they ask, which will make it possible for them to engage in coitus— and enable the young woman to enjoy it?

A woman of thirty reports that during her first marriage, sex was a transcendent experience. She loved her husband and cherished him and had shared many ecstasies with him. One characteristic of their life together was her experiencing six, eight, or even a dozen orgasms in rapid succession during a single sexual encounter; sometimes two or three such series might follow one another in the course of an evening of love-making. In her present marriage, however, all this is lacking. At best she experiences from time to time a single minor orgasm that leaves her still restless and dissatisfied. What has gone wrong, and what can be done about it?

A woman of fifty complains that she is losing her sexual attractiveness, and that troublesome changes seem to be occurring inside her genital tract.

Men, too, of course, often come to physicians with sexual complaints. Of these the most common are the inability to achieve an erection, the inability to maintain an erection, and premature ejaculation—the loss of semen before the penis enters the vagina, or while entry is being attempted, or within a few seconds after entry.

The physicians and others to whom patients bring such complaints, Dr. Masters knew, had many methods of handling them. Reassurance was one. "There's nothing to worry about. These things usually iron themselves out. Come back in six months if everything isn't all right." Medicines were often prescribed, or operations performed, or some sort of psychotherapy recommended as the treatment of choice. In many cases, the conclusion might be reached that a divorce, leaving both partners free to try again with someone else, was the only solution.

How effective were these methods of handling sexual complaints? No one really knew. But to Dr. Masters one point was clear: he and others could provide far more competent help to patients such as these if more was known about the actual sexual physiology of men and women, and about sexual response. Many problems might be solved at the medical level, or at the marriage counseling level, or at the psychiatric level which—in the absence of sound knowledge—were likely to end up in the divorce courts.

Finally, Dr. Masters was aware that many couples who were already enjoying their sexual activities were eager to learn more about sex in order to increase their enjoyment. This desire has led to a flood of "sex manuals" and other "how-to" books, not only in our own time but through the centuries since the days of the ancient Chinese, Indians, and Greeks.

This popular demand for detailed sexual information and advice is a valid one, and the enormous sale of sex manuals would no doubt contribute much to human happiness—*if* the information in them were reliable and the advice sound. But the authors of these manuals share with their readers and with scientists generally a basic ignorance of sexual physiology, and especially of the ways in which the male and female bodies respond to sexual stimulation of various kinds. No one knew because no one had objectively observed, with the aid of modern scientific equipment, the whole broad spectrum of erotic stimuli and of the human body's response to these stimuli.

WILLIAM H. MASTERS, RESEARCHER

Not all of these problems were in the mind of William Howell Masters when he first decided to devote himself to sex research.

Born in Cleveland in 1915, of parents in comfortable circumstances, Bill Masters attended a Kansas City high school for two years, Lawrenceville preparatory school in Lawrenceville, New Jersey, for four years, and then Hamilton College in Clinton, New York, where he received his bachelor of science degree in 1938.

At Hamilton, in addition to his science course, he somehow found time to play on the varsity football, baseball, and basketball teams, to run on the varsity track team, to participate in the Debate Club, to serve on the Honor Court (which oversees Hamilton's honor system), and to belong to a fraternity. "Here is a strange, dark man with a future," the Hamilton senior classbook for 1938 reported. "Has an easy time carrying three lab courses but a hard time catching up on lost sleep. . . . Bill is a boy with purpose and is bound to get what he is working for."

That description is still relevant. A perceptive science writer described Dr. Masters in 1966 as "a dapper, athletically trim gynecologist who starts his day at 5:30 with a two-mile jog." Then, says Arthur J. Snider of the Chicago *Daily News,* he puts on "a sport coat, slacks, and a bright bow tie and drives to one of the two large [St. Louis] hospitals where he operates." His surgical and other hospital chores completed, he reaches his office at the Reproductive Biology Research Foundation about 10 A.M. to begin his major work of the day. Four half-days a week he devotes to his gynecological practice; the remainder of his time is spent on treating patients with sexual problems, research, and administration. He works two evenings a week—and all through one night a week. Thus his work week at fifty, as at college, totals some eighty hours.

It was his laboratory courses at Hamilton that persuaded Masters to become a laboratory researcher, and he entered the University of Rochester School of Medicine and Dentistry in 1939 as a step toward that goal rather than toward the practice of medicine. His first year at Rochester, he had the good fortune to work in the laboratory of one of the country's foremost anatomists, Dr. George Washington Corner. "I remember him as a very serious and intelligent young man of more independent character than many," Dr. Corner recently recalled.

Dr. Corner in 1939 was already well into his comparative studies of the reproductive tract in animals and in humans—studies that were to lead to his pioneering investigations of the ovarian hormones and the reproductive cycle for which he is today best known. But his concerns were not narrowly scientific. The previous year he had published a little book entitled *Attaining Manhood: A Doctor Talks to Boys About Sex;* and in 1939 he published a companion book for girls, *Attaining Womanhood.* An inspiring teacher, he was precisely the kind of leader to whom any serious-minded young scientist-in-training would be attracted as a model.

The particular task to which Dr. Corner assigned Bill Masters profoundly affected the younger man's future. One of the baffling problems of comparative anatomy and physiology, in 1939 as today, is the relationship between the human menstrual cycle and the estrous cycle in infrahuman animals. To what extent are the monthly changes in the lining of the human uterus, preparatory to reception of a fertilized ovum, parelleled in other species? A study of the lining of the rabbit uterus was Bill Masters' assignment as a first-year medical student in Dr. Corner's laboratory.

The findings were never published. "The problem turned out to be one of those which does not give clear answers," Dr. Corner recently explained. But it did serve to focus young Masters' attention on reproductive biology as a challenging area concerning which very little was known. This first research undertaking, Dr. Corner has noted, illustrates "the serious and entirely proper interest in sex research which Dr. Masters exhibited in his student days."

Masters married in 1942, and secured his M.D. degree in 1943.

How did he reach his decision to make sex research his major scientific interest? Psychoanalysts might say, perhaps with some degree of truth, that deep unconscious drives and urges were involved. Some prurient men and women might suggest that the same motives which would have influenced them influenced Bill Masters. In the course of such speculations, a very simple explanation is usually overlooked altogether. Every ambitious young man starting out on a scientific career keeps a weather eye cocked for some field which is not already over-cultivated—a field where industry, perspicacity, and good luck are most likely to lead to fresh and significant discoveries instead of to mere refinements on the prior discoveries of established workers. In 1943, a decision to study the physiology of sex was a decision to study the least plowed and hence most inviting area of human physiology.

In the course of reaching his decision, Bill Masters went to Baltimore to consult Dr. Corner—who had left Rochester to become director of the department of embryology at the Carnegie Institution of Washington. Also present at this meeting was another of the nation's foremost authorities on comparative sexual anatomy and physiology, the zoologist Dr. Carl G. Hartman.

Both men were keenly aware of the pitfalls in choosing this area of study: the general prejudice against sex research, the criticism heaped upon those who dared to enter this long-tabooed field, the insinuations of prurient interests that sex researchers then faced (and still do), the difficulty in securing financial support for sex research, and many more.

They had in mind, when Masters came to ask their advice in 1942, the inquiries into human sexual behavior that Dr. Kinsey had quietly launched at Indiana University back in 1938. Dr. Corner was a member of the Committee for Research in Problems of Sex, an arm of the National Academy of Sciences–National Research Council. It was to this committee that Dr. Kinsey had turned for financing his undertaking; and after thorough investigation, they had supplied substantial funds. Among the many factors that may have influenced the committee in favor of Kinsey, three were quite obvious:

(1) He was a man of mature years.
(2) He had already earned his scientific spurs through intensive, competent research in another field—the anatomy of gall wasps.
(3) His work was being conducted under the impeccable auspices of a great university.

The prescription Dr. Corner and Dr. Hartman gave young Masters was along precisely these lines. If he really wanted to engage in sex research, they told him, he must wait until he was at least forty, until he had earned a sound reputation by research on some other topic, and until he could launch his program under the auspices of a major medical school or university.

Dr. Masters followed the prescription almost to the letter through the next ten years.

He spent four years (1943–47) as an intern, and as a resident in obstetrics and gynecology, at Barnes Hospital and Maternity Hospital, Washington University School of Medicine in St. Louis.

From 1947 to date, he has been successively instructor, assistant professor, and associate professor of obstetrics and gynecology there. In 1951 he was certified as a specialist in obstetrics and gynecology by the American Board of Obstetricians and Gynecologists. His two children, a girl and a boy, were born in 1950 and 1951. In addition to his university connection, he now serves as associate obstetrician and gynecologist at St. Louis Maternity and Barnes Hospitals, and at the Washington University Clinics; and as consulting gynecologist at the St. Louis Infirmary and at Salem Memorial Hospital in Salem, Illinois.

During the six years from 1948 to 1954, Dr. Masters published twenty-five contributions to the medical literature, covering a variety of obstetrical and gynecological topics. Fourteen of these papers were concerned with a major research project, pursued intensely for seven years—hormone replacement therapy for postmenopausal women. By 1954, Dr. Masters felt ready to enter the field for which he had been preparing—the study of human sexual response. In only one respect had he taken a shortcut from the path recommended by Dr. Corner and Dr. Hartman in 1943; he was only thirty-eight years old.

THE LABORATORY BEGINNINGS

Dr. Masters launched his sex studies—known initially as the "Sex Research Project" and later as the "Reproductive Biology Research Project"—at the Washington University School of Medicine in St. Louis. Financing came in part from the medical school and in part from a research grant of the U.S. Public Health Service. The project remained at the medical school until 1964, when Dr. Masters established his own Reproductive Biology Research Foundation near the medical-school campus, financed by St. Louis citizens and other individual donors, and by a number of small philanthropic foundations. Dr. Masters retains his associate professorship at the medical school. He receives no pay from either the Foundation or the medical school, supporting himself by his gynecological practice.

The launching of his Sex Research Project was aided by a change in the climate of public opinion, which was just then occurring. Dr. Kinsey and his associates had published the second of their classic reports, *Sexual Behavior in the Human Female,* in 1953, and had created a nationwide sensation. For the first time millions of Americans took an open-eyed look into the yawning chasm separating the accepted myths of human sexual behavior and the actual behavior of men and women as they themselves reported it to the Kinsey Institute researchers. While there were detailed criticisms of the Kinsey Institute procedures and findings, even most of its critics were agreed in 1954 that there was urgent need for more study of sexual problems. Thus the Masters research program received, from the beginning, understanding and approval from thoughtful people whose opinions counted most. Dr. Masters has since taken every opportunity to express his indebtedness to Kinsey for "opening the previously closed doors of our culture to definitive investigation of human sexual response."

But where was Dr. Masters to get subjects for his program of laboratory investigations? Middle-class and middle-Western in his own cultural orientation, it never occurred to him in the beginning that volunteers could be found in "respectable society." He accordingly turned to the one obviously available group—the professional prostitutes. This decision was cleared in advance with medical school and university officials, with the local police, and with others in authority. It met with no opposition.

As naïve at the beginning as any other gynecologist, Dr. Masters learned a great deal from the 118 female prostitutes who contributed their sexual and professional histories to his project. (He also interviewed twenty-seven male prostitutes, serving a homosexual clientele; but none of his work on either male or female homosexuality has been published, and none of it falls within the scope of the present volume.) The prostitutes "described many methods for elevating and controlling sexual tensions and demonstrated innumerable variations in stimulative techniques," Dr. Masters later reported. "Ultimately many of these techniques have been found to have direct application in therapy of male and female sexual inadequacy and have been integrated into the clinical research program."

During this early period, too, Dr. Masters was designing and establishing the laboratory in which his subsequent observations of human sexual response were to be made and recorded. Many problems had to be solved. Just how do you go about observing sexual relations? How large a room do you need? How do you hitch up the electrocardiograph, the electroencephalograph, the electromyograph, the X-ray machine, and all the other equipment helpful in physiological research? What kind of lighting is required—especially if responses are to be recorded on film? Eight of the women prostitutes and three of the men participated in "dry runs" of laboratory procedures during this preliminary period.

And then, for many months, research came to a dead stop. The prostitutes proved wholly unsuitable for the studies of normal human sexuality that Dr. Masters hoped to make.

In the first place, many of them were migrants, working in St. Louis one month and disappearing the next. An essential feature of Dr. Masters' research program was the prolonged observation of responses as they developed through the years in individual subjects. Without follow-up confirmations, observations would be of little value.

Many of the prostitutes, moreover, exhibited substantial degrees of pelvic pathology—including a condition of chronic congestion of the pelvic region, presumably the result of frequently repeated sexual excitation without orgasmic release. This condition affected precisely the bodily functions Dr. Masters was most concerned to study. Observations made on subjects with chronic pelvic congestion would be of little value in establishing what happens in normal women.

Stymied by the shortcomings of prostitutes, and unable for a time to believe that ordinary men and women would subject themselves to the laboratory procedures he knew were necessary, Dr. Masters turned to other problems, and let his sex research languish for almost a year.

THE STUMBLING BLOCKS

In the physiological laboratories of every major medical school, research studies are always going on. The functioning of the human heart, lungs, digestive tract, and other organs is studied in minute detail, using complex equipment to supplement direct observation. Medical students and other volunteers are recruited as subjects for these studies, and are paid for their time like any other employees. But a widely held and deeply rooted taboo prevented Dr. Masters from simply going out and recruiting volunteers similarly for his research project. This was, of course, the taboo against engaging in sexual activity in the presence of others.

Because the ultimate breaking down of this taboo was the step that made the Masters-Johnson research program possible, it is essential to examine its nature in some detail.

In our culture, the sex-in-public taboo is intimately related to the nakedness taboo. The nakedness taboo applies primarily to the male and female genitals and the female breasts, though the breast taboo seems currently to be weakening. In parts of the Moslem world, in addition, the female face is a major site of taboo. In a few primitive tribes, it is the anal region; a young woman surprised without clothing may throw herself down on her back to hide her buttocks.

In our culture, too, the nakedness taboo applies chiefly to nakedness in front of the opposite sex; but there are exceptions. Schools and camps are familiar with boys who are ashamed to bare themselves before other boys, and who go to extreme lengths to avoid gym classes, swimming pool lessons, and other occasions when they may be forced to do this.

Most Americans make an exception to the nakedness taboo when they go to a physician for a physical examination—but this is not universally true. Some men are embarrassed to be examined by women physicians. Some women delay for months or even years and run a grave risk of an incurable disease such as cancer because of their reluctance to let a male physician examine their breasts or their genital organs. In some cultures, no exception whatever is made for the medical profession. Male physicians, for example, may be forbidden to deliver babies, or may be forced to deliver them blindly, groping under a sheet or blanket by the sense of touch alone. In parts of China not so long ago, women avoided the embarrassment of a medical examination by pointing out the location of their symptoms on ivory dolls that physicians provided for the purpose.

In our culture the nakedness taboo varies according to the occasion. Respectable women would shudder to wear to church on Sunday morning the evening gown worn the night before, or the bikini worn without embarrassment at the beach on Sunday afternoon.

Society enforces this taboo in many ways. "Indecent exposure" may even be punished by imprisonment—but there are widespread variations. One city may permit bare breasts but not bare buttocks in nightclub acts; another city may permit bare buttocks but not bare breasts.

One extreme of the taboo in our culture was the teaching of children a generation or two ago to put on their nightgowns before taking off their underclothes, in order to spare themselves the sight of their own nakedness. Some older women still get ready for bed in this way.

At the other extreme, many thousands of American men, women, and children put aside their clothes and their nakedness taboos without qualms and without embarrassment each summer weekend on their visits to nudist camps. There they eat, play, swim, and engage in a wide range of social activities unclothed.

Those who have never visited a nudist camp are likely to think of them as immoral places where shocking scenes are enacted. Nothing could be further from the truth. Most of them are prim, almost puritanical. Despite abandonment of the nakedness taboo, most nudists retain the usual modesty taboos. They stand and sit modestly, for example. Any vulgar bodily display is frowned upon or punished by expulsion from the camp. Casual bodily contacts which would fail to raise an eyebrow in a strict New England junior high school remain taboo in nudist camps. In some, shaking hands is the only form of bodily contact not tabooed.

Behavioral scientists, moreover, report that nudists are *not* a breed apart. Most of them were brought up with the usual nakedness taboos. For various reasons and in various ways they have shed them—often because someone they liked, respected, and trusted had joined a nudist camp and had thus made nudism acceptable and respectable in their eyes. In this as in many other situations respectable behavior is defined by what people who are considered respectable do.

A very remarkable fact is the rapidity with which the nakedness taboo disappears completely at nudist camps once the decision to abandon it is reached. This seems to be true of both men and women in our culture. Men have an added fear when they appear unclothed for the first time—the fear that they may become sexually aroused and be embarrassed by an erection. This almost never happens. Within minutes of entering a nudist camp, newcomers of both sexes are as comfortable in the situation as those who have attended for years. "It isn't hard to get used to the lack of clothes; it's only hard to get used to incidental inconveniences like lack of pockets," is a common observation among recent converts to nudism.

In summary, the nakedness taboo varies from culture to culture, and from generation to generation within a culture. It also varies from person to person within a generation, and even within a single family. Individuals alter their nakedness taboos from hour to hour, depending on the place and circumstances; and once the decision is made, the entire taboo can, it appears, be cast off with amazing ease and promptness.

The taboo against masturbating or engaging in sexual intercourse or pursuing other sexual activities in the presence of observers may seem on first consideration quite different. But there are reasons for suspecting that it is more like the nakedness taboo than might be supposed.

Kissing, for example, is a sexual activity long tabooed in public. No one kissed hello or good-bye in the novels of Jane Austen. "When I was a girl, you didn't dare walk with a man after sunset, unless he was your husband," the late James Thurber quoted his mother as recalling, "and even then there was talk." Today kissing in public is quite acceptable.

Necking and petting in public appear to be going through a similar transition. Many older people in our culture would object to others necking or petting in their presence; but many teen-age couples seem to have relatively few taboos about doing so in the presence of other teen-age couples.

Dancing taboos also change. The court dances and square dances of an earlier generation were relatively nonsexual. The sensuous waltz was greeted by storms of protest when first introduced, but became ultra-respectable in due course. Cheek-to-cheek dancing and dancing in close embrace were accepted in their turn. Recently "the twist" and other dances featuring the overt pelvic thrusting characteristic of sexual intercourse have become increasingly acceptable.

Nor is the ultimate taboo against sexual intercourse in public a universal characteristic of human beings at all times and in all places. Students of primitive religion report that sexual intercourse was often a feature of primitive fertility rites. A priest and priestess, or a king and priestess might copulate before the assembled population to assure the success of the crop just planted; or the entire population might pair off and engage in public intercourse for the same or some other equally worthy and socially approved purpose.

In many parts of Europe during pre-Christian times, special holidays were set aside as periods of sexual license; often these holidays had a religious significance. At such times the taboo against sexual intercourse in public was temporarily suspended. Even virtuous matrons and statesmen of unblemished repute could—on the days specified—engage in both marital and extramarital intercourse in public without feelings of shame or risk of social disapproval. On other days, similar behavior would have shocked society to the core. Today's Mardi Gras, New Year's Eve, and some other festivals are no doubt modified survivals of these traditional periods of taboo suspension.

Among the Polynesians, sexual intercourse in public seems to have taken many forms, varying from island to island and from time to time. The English explorer, Captain James Cook, in his *Account of a Voyage Around the World,* noted that the Tahitians he visited "gratify every appetite and passion before witnesses." One Sunday in 1769, following Divine services, Captain Cook witnessed

> vespers of a very different kind. A young man, nearly six feet high, performed the rites of Venus with a little girl about 11 or 12 years of age, before several of our people and a great number of the natives, without the least sense of its being indecent or improper, but, as appeared, in perfect conformity to the custom of the place. Among the spectators were several women of superior rank, who may properly be said to have assisted at the ceremony; for they gave instructions to the girl how to perform her part, which, young as she was, she did not seem much to stand in need of.

The Swedish anthropologist Bengt Danielsson—one of the participants in the *Kon-Tiki* voyage—has collected in his book, *Love in the South Seas,* numerous other accounts of the extent to which privacy was not considered necessary for sexual intercourse. He quotes, for example, this account of a traditional wedding custom in the Marquesas Islands by a French anthropologist, L. F. Tautain:

> At a sign from the bridegroom, all the men present assembled, forming a queue, and each in turn passed before the bride, who, lying in a corner of the *paepae,* with her head on the bridegroom's knee, received them all as husbands. The procession was headed by the oldest men and those of lowest birth, then came the great chiefs, and last of all the husband. . . . A newly married woman was sometimes half dead and obliged to keep to her bed for several days afterwards.

This test of strength, Danielsson adds, was not regarded as in any way degrading or shameful; indeed, "the more men a bride had satisfied, the prouder she was."

All of the variations on the nakedness and sex-in-public taboos we have reviewed so far arose among respected and self-respecting members of society, men and women whose behavior was considered irreproachable within their own groups. When we look beyond these boundaries of respectability, we find in many cultures—and certainly in our own— countless examples of sexual activity in the presence of others on the fringes of polite society.

During the nineteenth and early twentieth centuries, sexual exhibitions before onlookers were a common feature of the brothels serving an upper-class clientele in large American cities, often patronized by leading citizens and tolerated by the police. Today the laws against such exhibitions are more strictly enforced, but they still occur, serving as a further reminder that taboos are remarkably flexible.

The Kinsey Institute interviewers were well aware of the existence of such fringe activities. Item 11 in Section VII of the questionnaire outline they used included the following:

Group heterosexual activities:

Circumstances, frequency
Number and nature of partners
Participation in strip poker
Fraternal and other group initiation activities
Observation of coitus

Of parents
Of friends
Of professional exhibitionists

Item 3 in Section III similarly covered "Experience in observing sex behavior." Item 12 of Section VII, addressed particularly to prostitutes, included numerous other topics concerning group sexual activities and sexual exhibitions. The findings based on these questions have not been published; but enough affirmative answers were secured to persuade Dr. Kinsey himself that a study of human sexual response based on direct observation would be a feasible undertaking in the United States of the 1950's.

Dr. Masters had never met Dr. Kinsey. He was unaware of Dr. Kinsey's belief that ordinary American men and women could be found willing to cooperate in scientific studies of sexual response. But slowly and tentatively, he reached much the same conclusion himself.

The prostitutes he had studied provided the major evidence for the feasibility of the project. They cited many examples of sexual activity occurring in the presence of others. A client might engage two prostitutes, for example, or two clients might engage two or more prostitutes, or other combinations might be arranged. There were both men and women, the prostitutes reported, who enjoyed engaging in sex in the presence of others. Much more important for Dr. Masters' research, there were also men and women who had no strong feeling about privacy one way or the other; they simply lacked, for some reason or other, the privacy taboos common in our culture.

If this was true, satisfactory volunteers might be found. The possibility was at least worth exploring; and in the spring of 1956, Dr. Masters began to explore it.

THE VOLUNTEERS

Dr. Masters' first step toward securing volunteers was absurdly simple. He merely let it be known through the medical school and university community that he was planning a study of human sexual response based on laboratory studies. News like this spreads quickly along the local grapevine. One medical school professor tells another, who tells his wife, who tells a neighbor. A medical student tells a nurse, who tells her sister-in-law.

The returns from this local gossip were of two kinds. A few of those who heard about the research came to Dr. Masters' office on the medical-school floor of the maternity-hospital building eager to volunteer "for kicks." They were promptly eliminated.

More welcome visitors were those genuinely concerned with some important human problem which sex research might help to solve.

Some couples were referred by their own physicians; some

came because they hoped to increase their own understanding and enjoyment of sex. Former patients of Dr. Masters sometimes came and brought their husbands along when they heard that he needed volunteers.

If a couple seemed to be likely candidates for the program, they were invited to return and supply a complete social, medical, and sexual history.

The participation of Mrs. Johnson at this history-taking stage was essential in several ways. Born Virginia Eshelman in the Missouri Ozarks in 1925, she had been brought up fully aware of the sexual superstitions and customs of the area, and with the sexual realism common to country-bred children—tempered by the influence of a paternal grandfather from one of Philadelphia's Main Line suburbs. She studied music at Drury College in Springfield, Missouri, then transferred to Missouri University—where she discovered the world of sociology and psychology. In 1950 she married; in 1952 she had a son and in 1955 a daughter. Separated from her husband soon afterward, Mrs. Johnson registered for a job with the Washington University Placement Bureau at just the time when Dr. Masters had applied there for a woman to assist in research interviewing. He had specified a woman with experience and interest in working with people, preferably a married woman with children. Mrs. Johnson was sent to fill the job, and has been working with Dr. Masters ever since. In addition, she has continued her graduate studies in psychology, and from 1960 to 1964 she served by appointment as research assistant and research instructor at the Washington University School of Medicine.

Dr. Masters soon found that a team composed of both a male and a female interviewer—himself and Mrs. Johnson— was exceedingly helpful in dealing with potential research volunteers and with patients as well. The interviewing procedure varied. Dr. Masters and Mrs. Johnson might talk together with a husband and wife; Dr. Masters might then talk with the husband while Mrs. Johnson talked with the wife; or Dr. Masters and the wife might confer while Mrs. Johnson consulted with the husband. The series of interviews might conclude with all four present again. Whether this or some other pattern was followed, the yield of information proved to be significantly greater when both sexes were represented on the interviewing team. Some people talk more freely with someone of the same sex, some with the opposite sex. Variations in the accounts that a person gives a man and a woman interviewer may also prove significant, and helpful in diagnosing clinical problems. The two-sex interviewing team has been a standard feature of the Masters-Johnson research and clinical programs since Mrs. Johnson joined the team in January 1957.

In all, 619 women and 654 men were interviewed by Dr Masters and Mrs. Johnson in the course of selecting subjects for the research study; the detailed sexual histories supplied by these 1,273 men and women provided a useful background of knowledge. The questions asked and answered during this history-taking were somewhat similar to the questions used by the Kinsey Institute group, plus a full medical history. Several hours might be devoted to the history-taking. In addition to asking questions, Dr. Masters also answered countless questions put to him as a gynecologist by the men and women he was interviewing.

These interview sessions served several important functions:

First, they gave the men and women being interviewed an opportunity to get to know and respect Dr. Masters and Mrs. Johnson. Those who came with any doubts about the scientific integrity and dedication of the two researchers soon had their doubts set at rest. Both Dr. Masters and Mrs. Johnson are the kind of people in whom it is easy to develop confidence.[1]

Second, Dr. Masters and Mrs. Johnson could learn more of the motives of those volunteering and could explain the project in terms relevant to their interests. "Pretty soon *they* would be giving *us* reasons why this research should be pursued, and urging us to explore some problems which they particularly felt needed solving," Mrs. Johnson recalls.

Third, potential volunteers who were uncomfortable in the processing period had an opportunity to drop out gracefully. "Most of our washouts occurred during or immediately after the history-taking," Mrs. Johnson states.

The detailed history-taking also provided Dr. Masters and Mrs. Johnson with an opportunity to weed out those who were unsuitable. These were thanked for their interest, but not invited to participate further.

[1] A striking example occurred in April 1966 at the press conference in Boston where the Masters-Johnson book, *Human Sexual Response*, was about to be published. One reporter came to the press conference obviously outraged by the Masters-Johnson research and loaded with cutting questions designed to prove their degeneracy. Within a short time, he was asking sensible questions and at the end of the conference he apologized for his misevaluation of their work.

Some were rejected because they were *too* eager. Dr. Masters was not seeking exhibitionists. They were easy to detect, for they were impatient with the long preliminary interviews and were unable to conceal their hurry to get to the part of the proceedings that concerned them.

Others were rejected because, even though they verbally expressed a willingness to participate, Dr. Masters and Mrs. Johnson sensed that there was resistance deeper down. The research program could succeed only if volunteers were comfortable in it.

Men and women unable to respond sexually and to reach orgasm were also weeded out. Since this was to be a study of human sexual responses, those unable to respond could contribute little to it. (Beginning in 1959, however, Dr. Masters and Mrs. Johnson developed a program for the *clinical treatment* of sexual inadequacy in both men and women; this program, though not experimental in nature, has provided insights concerning the nonresponding portion of the population. For details, see below, pages 203–219.)

Finally, applicants with any history of emotional disturbance or of mental illness or instability were rejected, for their own protection.

During these preliminary interviews, the Masters-Johnson security measures were explained—measures designed to assure the complete and permanent anonymity of the research participants. Prospective volunteers were assured that any files containing information that might identify them would be immediately destroyed in the event something should happen to the research team. The comings and goings of the volunteers were also safeguarded in several ways. The chief safeguard of anonymity was heavy traffic. Hundreds of people on scores of different missions came daily to the building in which the laboratory was housed. Many of them came to see Dr. Masters and his staff—obstetrical patients and their families, gynecological patients, other doctors, nurses, medical students, salesmen, friends. Volunteers cooperating with the research program could not be distinguished from the many other callers.

Following the history-taking and related discussions came a physical examination, including the genitals and internal reproductive organs. This, too, had several purposes. It enabled Dr. Masters to weed out applicants with gross physical abnormalities. Variations of the kind found in any random population, however, did not exclude an applicant; and for certain specialized portions of the research, women who had

had hysterectomies or other operations on their reproductive organs or whose anatomy was unusual in specific respects were sought out and welcomed.

In addition to this screening function, the complete physical examination established Dr. Masters' role as physician, the medical nature of his relationship with the volunteers. It provided the "medical aura" considered essential for successful laboratory work of this kind.

In these ways, almost everyone unsuitable for the project was eliminated, and almost everyone uncomfortable in the situation was able to bow out voluntarily. Of the 1,273 men and women who participated in the history-taking stage, 694 ended up as participants in the actual laboratory research.

Included in the 694 were 276 married couples, plus 106 women and 36 men who were not married when they entered the program; some married during the period when they were taking part in it. Ninety-eight of the 142 unmarried participants had been previously married. The unmarried participants were useful primarily in portions of the research that did not require sexual intercourse, such as studies of the ejaculatory mechanism in the male and of the way in which contraceptive materials behave in the female vagina.

The men ranged in age from twenty-one to eighty-nine; the women ranged from eighteen to seventy-eight. One of the two participants under twenty-one was a girl of eighteen, who participated with her husband; they had been married three years and had one child. The other was a twenty-year-old girl with an artificial vagina (see below, page 61); she was needed for a specific portion of the research program that did not require sexual intercourse.

Those accepted for the program, following the history-taking and physical examination, were taken on a tour of the laboratory—a suite of rooms resembling any other physiological laboratory, and similarly equipped. The questions asked by the volunteers were answered as fully as possible. "This is the electrocardiograph," Dr. Masters might explain. "With it we record the detailed behavior of the heart during the four phases of sexual response. This information may prove helpful in counseling elderly people and people with heart disease. There is so much that nobody yet knows—but that we may be able to find out with your help." Or Mrs. Johnson might explain the "pH meter" and the glass-coated electrode attached to it. "One of the subjects we are investigating," she would say, "is the relative acidity of the vagina under various conditions, a factor which may prove significant in helping couples who have been trying without success to have a baby. When the tip of this electrode is touched to the wall of the vagina, this meter records the acidity at the point touched."

Throughout these orientation procedures, the calm matter-of-factness of both researchers was a major factor in putting the participants at ease. Dr. Masters' and Mrs. Johnson's acceptance of sexual response in the laboratory as a commonplace routine helped the participants to accept it in the same way.

After volunteers had toured the laboratory, they were invited back for a practice session in privacy, to accustom them to sexual activity in the laboratory surroundings. During this practice session, they were not observed or intruded upon. Additional private sessions were available for those who wanted them, but few were requested.

During the first sessions with Dr. Masters and Mrs. Johnson present, considerable care was taken to make their presence as unobtrusive as possible. The researchers casually went about their other business. The whole procedure was structured to make it as much as possible like a routine hour in the laboratory—as different as possible from a staged performance before spectators. Under these circumstances, the vast majority of volunteers found it surprisingly easy to respond sexually in the laboratory in much the same way as they responded at home in private. Almost all of the resistances had been overcome during the earlier history-taking, physical examination, establishment of rapport, familiarization with the laboratory, and private sessions. And whatever barriers to simple, natural response might remain evaporated during the first few sessions with Dr. Masters and Mrs. Johnson present. The rapid disappearance of the nakedness taboo noted in nudist camps was almost precisely paralleled by the rapid disappearance of the privacy taboo in the laboratory.

Men, interestingly enough, had a somewhat higher failure rate in the laboratory than did women. Among more than 7,500 female sexual response cycles observed over an eleven-year period, there were 118 recorded failures to achieve orgasm. Among more than 2,500 male cycles, there were 220 failures. Thus the male failure rate, though less than ten percent, was roughly six times as high as the female failure rate. Cycles during the preliminary orientation period and cycles in which orgasm was not sought are excluded from these figures.) A higher anxiety level in men was no doubt the explanation for their higher failure rate; sexual failure is more embarrassing to men than to women in our culture—and fear of failure is a major factor in producing failure.

Participants continued to abide by all the social and modesty taboos compatible with the requirements of the laboratory program. "Overt exhibitionism has not been a factor in the laboratory," Dr. Masters and Mrs. Johnson report. Those who were shy and retiring in other settings remained shy and retiring in the laboratory.

How did participation in the program affect the lives of the volunteers outside the laboratory? Dr. Masters and Mrs. Johnson have been alert, of course, to note both favorable and unfavorable reactions. All program participants are questioned annually on this and related topics, and former participants are followed up at five-year intervals. During the eleven years of the program to date, Dr. Masters and Mrs. Johnson say none of the participants has developed symptoms of sexual inadequacy. On the contrary, participants report specific ways in which participation has significantly enriched their lives together.

A couple we shall call Mr. and Mrs. X are a case in point. They joined the volunteer group in 1960, when Mr. X was thirty and Mrs. X was twenty-six. Both were college graduates; Mr. X was a junior executive in an industrial firm and Mrs. X had been a school teacher in St. Louis before her marriage. At that time they had no children. They volunteered their services after hearing about the program via the local grapevine—explaining that they came because they wanted to contribute to scientific knowledge of human sexual response.

Orientation to the program proved easy for both Mr. and Mrs. X. They required only two sessions in the laboratory following the history-taking to feel at home there. ". . . Their coital response under observation was excellent," Dr. Masters and Mrs. Johnson report. "The husband never has had erective or ejaculatory difficulty. Over the five-and-a-half years of program participation [Mrs. X] has been orgasmic in 85 percent of recorded coital opportunities, occasionally developing multiorgasmic response. She always has been orgasmic, though rarely multiorgasmic, during an automanipulative sequence."

In addition to participating in the general research program, Mr. and Mrs. X cooperated in special projects for studying the effects of sexual activity on the heart and breathing. After two years, Mrs. X became pregnant; she and Mr. X continued their participation through her pregnancy and were thus a part of the especially significant pregnancy sub-project within the overall program. "Their contributions both individually and as a family unit have been invaluable," Dr. Masters and Mrs. Johnson state.

In 1965 both Mr. and Mrs. X were interviewed in depth, in part to determine the effects of the program on their married life. Dr. Masters and Mrs. Johnson report:

> Neither partner described any identifiable variation in individual or mutual sexual responsiveness in the privacy of their home as opposed to the research environment. There has been no erective or ejaculatory difficulty regardless of the environment, and [Mrs. X's] orgasmic return has not been altered by research equipment or personnel. This man and woman have stated categorically that they have found program participation of significant importance to their marriage. They have volunteered to continue in the research program so long as there is need for their contribution.

A quite different example is a couple we shall call Mr. and Mrs. Y. Mr. Y was shy as a boy and young man. He first began to "go steady" with a girl at the age of twenty-five; the girl broke off the relationship after six months because "she didn't think [he] was aggressive enough." He married Mrs. Y when he was twenty-six and she was a twenty-five-year-old secretary working in the same office.

The marriage was not completely successful from the sexual point of view. Mr. Y was concerned about his own over-controlled background, his lack of sexual experience, his shyness, and his sexual self-repression. His wife reported that she rarely achieved orgasm during intercourse. Both frankly stated that they were volunteering in order to learn more about sex and to "enhance the sexual component of their marriage in return for their cooperation with the program."

As might be expected, it was harder for the Y's than for the X's to become acclimated to the laboratory environment.

For orientation [Dr. Masters and Mrs. Johnson state], five episodes were necessary. . . . The first exposure was to background and equipment; during the second, coition was attempted without ejaculatory success. The third episode developed as successful coition for [Mr. Y], but his wife was not orgasmic. During the fourth session both husband and wife were successful in individual automanipulative episodes, and in the fifth episode no difficulty was encountered by either partner in response to coital or manipulative stimuli.

Once acclimated, moreover, the Y's had no further difficulty, "much to the surprise of both husband and wife." Mrs. Y, who had only rarely experienced orgasm during intercourse before joining the program, now experienced it four-fifths of the time.

> [Mrs. Y] has stated repeatedly that subsequent to program participation her husband has been infinitely more effective both in stimulating and in satisfying her sexual tensions. He in turn finds her sexually responsive without reservation. Her freedom and security of response are particularly pleasing to him. Together they maintain that they have gotten a great deal more out of cooperating with the program than they have contributed, and they wish to continue on a long-term basis.

In what respects did the 694 Masters-Johnson volunteers differ from other American men and women?

They were on the average more highly educated. More than two hundred of the 694, for example, had attended graduate school following college. But other educational levels were also represented; more than two hundred had not gone to college at all, and some had not finished high school.

Most of the volunteers were white, but eleven couples were Negro.

All of the volunteers, as noted above, were sexually responsive.

One factor that broadened the volunteer group was the payment of volunteers for the time devoted to the project. This helped in several ways. The payments made this research resemble other forms of laboratory research for which payment is customarily made. Couples in modest circumstances who might have hesitated to participate because of the cost of baby-sitters and taking cabs to and from the lab were enabled to join. And the payments provided an additional incentive to volunteer for young couples—graduate students and their wives, for example—who needed the money. Thus the research population was not limited to those wanting to help in the progress of science and those seeking to add to their own sexual understanding and responsiveness; it also came to include those who wanted the extra income. Finally, paid volunteers were more likely to be punctual for their appointments, as they would be for any other paid job.

Of special interest was the geriatric group—thirty-four married couples over the age of fifty, including some in their sixties and seventies, plus five men over fifty married to post-menopausal women in their forties. "Their contribution has been large," Dr. Masters and Mrs. Johnson state, "for their cooperation has extended over four years of concentrated investigations of geriatric sexual response." (For discussion, see pages 251–266.)

Clearly, these 694 men and women differ *statistically* from the same number selected at random. Thus some kinds of questions cannot be answered by a study of this group. The question, "What proportion of women achieve orgasm?" for example, cannot be answered from a study that excludes women who do not achieve orgasm. Similarly, this highly selected group cannot be used to answer the question, "What proportion of women commonly experience multiple orgasms in rapid succession?"

But for many other kinds of question, reliable answers *can* be secured. A striking example concerns the changes in vaginal acidity during the four phases of sexual intercourse. The higher-average educational level of the women volunteers is hardly likely to affect the acidity of their vaginal fluids. And if some doubting Thomas were to challenge the results on the ground that education *might* affect vaginal acidity, the issue could promptly be settled by comparing the results in the volunteers who attended graduate school with the results in the high school dropouts—all without going outside the basic sample.

Similarly, the question, "Does a series of multiple orgasms resemble a single orgasm?" could be answered directly by actual comparison of the two types of response—even though the *proportion* of women experiencing multiple orgasm might be higher or lower in the Masters-Johnson research group.

Like the population as a whole, the Masters-Johnson group included the young and the old, the tall and the short, the fat and the thin, the rich and the poor, Negro and white, the single, the married, and the widowed or divorced, the circumcised and uncircumcised, women who had not had children, women who had had one child, and women who had had two, three, or four children. Thus the universality of a phenomenon in many kinds of people—women with and without children, for example—could also be established. The only handicap resulting from the selective nature of the Masters-Johnson research population is the impossibility of determining what proportion of people react in one way or another. For that, the Kinsey Institute reports remain the best guide.

When Dr. Masters first launched his research, it will be recalled, he had only prostitutes to work with. His subsequent success in recruiting men and women from many walks of life—the shy as well as the forthright, the inhibited as well as the unabashed—has exceeded his own fondest expectations, and must come as a surprise to the rest of us. Only Dr. Kinsey had anticipated such a possibility. Dr. Masters and Mrs. Johnson, indeed, have found only one characteristic common to all of their 694 volunteers: their basic interest in and desire for effectiveness of sexual performance. "This one factor," Dr. Masters and Mrs. Johnson suggest, "may represent the major area of difference between the research study subjects and the general population."

MISS A, MISS B, AND MISS C

While from one point of view, the men and women participating in the Masters-Johnson research were just ordinary citizens, devoted husbands, chaste wives, loving and conscientious parents, from another point of view each was uniquely himself or herself, with a dramatic story to explain his willingness to participate. To illustrate, let us consider in more detail three remarkable women involved in the Masters-Johnson program—all three as patients, and two of them also as volunteers.

The first of these, identified only as "Subject A" in the *Western Journal of Surgery, Obstetrics and Gynecology* for May–June 1961, was twenty-seven years old when Dr. Masters first saw her as a patient. This was in 1953, before his laboratory research was launched. Miss A and the young man she loved had come to see him together because they were eager to get married, but were afraid that they could never have sexual intercourse.

As a child, Miss A explained, she had not known that anything was wrong with her, and she appeared to be quite normal on external examination. Her breasts, her pubic hair, and other secondary sex characteristics had developed quite normally at the usual time. Nor did she have any problem of sexual responsiveness. Like countless other girls, she had discovered how to masturbate, and she had no difficulty in reaching orgasm. At the age of sixteen, however, she still had not menstruated.

Her parents accordingly took her to a physician who found that, despite normal development of the external genitals, including the outer and inner lips, Miss A had been born without a vagina.

This is an uncommon developmental defect in girls, but not as rare as might be supposed. Reports of vaginal agenesis, as it is called, and of the attempts of surgeons to correct it, date back for many decades. Dr. Virgil S. Counsellor and his associates at the Mayo Clinic reported in 1949 on one hundred cases treated there. According to one estimate, eighteen thousand women and girls in the United States today were born without a vagina.

"Of the propriety of establishing a vagina, in cases in which this canal is absent either as a congenital defect or as an acquired deformity, there seems to be no question, even when the canal is thus established purely for coitional purposes," wrote Dr. James Fairchild Baldwin of Columbus, Ohio, in the *Annals of Surgery* back in 1904. But early surgical attempts to create an artificial vagina were stymied by the fact that the normal vagina is lined with mucous membrane rather than with skin, and no feasible way had been discovered to graft mucous membrane effectively. Surgeons accordingly developed techniques for grafting skin from the thighs or abdomens of patients to line a surgically produced vaginal barrel. The technique worked; in a few cases, indeed, girls with artificial vaginas thus constructed became pregnant and gave birth to babies—some by normal means and some by cesarean section.

The physician to whom Miss A was taken at the age of sixteen was not, unfortunately, familiar with this operation. Nor did he bother to look it up in a gynecological textbook or in the medical journals. He explained the girl's problem to her parents, but they left his office with no knowledge that it could be surgically corrected.

Shortly after her eighteenth birthday, Miss A's defect was explained to her in detail. She took the news in her stride. If she could never hope to marry and have children, she would seek a career for herself. She went to college and later found a job where her training could be of use. She did not withdraw from social contacts. "During the patient's late teens and early twenties," Dr. Masters and Mrs. Johnson report, "the growth of normal heterosexual interests was evidenced by an active social life, and by a positive history of the usual teen-age anatomical sexual experimentation."

Very attractive, and emotionally as well as physiologically responsive, Miss A was repeatedly urged by men who dated her to "go all the way." Unwilling to reveal her defect, she took refuge in the familiar protest, "I want to be a virgin when I marry." On a number of occasions, however, she did "pet to climax"—to use the phrase introduced by Dr. Kinsey. "She also developed a satisfactory reciprocal technique for manual relief of the male partners involved," Dr. Masters and Mrs. Johnson report.

At the age of twenty-three, Miss A fell in love and almost became engaged. For six months she and her young man maintained a happy relationship. Then she told him about her defect. He consulted a physician—another practitioner unfamiliar with the frequently announced success of the artificial vagina operation—and he, too, was told that there was no hope of their ever engaging in sexual intercourse. Understandably enough the young man broke off the engagement.

Miss A was heartbroken. For the next two years or so, she dated very little. She tried hard to concentrate on her studies and her career. For sexual relief she masturbated. But her natural sociability eventually came to the fore, and at twenty-seven she fell in love again. Together with her fiancé, she sought medical consultation to see if "anything new" had developed in the way of a cure.

This time Miss A and her fiancé had the good fortune to consult a physician—Dr. Masters—familiar with the literature of sexual physiology and with the many published reports of artificial vaginas.

"Once the anatomic situation was described in detail to both potential marital partners," Dr. Masters and Mrs. Johnson wrote, "there was no question of the subject's eagerness to undergo the corrective surgical procedures deemed necessary. . . ." The young man was similarly delighted by the good news—though he expressed his eagerness to marry Miss A "whether the surgery is successful or not."

The operation was performed in 1953. Postoperative procedures were prescribed, and the couple married one month later. Sexual relations were successful from the beginning. Miss A (now "Mrs. Q") experienced her first orgasm during intercourse after three months; and she later reported that she was experiencing orgasm nine-tenths or more of all the times she had coitus.

This gratifying outcome, occurring just before Dr. Masters launched his laboratory research program, must have helped him in his decision to go ahead. What better evidence could he have of the almost unlimited potentialities of sex research for solving the most poignant human problems?

Four years after the operation, Mr. and Mrs. Q learned of Dr. Masters' program of laboratory research and decided to volunteer.

The story of Miss B can be more briefly summarized. She, too, was born without a vagina. Her mother, suspecting that "something was wrong," took her to a physician when she was eight. Fortunately, the physician consulted not only made the right diagnosis, and briefed Miss B's mother on the potential distress that might result, but also emphasized the fact that the condition was surgically correctable. "A vagina can successfully be created when the young lady is ready for marriage," the physician was quoted as saying. (Some gynecologists might have recommended an earlier operation.)

Miss B, like Miss A—but unlike many other victims of vaginal agenesis—went through her teens with a normal heterosexual social life. Like Miss A, she learned the joys of sexual response and staved off sexual intercourse with the formula, "I want to be a good girl."

Then, at twenty-two, Miss B fell in love and became engaged to a young man of twenty-six. The two developed a mutual technique of sexual stimulation satisfactory to both. They consulted Dr. Masters, who offered surgery, but they decided to marry first.

Six months after their marriage, they returned for the operation; it was successful.

Two years after the operation, this couple, too, volunteered to become members of the Masters-Johnson laboratory study group.

Miss C's case was different, and is perhaps more typical of the psychological trauma girls suffer when they first learn (without proper briefing) that they have no vagina.

Miss C's parents first took her to a doctor when she was six years old. He was "reassuring." Dissatisfied, they sought consultation with a specialist, who explained to them in some detail both the condition and the probable necessity of future surgery. According to the mother, however, he gave no warning as to any possible psychological effect on the daughter.

Miss C reached the age of fourteen ignorant of her defect—a happy, extroverted, relaxed young lady with marked sociability. She did very well in school. Her sexual development was normal—except, of course, that she did not begin to menstruate when her friends and classmates did.

This troubled her very much; and toward the end of her fourteenth year, after she had frequently expressed her concern about her failure to menstruate, her mother undertook to tell her about her condition. "Either the mother's descriptive powers were inadequate, or unfortunately were expressed with emotional bias," Dr. Masters and Mrs. Johnson subsequently reported. "In any event, Subject 'C' apparently suffered severe psychological trauma. . . ." Miss C's parents did not take her to a physician again at this time; nor is there any evidence that they reported to her the doctor's statement when she was six that surgery might solve the problem.

> During the next two years [Dr. Masters and Mrs. Johnson report] Subject "C" underwent a marked personality involution. . . . She became chronically depressed and markedly involutional in interpersonal relationships. The mother describes significant evidence of excessive emotional disturbance . . . many crying spells, long periods of isolation, and repeated statements of "I want to die." [Her school grades fell far below average. Her teachers described] a marked reduction in concentration span and a classroom behavior that was primarily antisocial. Apparently there were no friends at school with whom Subject "C" shared confidences. The family also reports that she had no real interest in, or evidence of, friends of either sex. This antisocial attitude developed despite the fact that, until the age of fourteen, her personality had been primarily gregarious in nature.

After two years of this psychic suffering, Miss C's parents finally sought medical help for her. But they did not take her to a gynecologist. Although they knew about the corrective operation, they took her instead to a psychiatrist in "an attempt to provide relief from the progressive symptoms of neurotic behavior."

Psychiatry is not, however, the best treatment for vaginal agenesis, and during the next two years Miss C became even more unhappy and neurotic "despite active psychiatric support." Then, at the age of eighteen, she was referred to Dr. Masters for gynecological evaluation—her first since the age of six.

Dr. Masters noted total absence of a vagina; there was only a small dimple where the vagina should have been. This dimple, however, suggested the use of a nonsurgical technique, described by Drs. R. T. Frank and S. H. Geist in 1927, and further by Dr. Frank in 1938, involving the daily application to the dimple of a "perineal dilator" designed to stretch it gently over a period of months until a vaginal barrel was formed.

The details and advantages of the technique were exhaustively explained to the young lady [Dr. Masters and Mrs. Johnson state]. She became vitally interested in the reclamation project and promised complete cooperation. Application of the . . . dilators to the dimpled area of the perineum was instituted as a daily procedure.

With regularly recurring effort the perineal dimple slowly increased in depth and breadth. . . . [The girl] became a different individual once she knew she "was getting to be normal." After eight months of conscientious perineal dilation, a well-developed artificial vagina measured 7 cm. in depth.

Miss C then entered college, where she achieved excellent grades. "Her social activities have developed a marked heterosexual interest. Routine heterosexual dating has been established, and she has given every intent of real interest in interpersonal relationships." She engaged in coitus with two men and reported that neither of them noted anything different about her vagina.

A final statement of Miss C's indicates the psychological as well as the physiological success of her artificial vagina: "None of my friends, even my boy friends, knows that I am different—and *I* don't really feel that I am."

Miss C did not participate in the Masters-Johnson laboratory research program. She would have been refused if she had volunteered, for, as noted above, all volunteers are thoroughly screened for a history of past emotional instability before they are accepted. "No attempt has been made," Dr. Masters and Mrs. Johnson state, "to use her as a subject for experimentation in the field of sexual response." She did co-operate with the project, however, "to the extent of [supplying] multiple vaginal smears, a vaginal biopsy, cyclic vaginal pH recordings, and a detailed history. . . ."

Dr. Masters neither claims nor deserves special credit for the development of either the surgical correction of vaginal agenesis or the nonsurgical method of correction through the use of perineal dilators. He is simply one of the many gyne-cologists who make use of these methods of treatment. Yet his 1961 paper with Mrs. Johnson, entitled "The Artificial Vagina: Anatomic, Physiologic, Psychosexual Function," is one of the major contributions to the literature of vaginal agenesis; for it is the first report *based on long-term follow-up* of the detailed physiological and psychological results of the artificial vagina. The 1966 Masters-Johnson report, *Human Sexual Response,* provides further follow-up studies on Miss A, Miss B, Miss C, and four others.

A few of the follow-up findings are worth noting here.

The first concerns vaginal lubrication. Beads of lubricating fluid, as noted above (pages 19, 22), appear on the mucous membrane lining the natural vagina within ten to thirty seconds after the onset of sexual stimulation. This may be stimulation of the clitoral region, or of the breasts and their nipples, or it may be purely psychic—the occurrence of erotic thoughts without any physical contact. Regardless of the type of stimulation, the beads of moisture promptly ap-pear.

Since the artificial vagina is lined with skin rather than mucous membrane, no lubrication can be expected at first, and patients are advised to use a cream or jelly lubricant prior to coitus. But during the following weeks and months, an astonishing change occurs. Gradually the lining comes more and more to resemble the lining of the normal vagina, with mucous membrane characteristics. *And this mucous mem-brane begins to secrete lubricating fluid.* In the case of Miss A, for example, sufficient natural lubrication was established within four months of the operation to make cream or jelly unnecessary. In the case of Miss B, adequate lubrication made its appearance within six weeks.

The Masters-Johnson studies reveal that this appearance of lubricating droplets, in girls with artificial vaginas, occurs within thirty to forty seconds after the onset of either physical or psychic stimulation.

Another interesting observation concerns the relationship of vaginal lubrication to the menstrual cycle. Women with normal vaginas, the Masters-Johnson studies indicate, tend to lubricate more copiously during the luteal phase of the cycle —that is, during the days following ovulation and preceding menstruation. The same is true, Dr. Masters and Mrs. Johnson noted, of Subjects A and B.

Other significant observations on the seven patients with artificial vaginas can be summed up in a single broad generalization. In almost all significant respects, *these patients respond physiologically to effective sexual stimulation in precisely the same ways—including orgasm—as do women with natural vaginas.*

SOME LABORATORY PROCEDURES

One early concern of Dr. Masters and Mrs. Johnson was to determine whether bodily sexual responses vary with the type of stimulation applied. In search of answers to this question, male responses to intercourse and masturbation were compared; and female responses to eight different types of stimulation were also compared:

(1) Manual automanipulation—that is, masturbation with the hand or fingers.

(2) Mechanical automanipulation—that is, masturbation with an electric vibrator or massager of the kind on sale at most drug and department stores. Application of a vibrator to the mons area provides intense clitoral stimulation, and the vibrator is therefore recommended by a number of therapists to women patients unable to reach orgasm in other ways. Once a patient has learned to reach orgasm with the aid of the vibrator, the response pattern can be transferred to other forms of stimulation, including ordinary coitus (see pages 87, 161).

(3) Sexual intercourse with the wife in the "supine position"—that is, lying on her back.

(4) Sexual intercourse with the husband in the supine position.

(5) Sexual intercourse with the wife in the "knee-chest" position—that is, face downward and supporting her weight on her knees and elbows. Her husband's penis then entered her vagina from the rear.

(6) "Artificial coition," with the wife in the supine position, making use of an artificial penis. (This device proved to be of the greatest usefulness in securing data unavailable in any other way. It was made of plastic as clear as plate glass and as free of optical distortion. Both its length and its diameter could be selected to fit the user's vagina. It was powered by an electric motor; the user could adjust both the depth and the frequency of thrust to suit herself, and could alter the adjustments at will from time to time. An optical system within the artificial penis made it possible to observe internal changes and to record them in full color on motion-picture film. Many of the most significant findings of the study arose out of these artificial coition observations.)

(7) Artificial coition with the wife in the knee-chest position also provided highly significant data.

(8) Stimulation of the breasts alone, without genital contact; several of the women in the Masters-Johnson research group proved capable of reaching orgasm in this way. Observations of genital response were of course very easy in these cases, and hard-to-get data were secured.

As has been noted, some women proved more readily responsive to one of these eight types of stimulation than to another. Response might occur more quickly or more slowly, and might be more or less intense, depending upon the type of stimulation. Psychologically, the experience might be felt as quite different. But the basic responses described above—from initial lubrication of the vagina, through orgasm, to the end of the resolution phase—proceeded in precisely the same sequence regardless of the type of stimulation.

One hallmark of well-planned research is its ability to return useful data on a number of questions simultaneously. The Masters-Johnson research was well planned in this respect, as a detailed example will show.

Mr. and Mrs. K, after the usual practice sessions in privacy and orientation sessions with Dr. Masters and Mrs. Johnson present, agreed to participate in a special subsection of the research program concerned with variations in the relative acidity of the vagina under varying conditions. Earlier test-tube studies had shown that sperm cells are damaged by either too high or too low a "pH"—that is, too high or low a concentration of hydrogen ions, a factor known popularly as relative acidity or alkalinity. Semen contains a buffer that protects the sperm cells from acid; but Dr. Masters suspected that under some circumstances at least, the relative pH of the vagina might help or hinder the migration of the sperm cells through the vagina and cervix into the uterus and Fallopian tubes on their way to meet an ovum. All this was explained to Mr. and Mrs. K, and the strict experimental procedures to be followed were presented to them in detail.

The main experiment, they were told, would continue through three of Mrs. K's monthly menstrual cycles. Its primary purpose would be to measure the pH at five selected points inside Mrs. K's vagina under a variety of conditions. Since semen alters the acidity or pH, Mr. K was to wear a condom whenever he had intercourse with Mrs. K during the three-month period. Mrs. K was not to douche, and was not to use any vaginal jellies, creams, or suppositories. Weekly laboratory tests would be run to make sure that her vagina remained free of infection—for bacteria and fungi can also alter the pH of the vagina. Laboratory sessions were scheduled in advance, and the K's were instructed to refrain from sexual intercourse, even intercourse with a condom, for three days prior to each session. Mrs. K was also instructed not to masturbate during these three-day periods.

The first of the fully controlled experimental sessions following these preliminaries occurred on the eleventh day of Mrs. K's twenty-seven-day menstrual cycle—that is, immediately prior to the time when one of her ovaries was expected to release an ovum. The first laboratory procedure was to secure a sample of her vaginal secretion on a glass slide. The slide was then examined under a microscope; and the condition of the cells found in the fluid confirmed the fact that she had not yet ovulated.

Next an electronic probe or electrode sheathed in glass was inserted into Mrs. K's vagina. It was attached by wires to a standard pH meter which determined the relative pH of any region of the vaginal lining touched by the tip of the probe. The pH at five points was recorded in succession: two points near the entrance to the vagina, two near the middle and one at the farthest end, known as the *cul-de-sac*.

After this first or baseline recording, Mrs. K was requested to masturbate. The electronic probe was reinserted 2½ minutes later and another set of five pH readings was recorded. At this time, too, Dr. Masters and Mrs. Johnson checked the interior of the vagina to gauge the amount of lubricating moisture secreted; they rated the quantity on a five-point scale ranging from 1 (very little) to 5 (very copious lubrication). Thus in addition to determining pH, the same sexual sequence was being used to measure simultaneously Mrs. K's lubrication response as part of the broader overall study.

Three additional sets of pH readings, and of lubrication observations, were taken 5 minutes, 7½ minutes and 10 minutes after Mrs. K had started masturbating. On some occasions she was asked to stop while readings were being made; on other occasions she was instructed to continue without interruption. After the fourth set of readings, she continued to masturbate without further interruptions for an additional 9¼ minutes—at which time her orgasm occurred.

The electronic probe was reintroduced and five further meter readings were recorded within 10 to 15 seconds after the orgasm had subsided. All of the procedures were repeated five more times during the next 15 minutes of Mrs. K's post-orgasm recovery phase. These observations were useful in outlining the nature of the recovery phase as well as in the pH portion of the experimental plan.

At the very beginning of the session, Mrs. K had been asked a number of questions—how she felt, whether there had been any problems since her previous visit to the laboratory, whether her sexual tension seemed high, moderate, or low. Immediately after her orgasm, she was questioned again and asked to rate the intensity of the orgasm on a scale from 1 (mild) to 4 (very intense). (Grade 5 on the scale was reserved for multiple orgasm.) Thus the same response cycle useful in determining pH and lubrication responses was also being used to search for possible correlations between the subjective intensity of an orgasm and the physiological responses accompanying that orgasm. At the conclusion of her recovery period further questions were asked—whether, for example, she had made use of erotic fantasies during the buildup of sexual tension, and if so, what they were. She was also asked to describe in her own words everything she had experienced during the session, and the physiological changes she had felt. Similar questioning preceded and followed each of the subsequent sessions. The rich psychological data thus secured have not as yet been published, but will be included in future Masters-Johnson reports.

Mrs. K's next appointment came three days later. Microscopic examination of the vaginal slide on this occasion indicated that she had in fact ovulated since her last visit, as expected. The same masturbatory procedure and measurements were accordingly repeated to provide a comparison of vaginal pH, lubrication, intensity of orgasm, and nature of recovery phase before and after ovulation.

A third session on the twenty-fourth day of the same menstrual cycle—three days before her next menstruation—provided further comparisons of these and other factors. In all, 160 pH measurements were made inside Mrs. K's vagina this first month—eleven sets of five measurements each on two occasions, and ten sets on the third.

During Mrs. K's next menstrual cycle, she and Mr. K came to the laboratory together, and almost the same observations and pH measurements were made before, during, and following sexual intercourse. The glass microscope slide was used as usual to determine whether Mrs. K had as yet ovulated, and the electronic probe was used as usual to measure vaginal pH during a sexually unexcited state—that is, prior to the appearance of vaginal lubrication. Mr. K then joined Mrs. K, wearing a condom so that his semen would not affect the pH measurements. Sex play began, followed by sexual intercourse. The intercourse was interrupted when Mrs. K reported that she was fully aroused sexually; Mr. K withdrew his penis and pH measurements and other observations were made. These observations, of course, were useful in yet another facet of the overall research program; they could be used to determine whether Mrs. K responded in the same or in a different way to sexual intercourse and to masturbation. After this interruption was over, sexual activity was resumed and continued until Mrs. K had her orgasm. This orgasm could be compared with the orgasms she had had during the masturbatory sessions. Further pH measurements and observations were made during Mrs. K's resolution phase; the observations could be used to determine whether her resolution phase differed following intercourse and following masturbation. The whole procedure was repeated on two other selected days during this menstrual cycle. On each occasion, both Mr. and

Mrs. K were questioned intensively concerning their subjective experiences and emotional responses.

During Mrs. K's third menstrual cycle, the techniques of the first and second months were combined. Mrs. K first masturbated to orgasm; then, after her recovery phase was completed, Mr. K joined her and they engaged in sexual intercourse. The usual pH measurements and other observations were made, before, during, and after both orgasms—a rich source of further comparisons between masturbation responses and sexual intercourse responses.

In addition to Mr. and Mrs. K, three other married couples cooperated in the vaginal pH phase of the Masters-Johnson research. All three followed the same rigorously prescribed three-month schedule of experimentation. Two of the four couples had had several children each; the other two had no children. This made possible comparisons of many kinds between the responses of women with children and of women without children—including differences in vaginal pH at different phases of their menstrual cycle, and during different phases of their sexual response to both masturbation and intercourse.

In all, these four women were observed through some fifty orgasms during the three-month research schedule. Thousands of pH measurements, and countless observations relevant to many other aspects of the research, could be made during these fifty episodes—in addition to the subjective data which both wives and husbands supplied.

To confirm these findings, all four couples were then put through a second three-month cycle on the same schedule, and some of the couples were put through a third cycle.

Even this did not exhaust the scientific productivity of this one small subsection of the overall Masters-Johnson research program. For example, a participant, whom we will describe as Mrs. L, reached orgasm just three minutes after the onset of masturbation on the first of her regularly scheduled visits to participate in this part of the program. Orgasm occurred despite the fact that pH measurements had been taken half a minute earlier. Dr. Masters and Mrs. Johnson rated Mrs. L's vaginal lubrication on this occasion as only "fair." Mrs. L herself rated this first orgasm as moderately intense.

Since the orgasm had come so promptly, Mrs. L was asked to masturbate again after her ten-minute resolution phase was ended. This time Dr. Masters rated her vaginal lubrication as "good"; and a second orgasm, which Mrs. L rated as more intense than the first, occurred just 2¾ minutes after the onset of the second round of stimulation. Mrs. L's very rapid responses could be compared with Mrs. K's much slower responses—12 minutes, 19¼ minutes, and 23⅓ minutes—under comparable laboratory conditions. And the sequence also supplied data relevant to the portion of the Masters-Johnson research concerned with repeated orgasms. (Following her second orgasm, Mrs. L continued to masturbate for 30 minutes, but did not reach a third climax.)

On another occasion Mr. and Mrs. L came to the laboratory together. After the usual preliminary tests and measurements, Mrs. L began to masturbate, reaching orgasm in 5⅝ minutes. Following a ten-minute resolution phase, Mr. L joined Mrs. L and sexual intercourse began.

After seven minutes, Mrs. L reported that she was fully aroused. Intercourse was accordingly interrupted for vaginal examination and pH measurements. Dr. Masters and Mrs. Johnson noted that vaginal lubrication was "good." Sexual activity was then resumed, and Mrs. L reached orgasm 16⅔ minutes later, 23⅔ minutes after the onset of stimulation. Measurements were continued as usual during the resolution period. Mrs. L's responses to masturbation and to intercourse on the same day could thus be compared.

The thousands of measurements made with these four women and their husbands indicated a small but significant shift in vaginal acidity during various phases of the wives' menstrual cycles. These changes were presumably due to the varying amounts of sex hormones secreted by the ovaries at different times in the month. To confirm this hypothesis, two other women were invited to participate, and did. Both of them had had their ovaries removed during previous surgical operations, but had remained (as is usual in such cases) sexually responsive. Both were being maintained on artificial cycles by means of hormone replacement therapy, and the length of their cycles could thus be varied at will. The results confirmed the results on the four normally menstruating women and showed that the pH changes from one portion of the menstrual cycle to another are in fact due to ovarian hormones—natural hormones in the cases of the first four women, and hormones of pharmaceutical origin in the other two cases.

Another aspect of this pH research deserves mention. Many married Catholic couples rely on the "rhythm method" of contraception. This method depends on predicting quite precisely the time of ovulation—that is, the time when one of the woman's ovaries will release an ovum. Various ways have been recommended for making this prediction; none is completely satisfactory. The Masters-Johnson research conclusively demonstrates that *changes in vaginal acidity cannot be relied upon to predict ovulation for women using the rhythm method of contraception.*

Volunteers were assigned to various subsections of the research plan for a variety of reasons. A couple particularly interested in a specific problem, for example, might be assigned to research relevant to that problem. Women with particular capabilities—such as those able to have one orgasm right after the other, without an intervening resolution phase, and those able to reach orgasm by means of breast stimulation alone—were of course particularly valuable for research into these phenomena. In a few cases, too, women were selected because the particular type of observation to be made could more easily be made in their cases. An example was the portion of the study concerned with the response of the uterus to sexual stimulation.

Early observations had established the fact that the muscles of the uterus participate in the female orgasm. This was established both by placing an electrode sensitive to muscular contractions on the surface of the abdomen, and by placing one inside the uterus itself. The study indicated that the contractions proceed in a wavelike progression from top to bottom of the uterus—much as do labor contractions.

These preliminary observations, however, did not show whether the blood vessels of the uterus also became engorged during sexual response. Since muscle contractions and blood vessel engorgement are the two main features of the response of other organs to erotic stimulation, it seemed important to determine whether the uterus also exhibits *both* types of response. Engorgement, however, could not be checked with electrodes; it would be necessary to check for any swelling of the uterus by palpating it from the vagina—a routine gynecological procedure during pelvic examinations.

To perform the thousands of pelvic examinations necessary for firm conclusions would be a difficult and time-consuming task; but an important practical issue persuaded Dr. Masters to proceed. One of America's foremost gynecologists—Dr. Howard C. Taylor, Jr., of the Columbia-Presbyterian Medical Center in New York City, currently president of the American College of Obstetricians and Gynecologists—had described in a series of three papers published in 1949 a phenomenon called *chronic pelvic congestion*—the chronic engorgement of blood vessels of the uterus and associated pelvic organs. Dr. Taylor stated that a number of gynecological problems were related to this chronic congestion of the blood vessels; and he suggested that the whole "congestion-fibrosis syndrome," as he called it, was traceable at least in part and at least in some cases to a constantly recurring, year-after-year pattern of experiencing sexual arousal without orgasmic release.

Dr. Masters' early work with prostitutes at the beginning of his sex research project tended to confirm this explanation of the "Taylor syndrome." The prostitutes he examined reported that they frequently became erotically aroused without experiencing orgasm in the course of their work. Among these prostitutes, Dr. Masters quite frequently found the "congestion-fibrosis syndrome" described by Dr. Taylor.

One dramatic occasion during the prostitute phase of his work, moreover, focused Dr. Masters' attention even more sharply on the severe effects that might follow prolonged sexual arousal without orgasmic release. On this occasion, a prostitute agreed to subject herself to pelvic examination during her 6½-hour work shift and after her work was over. During her working period, she had intercourse twenty-seven times with almost that many men. She remained erotically excited during most of the 6½-hour period, and on five occasions reported she felt as though she had risen to the plateau phase. No orgasm occurred.

During a pelvic examination toward the end of her working period, Dr. Masters found that her uterus was enlarged to two or three times its unstimulated size. The broad ligaments attached to the uterus were thickened by congestion of the veins with blood. The walls of the vaginal barrel were grossly engorged and showed marked edema—that is, swelling due to fluids seeping into the tissues from engorged blood vessels. Both her major and minor labia were swollen to twice or three times their usual size. "Pelvic examinations and coital activity became increasingly painful toward the end of the 6½-hour working period," Dr. Masters noted. The whole pelvic condition strikingly resembled the chronic pelvic congestion that Dr. Taylor had described six years earlier—though in exaggerated form. Dr. Masters was accordingly concerned to see how long this congestion would last.

He continued his observations for the next six hours of

the resolution phase, during which no sexual stimulation was permitted. Throughout the entire period, he noted, "gross venous engorgement of the external and internal genitalia persisted—so much so, in fact, that the woman was irritable, emotionally disturbed, and could not sleep. She complained of pelvic fullness, pressure, cramping, moments of true pain, and a persistent, severe low backache."

At the end of the six-hour observation period, she was excused. She promptly masturbated, achieving orgasm and "immediate relief from the subjective pelvic distress and the low backache. The objective findings also disappeared rapidly. Pelvic vasocongestion was reduced an estimated 50 percent in five minutes and had disappeared completely ten minutes after the orgasmic experience."

Observations of one prostitute following so atypical a work period cannot be relied on for scientific purposes, of course; but the association between severe engorgement of the pelvic blood vessels, subjective feelings of distress, and failure to achieve orgasm, plus the prompt relief following orgasm, when viewed in the light of Dr. Taylor's earlier statement that this type of congestion can become chronic and lead to other problems, made it imperative that Dr. Masters check pelvic congestion in ordinary women following ordinary sexual stimulation.

Fifty women volunteers were selected for this phase of the Masters-Johnson research program extending over a four-year period. They were chosen for the ease with which they could be examined pelvically. In all other respects they differed widely. They ranged in age, for example, from eighteen to fifty-three years. Nineteen of them had never had a baby, thirteen had one child, seventeen had two or three, and one had four children. Each volunteer participated on five occasions—two occasions during the week immediately following a menstrual period, two during the week immediately prior to anticipated menstruation, and one at the height of menstrual flow (usually the second or third day of menstruation). During each of these occasions, of course, observations were made on many other aspects of response in addition to changes in the uterus.

The premenstrual and the postmenstrual observations were made preceding and following both masturbation and sexual intercourse; the observations during menstruation were made preceding and following masturbation alone. In all, several thousands of pelvic examinations were performed during five hundred response cycles to determine the response of the uterus to erotic stimulation of both kinds.

A typical session would open with a pelvic examination of the woman to determine the size of her uterus in an unstimulated state. She would then begin to masturbate or engage in sexual intercourse with her husband and continue well into the plateau phase. At the time when she felt that orgasm was imminent, sexual stimulation was stopped and pelvic examination of the condition of the uterus and of the attached broad ligaments followed.

In every instance, Dr. Masters noted, there was a significant increase in size of the uterus among women who had had one or more babies. In most cases he estimated the size increase at from 50 to 100 percent—a difference very easy to note between two pelvic examinations performed half an hour or less apart. Dr. Masters also noted that in individuals who had varicose veins in the pelvic region, there was an abnormal degree of venous engorgement of the broad ligaments.

Among the nineteen women who had not had babies, the findings were less precise. Some of them showed quite definite enlargement of the uterus; others either showed no enlargement, or else—a more likely possibility—a degree of enlargement too slight to be definitely determined by pelvic palpation alone.

Following the second pelvic examination, the women volunteers returned to masturbation or sexual intercourse, as the case might be. In about three-fourths of the five hundred episodes they reached orgasm. Another pelvic examination followed within a minute or two; five or six more were performed during the next half-hour, and a final pelvic examination was performed one hour after orgasm. The women who had not had children lost all detectable evidence of pelvic engorgement within ten minutes after orgasm; the same resolution process took ten to twenty minutes for women who had had babies.

In the cases in which women did not reach orgasm during further sexual activity, pelvic examinations were also made at five-minute intervals following the cessation of activity. These observations showed that the uterus remained detectably engorged for a significantly longer time in the absence of orgasmic release—as long as a half-hour or an hour in many cases.

The Masters-Johnson findings concerning prolonged engorgement of the uterus in the absence of orgasmic release should arouse no concern whatever among women who fail to reach orgasm from time to time. But the findings tend to confirm that countless repeated periods of sexual arousal not followed by orgasmic release may, over a period of years, contribute to the development of chronic pelvic congestion—the "Taylor syndrome."

In general, only married couples were used in portions of the research program that required sexual intercourse; the single men and women and the widows and widowers were used in portions that required only masturbation or artificial coition. But one exception was made to this general policy.

As it became increasingly clear through thousands of comparative observations such as those we have been describing that the physiological responses to stimulation are precisely the same in basic pattern, regardless of whether the stimulus is masturbation, intercourse, artificial coition, or breast stimulation, one flaw in the research design became increasingly apparent. All of the intercourse was being performed by married men and women, for the most part long familiar with one another's responses and accustomed to respond in relatively stereotyped ways. Would couples having intercourse with one another for the first time exhibit the same responses? Was uniformity of response a reliable finding for every act of intercourse, or was it just the result of the fact that responses in these married couples had gradually become uniform through long experience?

One way to close this gap in the research design would have been to study couples on their honeymoons. Since this was clearly not feasible, Dr. Masters and Mrs. Johnson departed from their established policy and studied a limited number of sexual response cycles occurring during intercourse between unmarried men and women who had not previously had intercourse with one another. The volunteers for this portion of the program were consenting adults for whom nonmarital intercourse was common in their own social setting. The data soon confirmed the fact that the same sequence of responses occurred under these conditions, and the nonmarital observations were terminated.

This review of some laboratory procedures does not, of course, exhaust the many variations in experimental design introduced during the eleven years of the Masters-Johnson program. It is perhaps sufficient, however, to indicate the ways in which research on small groups was used to solve subsidiary problems, while data were simultaneously being collected to confirm the broad general outlines of sexual response reported in the Masters-Johnson book, *Human Sexual Response,* and on pages 17–33 above. Further research may alter in detail the findings of the subsidiary research subsections; but the basic pattern of human sexual response, occurring uniformly during *all* of these sub-projects, stands in relatively little need of further experimental verification. What remains to be accomplished is further study of variations from the baseline thus established, and a search for the underlying neural and biochemical causes of the many responses observed.

Recording these sexual responses on motion-picture film was a minor but significant portion of the Masters-Johnson laboratory progam. Because it has been a target of criticism, a full discussion is warranted.

Though few laymen realize it, scientific recording on film plays an essential role in many kinds of physiological research and in medical diagnosis. A typical example is *cineradiography,* in which the moving-picture film is exposed to X-rays emerging from the patient. Prior to the development of cineradiography, a radiologist might have had to continue his examination of a patient with a fluoroscope for many minutes, in order to make sure that he had observed all the relevant detail revealed by the X-rays. If a second physician were later called into consultation, it might be necessary to repeat the entire procedure. With the X-ray data recorded on film, the radiologist can examine the same short film sequence repeatedly until he has mastered all the data it contains—instead of exposing the patient to substantial quantities of radiation during a prolonged examination. And a consultant can subsequently review the filmed sequence with the radiologist to assure consensus. In general, the recording of physiological data on moving-picture film (cinematography) is useful in at least five important ways:

(1) It enables the researcher to analyze occurrences so brief that they would otherwise be missed or misinterpreted. This can be done either by reprojecting a sequence repeatedly, seeing a little more each time, or by projecting it in slow motion.

(2) It enables the researcher to measure precisely changes he could otherwise only estimate. This is done by extracting a film frame from an early portion of a sequence and one from a later portion, and then

actually measuring the feature of interest on the surface of the two films.

(3) A change observed today can be compared with one observed weeks, months, or years before if the earlier change was recorded. Moving pictures taken before a surgical operation, for example, can be compared with pictures taken afterward to assess the degree of improvement. Similarly, Masters and Johnson could compare sexual responses of a married couple early in their laboratory participation with responses of the same couple many years later.

(4) Moving pictures can be used to document discoveries. It is common practice for physicians who have developed a new procedure, such as a new type of surgical operation or orthopedic treatment, to present films of it at subsequent medical meetings.

(5) Finally, medical moving pictures are extremely important in medical education and are in very common use for presenting techniques and observations to students.

Dr. Masters and Mrs. Johnson through the years have used films taken in their laboratories in all five of these ways. The use of films for documentation and for professional education have been particularly important in the case of their research because of the difficulties involved in inviting other scientists or students to observe for themselves in the laboratory. Many of the most important Masters-Johnson films portray internal changes, which could not otherwise be viewed, such as changes in the cervix. Others portray such external changes as the engorgement of the areolas surrounding the nipples or the color changes of the minor labia.

On several occasions, Dr. Masters and Mrs. Johnson have presented sequences filmed in their laboratory at meetings of professional groups such as the American Association of Marriage Counselors and the New York Psychoanalytic Society. The response of professional viewers has on the whole been favorable.

A few of those attending, it is true, seem to have come expecting to see a "sex movie" or "stag film." They have been disappointed, of course; and some who have attended in an unscientific frame of mind have even come away disgusted with what they have seen. For an example of this reaction to a Masters-Johnson film sequence, and for a description of the sequence itself, see the chapter by Dr. Leslie H. Farber, page 297.

THREE SEXUAL MYTHS
EXPLODED

Through the generations, men—and some women—have
speculated on the nature of sexual response, basing their
speculations on their personal experience and on the accounts
of others who, in turn, have had to rely on personal experience. Out of this vast sexual literature, several myths have
arisen, which the detailed Masters-Johnson observations dis-
prove. Among them are:

(1) The myth that a man's sexual performance is related
    to the size of his penis.
(2) The myth that women can have two kinds of orgasm—
    one clitoral and the other vaginal.
(3) The myth that a woman, like a man, is limited to one
    climactic orgasm that produces satiety.

Size of Penis

Many men and boys are worried by the small size of their
penis. A man generally reaches the conclusion that his own
is small by observing and comparing the unerected penises
of other men in showers, swimming pools, or other places. He
assumes that the larger organs he has observed will increase
in size during sexual stimulation proportionately more than
his own smaller penis. Psychiatrists report that the resulting
feeling of inferiority is a serious problem for substantial
numbers of men.

In reply, Masters and Johnson point out first that a penis
that is large in its unstimulated state does *not* increase in
length proportionately during erection. On the contrary, as
noted above (page 19), short penises as a general rule
increase in length more impressively than do long ones. A
striking comparison illustrates this point. One man in the
Masters-Johnson study group with an organ less than three
inches long in the flaccid state experienced a 120-percent
increase in penile length during erection, so that his erect

penis measured nearly seven inches. Another man in the group with a penis half again as long when flaccid (nearly four and one-half inches) experienced an increase in length during erection of only 50 percent. As a result, his fully erect penis was also a little less than seven inches long. In general, there is significantly less variation in length among erect than among flaccid penises. Penile size, moreover, turned out to have little relationship to a marital partner's satisfaction in sexual intercourse, for the vagina accommodates itself to the size of the male organ.

This accommodation reaction was repeatedly demonstrated during artificial coition (see page 69) with a plastic artificial penis whose length and diameter a woman could select to suit herself and could change from time to time. "Full accommodation usually is accomplished," Dr. Masters and Mrs. Johnson report, "with the first few thrusts of the penis, regardless of penile size."

The size of the vagina also has little effect on mutual satisfaction in most cases; and accommodation can be helped by suitable timing of the entry of the penis. If the husband has a relatively small penis and the wife a relatively large vagina, for example, he can introduce his penis into the vagina earlier in the excitement phase. When this is done, Dr. Masters and Mrs. Johnson report, "the fully erect smaller penis can and does function as a dilating agent as effectively as a larger penis." Conversely, a husband with a relatively large penis can help his wife with a small vagina by delaying entry until a more advanced stage of sexual excitation. "It becomes obvious," Dr. Masters and Mrs. Johnson conclude, "that penile size usually is a minor factor in sexual stimulation of the female partner."

Clitoral vs. Vaginal Orgasm

More than sixty years ago, Sigmund Freud presented, in *Three Essays on the Theory of Sexuality*, a theory that women can experience two kinds of orgasm—one clitoral, the other vaginal.

Little girls, he explained, discover that they can achieve orgasm by stimulating the clitoris. Later, in marriage, they must transfer their sexual responses from the clitoris to the vagina. Some women fail to make this transfer. As a result, even though they may continue to have orgasm following stimulation of the clitoris, they are "vaginally frigid."

Since Freud wrote, this doctrine of the vaginal orgasm as

distinct from the clitoral orgasm has permeated sexual literature and has troubled many women (see page 139). The
Masters-Johnson research should put these worries to
rest.

During ordinary vaginal intercourse, their studies show,
a remarkable feature of female anatomy comes into play. The
thrusting of the penis, as noted above (page 23) causes
motion of the inner lips, or minor labia, at the entrance of
the vagina. These lips come together above the vaginal opening to form the "hood" or prepuce of the clitoris. The rhythmic motion of the inner lips produced by rhythmic coital
thrusting slides the hood rhythmically back and forth against
the exquisitely sensitive glans of the clitoris, stimulating it
lightly but most effectively. Thus the clitoris participates fully
in ordinary vaginal intercourse, even though neither husband
nor wife makes special efforts to stimulate it directly.

There are undoubtedly great psychological differences between masturbation and sexual intercourse—but these differences cannot be traced back to two different kinds of orgasm.
To quote directly from the paper by Masters and Johnson in
the *Western Journal of Surgery, Gynecology, and Obstetrics*
for September–October 1962:

> From an *anatomic* point of view, there is absolutely no
> difference in the response of the pelvic viscera to effective
> sexual stimulation, regardless of whether stimulation occurs
> as a result of clitoral area manipulation, natural or artificial
> coition, or, for that matter, from breast stimulation alone. . . .
> The human female's physiologic responses to effective sexual
> stimulation develop with consistency regardless of the source
> of the psychic or physical sexual stimulation.

Women concerned by their failure to reach "vaginal orgasm" can thus be reassured. There is neither a purely clitoral
orgasm nor a purely vaginal orgasm. There is only one kind
of orgasm from the physiological point of view—a *sexual*
orgasm.

Multiple Orgasms in Women

Most men, as noted above, experience a "refractory period"
following orgasm and ejaculation. They cannot experience a
second erection and orgasm for many minutes or even hours.
This is not true of women.

If a woman who is capable of regular orgasms is properly

stimulated within a short period after her first climax [Dr. Masters and Mrs. Johnson report], she will in most instances be capable of having a second, third, fourth, and even fifth and sixth orgasm before she is fully satiated. As contrasted with the male's usual inability to have more than one orgasm in a short period, many females, especially when clitorally stimulated, can regularly have five or six full orgasms within a matter of minutes.

The possibility of multiple orgasms in women was not a Masters-Johnson discovery, of course; 14 percent of the women interviewed by Kinsey and his associates reported that they sometimes had multiple orgasms, and the same was true of 13 percent of the women interviewed by Terman. But these findings were often dismissed as unreliable by male writers who referred to multiple orgasms as "minor," and who even called multiorgasmic women "frigid" and incapable of experiencing true orgasm (see below, pages 136–138).

This kind of nonsense has now been laid to rest by the Masters-Johnson laboratory observations. Multiple orgasms do not differ physiologically in any significant respect from single orgasms, they report, except in their multiplicity. And they are not "minor" experiences:

> When female study subjects were interrogated in the laboratory after multiorgasmic experiences, the second or third orgasmic episode usually was identified subjectively as more satisfying or more sensually pleasurable than the first orgasmic episode.

The physiology of multiple orgasm in women can be simply explained. Three events in the genital region occur rapidly after a woman's first orgasm: her clitoris descends to its resting position overhanging the pubic bone, the orgasmic platform relaxes and loses its engorgement with excess blood, and her outer and inner lips (major and minor labia) also lose their engorgement. All three of these events, however, are reversible. With renewal of erotic stimulation—or with continuing stimulation—the clitoris again elevates, the veins refill with blood, the muscles again contract, and another orgasm is initiated.

Some women prefer continuous stimulation, going from one orgasm to another with practically no time lapse; others prefer to fall back to the plateau or excitement phase before stimulation is renewed.

Masters and Johnson report that multiple orgasms are more apt to occur with autostimulation (masturbation) than with intravaginal coition. The reason should be obvious: few men can maintain an erection long enough to produce multiple orgasms in their partners. The limit is not the woman's responsivity, but the male's erectile endurance.

In sexual cycles produced by direct stimulation of the woman's mons area, in contrast, her responsivity is the sole limit and she can match her self-stimulation to her responsive needs. Under such circumstances, Masters and Johnson report, a woman may "experience five to 20 recurrent orgasmic experiences with the sexual tension never allowed to drop below a plateau phase maintenance level until physical exhaustion terminates the session."

The belief that masculine endurance rather than feminine responsivity limits a woman's coital responses is confirmed by another remarkable set of Masters-Johnson findings. Five of the men seen in their clinic for infertile couples, they report, were fully potent sexually in all other ways, but were unable to ejaculate into a vagina. As a result, these five men "can and do maintain coital connection for 30 to 60 minutes at any given opportunity." In three of the five cases, the wives reap the full benefit. They "are multiorgasmic as a result of the constant opportunity for long-maintained coition." As in the cases of other women in self-stimulatory episodes, these women have one orgasm after another until "coition is terminated by the female partner's admission of sexual satiation." Multiple orgasm, in short, is not a characteristic of self-stimulation; it is a characteristic of any effective stimulation sufficiently prolonged to trigger multiple responses.

Dr. Masters and Mrs. Johnson have indicated just how far this process can go:

> The average female with optimal arousal will usually be satisfied with 3–5 manually induced orgasms; whereas mechanical stimulation, as with the electric vibrator [see page 161] is less tiring and induces her to go on to long stimulative sessions of an hour or more during which she may have 20 to 50 consecutive orgasms. She will stop only when totally exhausted. Such sessions, occurring as often as 2–3 times a week, create a chronic passive congestion of the pelvis and work hypertrophy of the clitoral shaft.

A practicing psychiatrist, Dr. Mary Jane Sherfey, has confirmed a portion of this finding, which she reported in the

Journal of the American Psychoanalytic Association for January 1966:

> In clinical practice a number of married and single women using the electric vibrator to achieve up to fifty orgasms in a single session have come to my attention in the past few years. To have the comfort of a label, I had considered them to be cases of nymphomania without promiscuity. From the standpoint of our cultural norm, this may be an accurate enough phrase. From the standpoint of normal physiological functioning, these women exhibit a healthy, uninhibited sexuality—and the number of orgasms attained, a measure of the human female's orgasmic potentiality.

In the past it was reasonable to believe, on the basis of the Kinsey and Terman studies, that the capacity for multiple orgasm was limited to a minority of women—thirteen or fourteen out of every one hundred. The Masters-Johnson work indicates that this is not true. In addition to their research with erotically responsive subjects, Masters and Johnson since 1959 have also been treating married couples for sexual inadequacy (see page 203). Some of the wives in this treatment group were "frigid" by even the strictest standards. They were incapable of achieving orgasm by any means whatever, and had never achieved orgasm throughout their lives, including five years or more of marriage. All of them had received prior medical or psychiatric treatment without results. These women, in short, were as far removed from the rapidly multiorgasmic women as could possibly be imagined. Yet following successful short-term therapy, they began within ten days to three weeks to experience not only orgasm but, in many cases, intense multiple orgasms; and once this capacity was achieved they were able to respond with increasing ease and rapidity. Details are not yet available; but in the light of what is already known concerning the Masters-Johnson therapeutic program, it would be dogmatic indeed to assert that even the seemingly most "frigid" women are not in fact capable, under suitable conditions, of experiencing intense multiple orgasms.

SEX DURING AND AFTER PREGNANCY

Some of the married women taking part in the Masters-Johnson laboratory research became pregnant during their participation. Four of them and their husbands volunteered to continue in the program during and after pregnancy. Two other couples volunteered for the first time early in pregnancy—in one case seven weeks and in the other case eight and a half weeks after the wife's last menstrual period. The six pregnant wives ranged in age from twenty-one to thirty-six. Two had never been pregnant before, while for the thirty-six-year-old this was the fourth pregnancy.

Thanks to these six couples, Dr. Masters and Mrs. Johnson were able to compare sexual responses during pregnancy with responses at other times under a wide range of circumstances. In most respects, they learned, responses were very much the same during pregnancy. Only a few differences need be noted here.

As described above, the female breasts become engorged during sexual stimulation. They also become engorged during pregnancy. The combination of these two types of engorgement, Dr. Masters and Mrs. Johnson report, led some women who had not had babies before to complain of severe breast tenderness, especially in the nipples and areolas, during advanced stages of sexual arousal early in pregnancy. This tenderness did not recur during sexual arousal later in pregnancy.

All six of the study subjects, Dr. Masters and Mrs. Johnson report, became conscious of heightened levels of sexual interest and responsiveness toward the end of the first three months of pregnancy or early in the second three months. "Two subjects who had never been multiorgasmic in prior sexual experience described and demonstrated this high-tension response for the first time during the second trimester of their pregnancies." The other four women had had multiple orgasms before pregnancy and continued to have them during pregnancy. Sexual interest and responsiveness continued high throughout the second three months and well into the final three months for all six women.

Four of the six described "occasional cramping and aching in the midline of the lower abdomen" during and immediately after orgasm; and two of the four complained of low backache after the cramping. Several were aware of uterine contractions following sexual stimulation.

The "orgasmic platform" surrounding the outer third of the vagina (see pages 27–28) was even more noticeable during pregnancy than at other times, so that the penis was even more tightly clamped than usual by the platform. During orgasm, the women *experienced* the rhythmic contractions of this platform as usual—but the region was so engorged that the contractions were much less visible to an observer.

Dr. Masters was concerned, of course, with the effect of maternal sexual activity on the unborn baby. He listened to the fetal heartbeat during orgasm, and reported that while it sometimes slowed down a little, this reaction quickly passed, and the fetal heart resumed its normal rate. Instead of the usual rhythmic series of contractions during orgasm, the uterus late in pregnancy sometimes engaged in a single contraction lasting as long as a minute.

Only the resolution phase differed markedly during pregnancy; it took longer and was less complete. "The study subjects frequently stated that orgasmic experience, although objectively most severe and subjectively quite satisfying, did not relieve their sexual tensions for any significant length of time." It was perhaps for this reason that the two women in the group who had not previously had multiple orgasms experienced them for the first time during pregnancy.

All six women came in for checkups four or five weeks after their babies were born, again between the sixth and eighth weeks, and again at the end of the third month. Four of the six reported a return of sexual desire before the time of the first checkup; and pelvic examination of all six showed sufficient healing to make intercourse permissible. Sexual intercourse in the laboratory at this time was reported as fully satisfactory subjectively by the six women, particularly among the mothers who were breast-feeding their babies; but both the intensity and duration of the observed physiological responses were diminished.

Three of the six mothers breast-fed their babies. Sexual interest and responsiveness returned earlier after childbirth in these three. The uterus also returned to normal size and position earlier, for an interesting reason. During breast-feeding, the baby's sucking on the nipples causes the pituitary to release a hormone, oxytocin, which contracts the chambers in the breast and squeezes milk out into the channels leading to the nipples. This same hormone also shrinks the uterus; indeed, injections of oxytocin are sometimes given women after childbirth to hasten the uterine shrinking. The Masters-Johnson findings confirm the view that the oxytocin secreted during breast-feeding plays a helpful role in returning the uterus to its normal nonpregnant condition.

Another fascinating observation concerned involuntary secretion of breast milk during orgasm. Two of the three women who breast-fed their babies reported that this happened at home, and the occurrence was confirmed in the laboratory. It strongly suggests, though it does not prove, that the same hormone, oxytocin, may also play a role in the female orgasm.

Six couples, of course, constitute a very small sample. Hence Dr. Masters and Mrs. Johnson supplemented it with a much larger sample of pregnant women and husbands who agreed to come in from time to time and report verbally on their sexual feelings, behavior, and responses.

In all, 113 pregnant women were invited to participate in this program of repeated interviews; 111 of them, aged twenty-one to forty-three, accepted the invitation—a gratifying illustration of how willing people are to cooperate in sex research programs. All of them, of course, were aware of how dependent pregnant women are on their doctors to advise them concerning sexual intercourse during and after pregnancy; and when told that the program would help doctors give sounder advice, only two were unwilling to help.

Ten of the women who had volunteered lost their babies during the first six months, leaving 101 who participated throughout pregnancy. Of these, nine were unmarried. The husbands of the ninety-two married women who continued to the end were also invited to report their reactions to their wives' pregnancies—and seventy-nine accepted.

Sixty-eight of the 111 women who participated had had babies before; the other forty-three had not.

During the first three months of pregnancy, the sixty-eight women who had had previous babies reported very little change in sexual interest or responsiveness. The main exceptious were four women who reported an increase, and seven who reported a decrease; these seven all suffered from nausea and vomiting during early pregnancy. Most of the women having their first baby did report a reduction in erotic interest and responsiveness—perhaps due in part to an unwarranted fear that the unborn baby might be injured, and in part to the chronic fatigue or other symptoms of early pregnancy they were experiencing.

"During the second trimester," Dr. Masters and Mrs. Johnson state, "sexual patterns generally reflected a marked increase in eroticism and effectiveness of performance regardless of the parity or ages of the women interrogated. This evidence of elevated sexuality was reported by the women not only as interest in sexual encounter, but also as planning for sexual encounter, fantasy of sexual encounter, and sex-dream content." Basic sexuality was increased not only as compared with the first three months of pregnancy, but also as compared with the period before pregnancy. The increase was reported by eighty-two of the 101 women who continued through the second three months.

Responses during the final three months were affected by the fact that seventy-seven of the 101 women were warned by their own physicians not to engage in sexual intercourse until after the baby was born. Some doctors forbade intercourse during the entire last three months; others specified periods as short as one month. Many women reported that they gradually lost interest in sex during the last three months quite independently of the medical warnings; and twenty of the 101 women reported that their husbands gradually lost interest in them—either because of the gross physical signs of their pregnancy, or because of fear that sex would be uncomfortable for their wives, or for fear of hurting the baby.

After the babies were born, strong sexual interests returned within two or three weeks in some women, while others were still sexually uninterested when questioned during the third month after childbirth. Twenty-four of the mothers were breast-feeding their babies at the time of the third-month checkup; and these mothers as a group reported a prompter return of sexuality and a return to higher levels of sexuality than the others. These women also expressed an interest in resuming sexual intercourse with their husbands earlier in the postpartum period.

The mothers who breast-fed their babies reported another very interesting physiological phenomenon: sexual stimulation during breast-feeding. Frequently this stimulation carried them to plateau levels of response, and on three occasions orgasm was experienced during breast-feeding—another indication that the hormone oxytocin, released during breast-feeding, may also play a role in female orgasm.

On the psychological side, six of the twenty-four women who breast-fed their babies expressed deep guilt-feelings about their sexual arousal during nursing; and six of the women who were not breast-feeding gave as their reason the fact that they had found themselves sexually aroused during breast-feeding of a previous baby. (Several psychologists and psychiatrists have reported this sense of guilt some women feel on discovering that breast-feeding is sexually arousing.) Dr. Masters and Mrs. Johnson reassured them that there is nothing "perverse" in these feelings; indeed, this may be just another of nature's subtle ways of encouraging mothers to take good care of their babies during the early months, and of establishing close rapport between mother and baby.

It is a shocking commentary on American prudery and rejection of sex, let us here add parenthetically, that a significant number of women feel guilty, and some even refuse to breast-feed their babies, when sexual feelings accompany breast-feeding. The need for the education of young girls on this point can hardly be overemphasized.

All of the married women, except those whose physicians forbade it, had full sexual intercourse with their husbands within two months or less after childbirth—and some whose physicians did forbid it also resumed despite the prohibition. A few, in defiance of their doctor's advice, had intercourse as early as three weeks after childbirth.

Meanwhile, what of the husbands?

In many cases, to follow medical advice would have meant going without sexual intercourse for six successive months —three before and three after delivery.

Of the seventy-seven women whose physicians had warned against sexual intercourse, sixty-eight expressed concern, in their talks with Dr. Masters and Mrs. Johnson, over the effect of the prohibition on their husbands, and forty-nine reported that they made deliberate efforts to relieve their husbands sexually during the period of medically recommended continence by masturbating them or in other ways. Three women reported that they knew their husbands were finding sex elsewhere during this period.

Of the seventy-nine men participating in the interview project, seventy-one were married to women whose doctors had forbidden intercourse for periods of from two to six months. *Only twenty-one of the seventy-one stated that they understood, agreed with, and honored the prohibition.*

In all, eighteen of the seventy-one husbands for whom intercourse with their wives was forbidden admitted to Dr. Masters and Mrs. Johnson that they engaged in extramarital sex activities during this period. Several insisted that this was the "first time" they had been unfaithful. Of the twelve who began extramarital sex activity before the baby was born, all twelve continued it after the baby was born.

Nearly a third of the men reported that they did not understand the reason for the prohibition, or were not sure that the doctor had really said it, or wished that he had explained it to them as well as to their wives. Several clearly suspected that their wives had made up the story in order to avoid intercourse.

Here is a major problem of pregnancy which has never been adequately explored. Several basic changes in obstetrical advice are indicated.

The first is very simple:

Whenever a physician forbids sexual intercourse—before pregnancy, after pregnancy, during or after an illness, or at any other time—he should take pains to explain the reasons in full to *both* husband and wife. It is unfair to both partners, and hazardous to the marriage, to leave one partner in the dark, with all the misunderstandings and suspicions that can arise.

The second is more complicated. Some physicians no doubt prescribe long periods of abstinence during pregnancy, or after pregnancy, or at other times, in order to "play safe." In the absence of precise information, they think it prudent to prohibit intercourse. The Masters-Johnson data indicate that far from being prudent, an unnecessary sexual prohibition, or one that is not fully understood by both partners, gravely jeopardizes the marriage in a substantial proportion of cases.

But what of the physical risk to mother and baby? Marital psychology aside, what *should* a doctor tell his patient and her husband about sex during pregnancy?

Dr. Masters and Mrs. Johnson do not have all the answers. They are planning a further report on this subject later on. Meanwhile, their data are the best available anywhere. The four most important points can be summed up as follows:

(1) For the overwhelming majority of women, there is no reason whatever to refrain from sex during the first three months of pregnancy.

The major exceptions may be a small group of women known as "habitual aborters," who have already lost three or more babies through spontaneous abortion during the first trimester, and who want very much to carry this baby to term. For this small group of women, physicians customarily recommend no sexual intercourse during the first three months.

The Masters-Johnson findings neither confirm nor cast doubt on this recommendation. Here, perhaps, is a group for whom it really is prudent to refrain. *But,* Dr. Masters and Mrs. Johnson state, the prohibition must go further if it is to have its intended effect. Their studies clearly show that *masturbation to orgasm* triggers even more intense contractions of the uterus than does orgasm following intercourse. Thus a habitual aborter who refrains from intercourse during the first three months should also be instructed to refrain from orgasm achieved in other ways.

(2) For the overwhelming majority of women, there is no reason whatever to refrain from sexual activity during the second three months of pregnancy.

(3) Late in the final three months, as delivery day approaches, the problem becomes more complex.

Some physicians warn against intercourse toward the end of pregnancy for fear of infection. Dr. Masters and Mrs. Johnson regard this as "a residual of the preantibiotic days." There is no more risk of vaginal or cervical infection late in pregnancy than at any other time, they state; and if infection should occur, it can be as readily and effectively controlled as at any other time.

More relevant is the fact that in some women toward the end of pregnancy, the baby's head engages in the cervix, and the cervix descends into the main axis of the vagina. *After* this descent occurs, vigorous coital thrusting may cause the glans of the penis to strike the infant-laden cervix. A little "spotting" or bleeding may result. In this case, Dr. Masters and Mrs. Johnson conclude, coition should be given up. But they point out that in many women, especially those who have had babies before, the baby's head does not engage and the cervix does not descend until labor actually begins. There seems little reason to prohibit intercourse for these women merely because the head has descended into the cervix in some *other* women.

Further, there is a possibility that an orgasm on the eve of a baby's birth may actually trigger the onset of labor. Dr. Masters and Mrs. Johnson describe four cases—none of them in their research program—in which women continued to have intercourse through the ninth month, and in which labor began immediately after an orgasm. Similar cases have been described by others. In none of these, however, was the baby born prematurely. "Whether or not premature labor can be or has been induced by orgasmic response is of major clinical moment," Dr. Masters and Mrs. Johnson state. "There is no secure information available on this subject." There are certainly cases in which women have had orgasm in the ninth month of pregnancy *without* triggering labor.

(4) After the baby is born, three factors may properly delay resumption of sexual intercourse. The wife may not feel like it. The surgical incision made to ease the birth of the baby—the episiotomy—may not have healed fully. And there may still be some uterine or vaginal bleeding or spotting. All three of these conditions, Dr. Masters and Mrs. Johnson report, usually (though not always) end after the third postpartum week.

In sum, then, they recommend that "the whole problem of coition during the third trimester of pregnancy and the postpartum period should be *individualized*." A physician should advise each woman and her husband on an individual basis. "Their situation should be discussed, personal reasons examined, fears explained away, and a firm understanding between both members of the marital unit reached." In most cases it will not prove necessary to forbid sex for prolonged periods—such as six weeks before and six weeks after the baby is born. In those selected cases where there is good reason to abstain, a physician following this individualized procedure can with sympathy and clear explanation minimize any unfortunate psychological effects.

INFERTILITY PROBLEMS

About one American couple in eight, it has been estimated, is trying without success to have a baby; many have been trying for five, ten, or even fifteen years. Thus infertility is one of the most tragic of all marital problems.

Dr. Masters had been concerned with infertility before he began his sex research project, and had established an "infertility service" for such patients at the Washington University School of Medicine. Indeed, some of the first volunteers for his sex research project were former infertility patients, and the new research program soon turned up valuable data on the problem.

The Masters-Johnson observations, for example, show how in a number of ways the detailed male and female responses to sexual stimulation aid in achieving pregnancy. The expulsion of semen from the penis with great force ensures that the semen will reach the cervical end of the vagina, even though ejaculation occurs while the penis is being withdrawn following a deep thrust. The engorged vaginal barrel, gripping the penis, holds the semen in the vagina after ejaculation. Equally important, the "ballooning" of the vagina during a woman's sexual response (see page 25) provides a useful cuplike receptacle for semen—a receptacle that in most cases lies directly under the cervix when intercourse is performed with the wife on her back in the supine position and her husband above her. Following his ejaculation, a pool of semen collects in this receptacle; and as her sexual tension subsides, her cervix promptly dips down into this pool of semen. At about the same time, the opening in the cervix, known as the cervical *os*, enlarges. All this, it seems likely, makes it easy for the sperm cells to swim up through the os into the uterus, and on up the Fallopian tubes to meet a descending ovum and fertilize it. The Masters-Johnson findings thus confirm in most cases the advice ordinarily given to infertile couples:

intercourse with the wife on her back, perhaps with a pillow under her buttocks to discourage the semen from escaping, is the position ordinarily most favorable for achieving pregnancy. The wife should hold this position for some minutes following her husband's ejaculation.

It is well known that a wife need not reach orgasm in order to become pregnant. Dr. Masters and Mrs. Johnson suggest that in very difficult cases where pregnancy has long been sought without success, it may be better for the wife to reach a plateau phase of excitation without immediate orgasm. This is because, shortly after the female orgasm, the inner two thirds of the vagina returns to its normal shape, and the cuplike receptacle filled with semen flattens out; the semen then has a tendency to drain out of the vagina. For seven couples out of eight, of course, such advice is irrelevant; pregnancy is easily achieved without regard for such details.

The Masters-Johnson data further reveal that for a certain minority of women, the usual advice to lie on the back in order to encourage pregnancy is mistaken. These are women with a severely "retroverted" uterus; the cervix in such cases lies on a line with the end of the vagina instead of more or less at right angles to it. In such cases, Dr. Masters and Mrs. Johnson have found, the cervix gains easier access to the seminal pool if intercourse is performed with the wife in the knee-chest position—face down, hips raised, supporting her weight on her knees and elbows, with her husband behind her. The wife should hold this position following her husband's ejaculation; but "a few minutes," Dr. Masters and Mrs. Johnson state, "are quite sufficient to allow effective contact between the cervical os and the seminal pool."

These observations, it should be noted, were among the many that could not have been made without the Masters-Johnson technique of "artificial coition," using an artificial plastic penis through which the detailed reactions of the vaginal walls and of the cervix and os could be directly observed and recorded on motion-picture film. The artificial penis used in their laboratory includes an ejector for injecting either semen or a fluid with the consistency of semen into the vagina. The pooling of the semen, the enlarging of the os, and other details were discovered in this way.

Like other authorities, Dr. Masters and Mrs. Johnson stress the importance of intercourse at the right time—that is, at about the time that one of the woman's ovaries releases an ovum—in order to achieve pregnancy. Much of their work has been concerned with techniques for establishing precisely the time when the ovum is released. But, like others, they have not yet made much progress on the essential task of predicting the exact time of ovulation.

In the course of working with infertile couples, Dr. Masters found in five cases a strange cause of infertility. Just as some women can experience orgasm during masturbation but not during sexual intercourse, so the husbands in these five very unusual cases were unable to ejaculate so long as the penis remained in the vagina. As a result, they could not impregnate their wives. Artificial insemination proved the treatment of choice in these cases. The husbands masturbated, the semen thus secured was introduced into the vagina or cervix, and pregnancy followed.

One cause of infertility, of course, is an inadequate number of sperm cells in the male semen, or sperm cells that do not move with sufficient vigor toward their goal, or that are deficient in other respects. There are various ways to evaluate a sample of male semen from the point of view of fertility. One way is to have the husband masturbate, and examine the semen under the microscope. Another way is to recover fluid from the vagina or cervix immediately after sexual intercourse, and examine the sperm cells found in the fluid. Dr. Masters used both methods of evaluation in a number of cases—and was rewarded with a discovery of great potential importance.

In thirty-nine cases, he found that the husband's semen contained tens of millions of living sperm cells, vigorously swimming in definite directions, when the semen sample was secured by masturbation. But when the test was performed using seminal fluid from the vagina or cervix, only inactive sperm cells were recovered. The cells must have been inactivated very promptly, for none of them had managed to get even as far as the cervix.

To check on this phenomenon further, these infertile couples were asked to have intercourse in the laboratory, in complete privacy, and to ring a bell the moment the husband ejaculated. In this way, fluid from the cervix and vagina could be examined within ten or fifteen seconds after ejaculation. Even so, only immobile sperm cells were found in the vagina, indicating that something was damaging or killing them with astounding rapidity.

In another test, the husband ejaculated by means of masturbation. A small sample of the semen thus secured was examined under the microscope, and the remainder was placed in his wife's vagina. The sperm cells viewed under the microscope were moving vigorously and in definite directions; the sperm cells recovered from the vagina were inactive—in all probability dead. The conclusion was thus inescapable: some previously unidentified factor was very promptly inactivating sperm cells in these thirty-nine cases.

Three explanations were possible. (1) The husband's sperm cells might be sensitive to something in normal vaginal fluids. (2) There might be some harmful kind of interaction between the husband's particular sperm cells and his wife's particular vaginal fluids. (3) There might be some factor in the wife's vaginal fluids harmful to all sperm cells.

To rule out the first possibility, Dr. Masters placed samples of the husband's semen in the vaginas of two other women. (The cervix in each case was capped to prevent the woman from becoming pregnant.) The sperm cells survived undamaged, indicating that it was not *their* sensitivity which was causing the trouble.

Next, Dr. Masters placed semen from two male donors into the wife's vagina, again with the cervix capped. In both cases, the sperm cells were promptly immobilized. This conclusively proved that the third alternative was the true one; these thirty-nine women had some factor in their vaginal fluids—Dr. Masters calls it "the lethal factor"—that is capable of inactivating sperm cells within a few seconds.

In two other cases, an apparently similar factor was identified in fluids from the wife's cervix. The sperm cells in semen deposited in the vagina remained normally active and moved up to the cervix—but when they got there, they were promptly immobilized.

In a few cases, the wives with a lethal factor in their vaginas became pregnant after Dr. Masters detoured around the lethal factor and inserted semen from the husband directly into the interior of the uterus through the cervix. While this does not always work, it is a procedure worth trying in such cases.

Efforts to identify the "lethal factor" chemically have to date been unsuccessful. It acts far more rapidly and more completely on the sperm cells in semen than the most effective of the spermicidal agents currently used in contraceptive jellies, creams, and foams. If it could be identified and mass-produced, it might add one more highly effective means of contraception to the number already available.

CONTRACEPTION AND
SEX RESEARCH

Prior to 1950, there was an accepted procedure for testing new contraceptives intended for use inside the vagina, such as jellies, creams, foams, tablets, and suppositories. Fresh semen was exposed in a test tube to the substance being tested. The faster the sperm cells in the semen were inactivated, the more completely they were inactivated, and the longer the substance retained its ability to inactivate sperm cells, the more highly it was rated. Following these test-tube studies, promising products were distributed to hundreds or to thousands of women, and the number who became pregnant in spite of the use of any particular contraceptive was the measure of its effectiveness.

But there were flaws in this procedure. Some researchers actively stirred the semen up with the contraceptive substance in the test tube; others refrained from stirring. The results were different in the two kinds of test—and no one knew which test was a better predictor of effectiveness in actual use. As more and more effective contraceptives became available, moreover, questions arose concerning the moral justification of supplying women with a substance of unproved effectiveness to learn whether or not it would protect them. The potential cost to the woman was extremely high—an unwanted baby.

In 1953 and again in 1960, papers were published on the preliminary testing of new contraceptives inside the human vagina instead of in a test tube. These papers marked a step forward; but they involved testing women immediately after ordinary intercourse and therefore raised a number of problems. The development of the technique of artificial coition by Dr. Masters and Mrs. Johnson marked another step forward.

The latest Masters-Johnson paper on the testing of intravaginal contraceptives, published in 1965, describes the procedure in some detail. Eight commercial contraceptive products were tested—a vaginal jelly, two creams, a foam, a gel, a tablet, a suppository, and a liquid. Each woman participating in the test introduced the contraceptive in accordance with standard instructions, and then engaged in artificial coition with the plastic penis until she reached orgasm. At orgasm, a specimen of semen from a man known to be fertile was injected into the vagina, with the cervix capped. A sample of the vaginal contents was then withdrawn within one to five seconds, a second sample after fifteen seconds, and subsequent samples after thirty seconds, one minute, two minutes, and five minutes. The samples were examined immediately under the microscope for moving sperm cells. The samples were taken from various portions of the vagina—one near the entrance, one at the furthest end or cul-de-sac, and four from the middle region close to where the cervix dips down into the vaginal pool.

After one hour, the woman engaged a second time in artificial coition, a second semen sample was injected, and the tests were repeated. A third sequence followed after five to eight hours. No further contraceptive was introduced into the vagina for the second and third sequences; thus the tests established the effectiveness of the contraceptive as long as eight hours after its introduction.

In all, thirty women participated in the test of each contraceptive, and eighteen semen samples from each woman's vagina were examined. Absence of moving sperm cells during all 540 examinations would have earned a product a score of 540. None of the eight products tested achieved this perfect score. But two achieved perfect scores during the one-to-five-second tests and four during the one-hour tests. Total scores varied from 508 for the best product to a low 222 for the worst.

Another Masters-Johnson contraceptive research undertaking was designed to determine the reasons for the occasional failure of the vaginal diaphragm to prevent pregnancy. The behavior of the diaphragm inside the vagina was studied under four conditions: artificial coition with the woman in the supine position, artificial coition with the woman in the knee-chest position, natural intercourse with the wife above and her husband in the supine position, and "multiple mounting" in which husband wife engaged in intercourse in a variety of positions, one after the other.

A number of failures of the diaphragm were observed, the great majority of them occurring during the reinsertion of the penis after it had once been withdrawn. When a diaphragm is first inserted, Dr. Masters and Mrs. Johnson explain, a properly instructed woman can readily place it in its proper position, with the front edge firmly tucked under the pubic bone so that the penis cannot slip behind the diaphragm. As sex play and intercourse proceed, however, the vagina doubles or even trebles its usual diameter. One result is that the fit of the diaphragm is now much less snug. If, while the wife is in this stage of excitement, the husband withdraws his penis from the vagina altogether—either as a variant on ordinary coital thrusting, or in the course of changing coital positions—he may reinsert it on the cervical side of the diaphragm. This happened with eight of the thirty couples participating in the diaphragm tests. Faulty reinsertion of the penis was particularly likely to happen with wives who had previously had babies.

A final Masters-Johnson contribution to the improvement of contraceptives should be briefly noted. The traditional tests of new contraceptives intended for use inside the vagina were aimed primarily at establishing the effectiveness of the chemical contents of the contraceptive in rendering sperm cells inactive. A second important factor, their studies indicate, is the physical consistency of the material, which determines its ability to spread promptly throughout the vagina and maintain an effective barrier. Thus even a highly spermicidal chemical may be relatively ineffective if the substance in which it is contained lacks the proper consistency. The same spermicidal chemical may be highly effective in a well-designed foam but relatively ineffective in a poorly designed jelly, cream, or foaming tablet.

The effectiveness and current popularity of oral contraceptives—"the pill"—and of the intrauterine contraceptive device (IUD), which is inserted into the uterus by a physician to provide protection year after year, has drawn attention away from the diaphragms and intravaginal substances which Dr. Masters and Mrs. Johnson have been testing. For the minority of women who either cannot or do not want to use "the pill" or the "IUD," however, the Masters-Johnson contraceptive research remains of practical importance.

"SHOULD THIS SEX RESEARCH
BE ALLOWED TO GO ON?"

Five hundred years ago, broad areas of nature and of human nature were closed to scientific investigation. The interior of the human body could not be explored, for example, even after death. Thus knowledge of human anatomy was gained by reading Aristotle or Galen, and by dissecting the lower animals—or by defying the taboo and making private arrangements with a hangman or graveyard custodian. Even in those days, however, exceptions might be made for particular projects. Artists engaged in portraying St. Bartholomew, who had been flayed alive, were permitted to examine the interior of a body in order to achieve verisimilitude. St. Bartholomew, carrying his skin over his shoulder, became a popular subject for painters and sculptors.

Considerable progress toward scientific freedom has been made since then. The burden of proof has for the most part shifted. Most people today would no doubt agree that any scientific inquiry is permissible for its own sake, in the absence of compelling ethical objections to it.

This change of attitude was illustrated when the Masters-Johnson book, *Human Sexual Response,* was published in April 1966. Even the staid *Journal of the American Medical Association* agreed in an editorial that the research was useful and justified. "To some," the editorial noted, "sex is the ultimate area of privacy, and hence not appropriate for study and evaluation. No scientific criteria can justify such a conclusion. It is no more reasonable to teach students the anatomy of the reproductive organs and ignore the way these organs function during their ordered activities than it would be to study the anatomy of the stomach but disdain any knowledge of [how it works]."

But ethical questions were raised by others when the Masters-Johnson book appeared, and these deserve answers.

An act can be judged moral or immoral in a number of ways. What motives produced it? What are its consequences? Does the act contribute to human happiness, or produce misery, or does it detract from human dignity? Was it a free act, or coerced? Does it violate the Golden Rule? If all mankind acted similarly, would the results be catastrophic?

All of these are valid ethical questions, and most people judge an act in one or another of these ways.

When judged from the point of view of motives or intentions, the justification for the Masters-Johnson research seems to us quite clear. These motives have been described above (see pages 33–39). They are in part the same motives that impel other scientists to study earthquakes, planetary orbits, or the human cardiovascular system—a desire to expand the boundaries of scientific knowledge. In part, too, they are the motives of the men engaged in clinical medical research—a desire to develop more effective methods of therapy for human illnesses, physical and emotional.

The motives of the volunteers have also been reviewed above (see pages 51–61)—primarily a desire to contribute to scientific and clinical progress, and also in some cases to enhance their own understanding and enjoyment of sex. Those who consider these motives evil may well conclude that the research program itself is evil.

Next, let us consider consequences.

As a result of the Masters-Johnson research and clinical programs, some husbands and wives who were sexually incompatible have found joy together. Some men and women deeply troubled by their sexual inadequacies have learned to respond fully and joyfully to sexual stimulation.[2] Some women, who desperately wanted children, were enabled to conceive. Other couples were helped to avoid bringing unwanted children into the world.

If such benefits were earned at the cost of suffering to participants in the research program, a moral issue would arise: did the good outweigh the evil? But, as we have seen, the participants in the research were also among the beneficiaries.

The research of Dr. Masters and Mrs. Johnson, moreover, abides by two cardinal rules of safety.

[2] ". . . Even the most critical should admit that, if we are able to free some individuals from neurotic guilt feelings about sex and if we can utilize scientific research to stabilize even a few apparently unsuccessful marriages, some good has been served. None of these admirable designs is achievable through ignorance." Editorial, *Journal of the American Medical Association*, July 18, 1966.

The first is that any research on human beings be started on a very small scale, so that possible harmful effects can be identified before hundreds or thousands are exposed to the hazard. Dr. Masters started with a handful of willing volunteers. The volunteer group grew very slowly—to 694 over a period of ten years. The harmlessness of the procedures—indeed, their helpfulness—had been fully established while the research group was still numbered in the tens rather than the hundreds.

The second cardinal rule is that researchers are under an ethical duty to search conscientiously for harmful as well as beneficial effects. The annual checkups on active participants and the five-year follow-ups of former participants in the Masters-Johnson research have been described above (pages 57–59).

It is possible, of course, to cast doubt on the safety of any research program. At a meeting addressed by Dr. Masters and Mrs. Johnson in May 1966, for example, a psychoanalyst rose to ask how many participants in the Masters-Johnson research had gone crazy as a result. (He used the term "psychotic" instead of "crazy.") The simple answer was "none." Insinuations like this, based on no evidence of any kind, can be raised to impugn any research. However, instead of leading to safety, they lead to scientific paralysis.

Some people do not judge an act by either its motives or consequences, but by its inherent nature. They may say, for example, "It is wrong (or bad, or sinful, or immoral) to masturbate."

Since men and women masturbated in the Masters-Johnson laboratory, and performed other sexual acts under observation, absolutists may well conclude that the Masters-Johnson research was immoral. Even absolutists, however, have one "escape hatch." They may very well hold that the acts performed in the Masters-Johnson laboratory are so different in quality, both with respect to motives and with respect to consequences, as not to belong in the category of condemned acts—even though the same names may be applied to them.

Almost all of the sexual intercourse in the Masters-Johnson laboratory was between wives and husbands. The sole exception and the reason for it—to secure data not available in any other way—was described on page 79. Absolutists may conclude that this small portion of the research program was immoral because intercourse between unmarried persons is always and everywhere immoral. Others will judge for themselves.

There has been much criticism in the past few years of research on human beings who did not know in advance that they were being used as experimental subjects. One objection concerned the prescription of experimental drugs to patients who thought they were getting drugs of established merit and safety. A second example, roundly condemned at the time, was the injection of living cancer cells into residents of an old people's home without full disclosure to them of what was being done. A third example was psychological research on men and women who thought they were being interviewed for a job opening when in fact they were being subjected to psychological testing for research purposes. We agree with the critics in all three of these cases. But all such objections are irrelevant to the Masters-Johnson research. The St. Louis volunteers knew precisely and in detail what they were volunteering for.

Subtle problems are raised by the question of coercion as distinguished from free consent. Consider, for example, the physician who requests cooperation in an experiment from a seriously ill patient in his personal care. Rightly or wrongly, the patient may conclude that consent is the price he must pay for the physician's continued concern. We think this kind of coercion should be guarded against. But again, there was no such coercion in the Masters-Johnson research. Some former patients were accepted as volunteers—but patients were not.

In some cases, payment may constitute coercion. Our own consciences are troubled by the commercial blood-donor centers found on the "skid rows" of many large cities. There, down-and-outers desperate for a few extra dollars for a meal, a few drinks, or a narcotic "fix" sell a pint or two of blood. We do not think the sale is uncoerced in such cases. Payment was made to the Masters-Johnson volunteers—but not to down-and-outers lacking all other means of support. It is difficult to see the slightest evidence of coercion—physical, psychological, or financial—in the St. Louis research.

The objection has been raised that the initial Masters-Johnson findings made public to date, because of their emphasis on physiological rather than psychological factors, may tend to dehumanize sexual relations or to reduce them to a mechanical search for full orgasmic response. One reviewer even suggested that their book should be called *Sexual Body Mechanics*. Dr. Harold I. Lief, professor of psychiatry at the Tulane University School of Medicine, has supplied ar eloquent rejoinder:

> As for the criticism of mechanization or of dehumanization of human sexuality, it is possible to marvel that one can compare the narrowing of the focus upon the orgasm *for the purposes of scientific investigation* with the daily sexual bombardment and titillation by advertising and other mass media whereby every conceivable product is sexualized, or advertised with the aid of sex. If sex has become a commodity dispassionately bought and sold instead of a basic aspect of human feeling and interaction, the blame must be fixed on our culture and its institutions, rather than on sober scientific investigators into a vital but hitherto neglected area of human research. Before man can determine what is *right*, he must find out what *is*.

For generations, human sexuality has been primarily the province of the novelists and poets, the psychologists and sociologists. The Masters-Johnson research does not supersede these other approaches, but provides new facts and insights to supplement them. Surely this is a step toward enrichmen rather than impoverishment of the human sexual experience

Part II

OTHER SEX RESEARCH

THE MASTERS-JOHNSON REPORT
AND THE KINSEY TRADITION

Wardell B. Pomeroy, Ph.D.

Editors' note: Dr. Pomeroy, a clinical psychologist, was
one of Dr. Alfred C. Kinsey's closest associates from
1943 until Dr. Kinsey's death in 1956. He remained in
charge of field research for the Kinsey Institute until
November 1963, and is currently engaged in marriage
counseling in New York City. In the chapter that follows,
Dr. Pomeroy presents fresh data on Dr. Kinsey's early
concern with sex research and on the Kinsey Institute's
pioneering observations of human sexual responses—observations that foreshadowed the Masters-Johnson research to a remarkable extent.

An evolution in American attitudes toward sex has been
under way throughout the past several decades. The roots
of these changes are manifold and complex. I shall consider
in this chapter one of the many factors that contributed to the
changes: a decision by Indiana University back in 1937 to add
to its hundreds of other undergraduate courses a course in
marriage.

Seldom has so minor a decision had such far-reaching

consequences. The man selected to run the course was an
indefatigable zoologist, Dr. Alfred C. Kinsey—and man's
knowledge of his own sexual behavior has burgeoned as a
direct result of this appointment. Ultimately, Dr. Kinsey
not only presented the fullest account to date, based on first-
person recollections, of how men and women behave sexually;
he also stands as the most important predecessor to Masters
and Johnson in presenting an account of male and female
sexual responses based on direct observation.

Dr. Kinsey wrote no autobiography, and his biography has
never been written. In the furor raised by his reports on
human behavior, his detailed descriptions of the physiology
of sexual response have almost been forgotten. Publication of
the Masters-Johnson report, *Human Sexual Response*, seems
an appropriate time to present some relevant aspects of the
life and work of Dr. Kinsey, and to call attention to some
contrasts and some remarkable parallels between the careers
of Kinsey and Masters.

Both men came to sex research after their lifelong commitment to scientific investigation had already been made.
In Dr. Kinsey's case, an interest in sex research came very
late.

Alfred C. Kinsey was born in Hoboken, New Jersey, in
1894. His parents were religious people, and his upbringing
was strict. At college he was the young man who played the
piano at fraternity parties while the others danced. He never
dated. His acceptance of traditional attitudes toward sex are
revealed in a story he later told me.

One of his friends had come to him during Kinsey's college
days, deeply worried about a sexual problem: masturbation.
The friend was so upset that he felt he had to seek advice
from someone. Kinsey was shocked, but according to his
upbringing knew exactly what to do. At his suggestion, the
two young men knelt down in the college dormitory and
together prayed that the friend be given strength to stop his
masturbation.

Kinsey had been ill with rheumatic fever and rickets during
the first ten years of his life, and this kept him from many of
the activities of his peers. In compensation, perhaps, he discovered the outdoors. He joined the Boy Scouts, was one of
the first Eagle Scouts in this country, and organized his own
scout troop at 17. His first publication, written during his
scouting days and based on many hours of observation in the
woods in the rain, was entitled, "What Do Birds Do When
It Rains?" He remained an observer of nature for the rest of

his life; and one of the things that irked him most in later years was the fact that our sexual mores and taboos made it so much more difficult to observe human sexual responses than other natural phenomena. Yet, as we shall see, he did not allow such difficulties to stand in the way of his work. In later years Dr. Kinsey probably observed directly more human sexual responses than any other scientist—except Dr. Masters and Mrs. Johnson.

At the Stevens Institute of Technology, where he studied for two years, and later at Bowdoin College, where he took his B.S. in biology in 1916, no signs had yet appeared of his later interest in sex. During his graduate work in entomology at Harvard, he became interested in gall wasps; and they remained the center of his professional concern until 1937.

Gall wasps are found primarily in oak trees; and in the course of collecting specimens, Dr. Kinsey hiked through many parts of the country, camping out, carrying his pack on his back. To find the oak trees and gall wasps in a backwoods region, he would have to introduce himself to country folk, explain his mission, win their confidence, and persuade them to show him around the area. He was shy, almost intimidated by the country people at first, but soon learned to speak their language and developed a real liking for them. This became one of his major assets; later, he was able to secure from such people as well as from other strata of society full and frank accounts of their sexual behavior.

Over a period of twenty years or so, Dr. Kinsey collected somewhere between two and four *million* gall wasps. He examined and classified 150,000 specimens while preparing a single paper on a single aspect of their structure. One of his techniques was to collect all the gall wasps on a given tree or in a given grove of trees in order to minimize sampling errors. This "100 percent-sample" technique was carried over when he later turned from gall wasps to the study of human beings.

To record the enormous volumes of data supplied by his millions of gall wasps, he invented a simple code that enabled him to record on a single sheet of paper as much information as would otherwise fill twenty or twenty-five typewritten sheets. This code, too, proved invaluable when he was asking three hundred to five hundred questions of each of thousands of human respondents.

After taking his doctor of science degree at Harvard in 1920, Dr. Kinsey became instructor in biology at Indiana

University. There he met and married a graduate student in
chemistry, Clara McMillan, the first girl he ever in his life
"went steady" with. Their honeymoon was, not surprisingly,
a camping trip. The Kinseys had four children,
and the marriage continued until Dr. Kinsey's death in
1956.

Dr. Kinsey referred in later years to two experiences
during his gall-wasp-collecting days that opened his eyes at
least a crack to the narrowness of his early sexual attitudes.

The first was on an expedition to Mexico, where he happened
to attend an American movie in a run-down old
theater. When the hero and heroine kissed, the audience
hissed and booed. Suddenly it was borne in on him that attitudes
toward such sexual activities as kissing can vary from
culture to culture. This concept of cultural variability became
one of the keys to his later research success. His initial
lack of sexual sophistication helped him to perceive more
clearly, and to be more sharply impressed by differences
in behavior and attitude among people of different backgrounds.

The second eye-opening incident occurred on Dr. Kinsey's
trip to Guatemala with two graduate students. On a miserably
hot day they visited a Guatemalan official in their shirt sleeves
and hiking shorts and were criticized rather sharply for appearing
in his office with bare arms. That afternoon Dr.
Kinsey and his students went down to the local river for a
swim. Most of the town was gathered there, all completely
naked. Dr. Kinsey was so embarrassed that he and his students
walked upstream to find a bit more privacy. But the official
who had chided him earlier spotted him; and accompanied by
his wife and fifteen-year-old daughter, all without bathing
suits, he followed Kinsey upstream to pass the time of
day.

Later, Dr. Kinsey was surprised to observe how quickly
the most ingrained attitudes toward nudity can be altered. At
first he and his students shied away from the beaches where
people were nude—afraid, he said, that they might show signs
of being sexually aroused. Soon they were able to accept
nudity as a matter of course. Others with similar cultural
inhibitions have had the same experience of rapid adjustment.

Knowing a good deal about gall wasps but little about
human sexual behavior when he first took charge of the
Indiana marriage course, Dr. Kinsey went to the library to

learn more. He soon discovered that no one else knew very much either. In order to teach the facts he would have to gather them himself—much as he had been gathering gall wasps.

At the end of six months, he had collected sixty sexual histories, most of them on the Indiana University campus. He then began interviewing men and women off the campus, and was amazed to discover how different noncollege people were both in their sexual attitudes and in their sexual behavior. A campus policeman was one example he liked to cite. College students must all be perverts, this man, who had had no more than an eighth-grade education, complained to Dr. Kinsey one day. They would lie under the trees in pairs and just pet and pet. Sexual intercourse the policeman could understand; but this interminable petting must be some form of perversion!

By the end of his first year, Dr. Kinsey had collected three hundred sexual histories; his main interest had clearly shifted from wasps to human beings. For both his students and the other men and women he interviewed were now asking *him* questions—questions that reached to the very core of their lives: "Will masturbation make me insane?" "Will premarital intercourse spoil my marriage?" "Am I normal?" "What should I do about my homosexual desires?" Dr. Kinsey set his gall-wasp collection aside—he later donated it to the American Museum of Natural History—and spent the rest of his life seeking answers to urgent questions like these.

When news of his project got around, a few of the more conservative faculty members went to the president of Indiana University and urged him to put a stop to such a disgraceful academic undertaking. President Herman B. Wells of Indiana University, despite the fact that he had only recently been appointed, had the courage to state that he would defend the right of any faculty member to conduct research of his own choosing—and the board of trustees backed him up. A few of Dr. Kinsey's friends on the faculty stopped speaking to him, but this only amused him; he viewed it as another example of our curious sexual folkways. There were occasional subsequent flurries of opposition, including speeches in the legislature which supplied the university's funds, but university support has continued to the present day. It is encouraging to know that Dr. Masters and Mrs. Johnson have had similar support from Washington University in St. Louis.

By February 1943, when I joined Dr. Kinsey's staff, more than three thousand sexual histories had been collected. The total today is more than eighteen thousand.

If, before Dr. Kinsey started his work, a thousand psychologists and sociologists had been asked: "Will people of all kinds, in all walks of life, tell the truth about their past sexual behavior, including their past crimes and sins, to an interviewer who comes calling?", I am sure the overwhelming majority would have dismissed the possibility as ridiculous— just as almost everybody would have advised Dr. Masters in 1954 against launching his laboratory observations of sexual response. But Dr. Kinsey went ahead without consulting the experts, and in a remarkably short time he developed interviewing techniques that worked.

The standard interviewing authorities of the time warned that people would clam up if you wrote down their answers in their presence. At first Dr. Kinsey just listened, rushing out at the end of the interview to write down what he had heard. He very quickly learned that he could not remember all the answers, so he tried recording the interview as it progressed, on a coded data sheet much like the one he had developed for gall wasps. Soon he discovered that people were just as willing to talk frankly when he had a pen in his hand. The recording of answers is now accepted procedure in many forms of interviewing. He developed many other techniques as well for getting frank answers, from even the most reluctant informants, and for cross-checking the reliability of their replies. Interested readers will find these methods described in the opening chapters of the 1948 and 1953 Kinsey Institute publications, *Sexual Behavior in the Human Male* and *Sexual Behavior in the Human Female*. Dr. Kinsey summed up what he and his associates had discovered in the earlier of these reports:

Learning how to meet people of all ranks and levels, establishing rapport, sympathetically comprehending the significances of things as others view them, learning to accept their attitudes and activities without moral, social, or aesthetic evaluation, being interested in people as they are and not as someone else would have them, learning to see the reasonable bases of what at first glance may appear to be most unreasonable behavior, developing a capacity to like all kinds of people and thus to win their esteem and cooperation—these are the elements to be mastered by one who would gather human statistics. When training in these things replaces or at least precedes some of the college courses on the mathematical treatment of data, we shall come nearer to having a science of human behavior.

With such standards, it was hardly surprising that the Kinsey staff grew slowly. Clyde E. Martin joined Dr. Kinsey in 1939, I came along in 1943, and Dr. Paul Gebhard followed in 1946. Dr. Kinsey's only woman interviewer, Cornelia Christianson, joined the staff soon after, although she did not begin to interview until 1957. There were nine interviewers in all; but three stayed only a short time. Dr. Kinsey and I took about 85 percent of the eighteen thousand histories now on file at the Institute. Dr. Kinsey was extremely fussy about hiring interviewers, and I sometimes wonder how any of us managed to qualify. For he wanted people who were happily married—yet willing to spend half of their time traveling around the country. He wanted M.D.'s or Ph.D.'s—yet broadly experienced people who liked and could get along with criminals, prostitutes, and men and women from the lowest socio-economic levels. Finally, he wanted typical, run-of-the-mill, through-and-through Americans—yet people who had somehow escaped the moralistic attitudes toward sex and sexual behavior different from their own—attitudes that were then (and perhaps still are) so typically American. This third point was the major stumbling block, and Dr. Kinsey was ruthless about it. I recall his turning down one psychologist who applied for a job as interviewer with the remark, "You don't really want to do sex research."

"But I do," the psychologist insisted.

"Well, look at your attitudes. You say masturbation is immature, premarital intercourse and extramarital intercourse harmful to marriage, homosexuality abnormal, and animal contacts ludicrous. You already know all the answers, so why waste time on research?"

Very early in our research, as has been pointed out in Part I (page 34), we at the Kinsey Institute were aware that some kinds of questions could not be answered by respondents from their own knowledge. Direct observations of sexual response would be required to supplement reports secured in interviews. In our 1948 report, for example, we stated quite bluntly:

Erotic arousal is a material phenomenon which involves an extended series of physical, physiologic, and psychologic changes. Many of these could be subjected to precise instrumental measurement *if objectivity among scientists and public*

*respect for scientific research allowed such laboratory inves-
tigation.* (Italics added.)

This was a theme that recurred continually in our staff
conferences; it permeated all our thinking, and Dr. Kinsey
was always alert for opportunities to make precise human
observations himself.

Observation of homosexual activity proved to be easier than
observation of heterosexual behavior, but both types were
made available to us. Also many thousands of feet of motion-
picture film showing a great range of human sexual activity
came into our possession, and were of substantial scientific
value.

In addition to taking advantage of such ready-made material, Dr. Kinsey began quite early to plan a program of
laboratory observation similar to the one Dr. Masters and Mrs.
Johnson subsequently established. Space for a physiological
laboratory was set aside in the Kinsey Institute quarters in
Wiley Hall on the Indiana University campus; and when the
Institute moved to Jordan Hall in the early 1950's, blueprints
were drawn up for a laboratory in which sexual responses
could be observed. During the 1950's Dr. Kinsey began interviewing physiologists who might supervise the work, but
the right man was never found.

We never had the slightest doubt that men and women
willing to cooperate as subjects in laboratory research were
available. This was clear from our interviewing. Let me cite
a specific example. A medical-school researcher from another
university, concerned with infertility, wanted to find out
whether the number of sperm cells per ejaculation, or per
cubic centimeter of semen, was lowered in cases where a man
ejaculated two or more times in rapid succession. He came
to us and asked if we could find subjects in his area who
were capable of repeated ejaculation and who would come to
his laboratory. On our next trip to that part of the country
we located a number of men willing to cooperate in an infertility research project in this way.

Much the same was true of women. Some women who
had multiple orgasms, for example, and were told that
science was almost completely ignorant of this phenomenon, indicated their willingness to have coitus under observation.

I think of one woman who was capable of from fifteen to
fifty orgasms in twenty minutes. Even the most casual contact
could arouse a sexual response. We actually did observe her,

both during masturbation and during sexual intercourse. During intercourse her first orgasm occurred within two to five seconds. She was in her sixties when we made these observations, and curiously enough, had never had an orgasm before she was forty. What we would have liked to explore was the possibility of a physiological difference between such a woman and one who must experience thirty minutes or more of intense erotic stimulation before she achieves a single orgasm. We were, however, never able to make the observations that might have resolved the issue of these extreme variations in response.

Another remarkable fact about our multiorgasmic sixty-year-old was her ability to achieve full relaxation as soon as her partner did. Immediately after his ejaculation, she relaxed in complete satisfaction. She might have had twenty orgasms by then, or only one or two. In any event, her partner's ejaculation marked a happy termination to her sexual drive. It was a variety of such phenomena, encountered in the course of our interviewing, that made us especially eager in the 1940's and early 1950's to supplement our interview studies with controlled laboratory observations.

We were bitterly attacked, incidentally, for our statement that many women have multiple orgasms. Dr. Edmund Bergler and Dr. William S. Kroger even wrote a book entitled *Kinsey's Myth of Female Sexuality*, in which they dismissed our reports of multiple orgasm as "fantastic tales which the female volunteers told Kinsey." Kinsey hardly ever answered criticism—just as Masters and Johnson don't. But whenever we thought of the Bergler and Kroger attack, we remembered our sixty-year-old subject and smiled.

Despite our lack of an operating physiological laboratory, we managed to accumulate a substantial body of data (judging by pre-Masters standards) on human sexual anatomy and physiology. Thus in our 1953 report on female sexual behavior, we were able to include two chapters—"Anatomy of Sexual Response and Orgasm" and "Physiology of Sexual Response and Orgasm"—which laid the foundation upon which Dr. Masters and Mrs. Johnson were later to erect so remarkable a structure of hard scientific fact.

We noted, for example:

In connection with the present study, five gynecologists have cooperated by testing the sensitivity of the clitoris and other parts of the genitalia of nearly 900 females. The results . . . constitute a precise and important body of data on a matter which has heretofore been poorly understood and vigorously debated. The record shows that there is some individual variation in the sensitivity of the clitoris: 2 percent of the tested women seemed to be unaware of tactile stimulation, but 98 percent were aware. . . . Similarly, there is considerable evidence that most females respond erotically, often with considerable intensity and immediacy, whenever the clitoris is tactilely stimulated.

The labia majora of the female are [also] sensitive to tactile stimulation. This was so in some 92 percent of the women who were tested by the gynecologists. . . .

A broad, funnel-shaped vestibule . . . leads to the actual entrance (the orifice or introitus) of the vagina. . . . Nearly all females—about 97 percent according to the gynecologic tests—are distinctly conscious of tactile stimulation applied *anywhere* in this vestibule, and only a very occasional female out of the 879 who were tested proved to be entirely insensitive in the area. For nearly all women the vestibule is as important a source of erotic stimulation as the labia minora or the clitoris. Since the vestibule must be penetrated by the penis of the male in coitus, it is of considerable importance as a source of erotic stimulation for the female.

In most females the walls of the vagina are devoid of end organs of touch and are quite insensitive when they are gently stroked or lightly pressed. For most individuals the insensitivity extends to every part of the vagina. Among the women who were tested in our gynecologic sample, less than 14 percent were at all conscious that they had been touched. Most of those who did make some response had the sensitivity confined to certain points, in most cases on the upper (anterior) walls of the vagina just inside the vaginal entrance.

One of the major discoveries of Dr. Masters and Mrs. Johnson, of course, is the way in which motion of the inner lips (minor labia) pulls on the hood of the clitoris and thus produces friction between the hood and the sensitive glans of the clitoris. We missed that important point—but we came close. "As sources of erotic arousal," we wrote in 1953, "the labia minora seem to be fully as important as the clitoris. Consequently, masturbation in the female usually involves some sort of stimulation of the inner surfaces of these labia. Sometimes this is accomplished through digital strokes which may be confined to the labial surfaces; usually the strokes extend to the clitoris which is located at the upper (anterior) end of the genital area where the two labia minora unite to form a clitoral hood." Dr. Masters and Mrs. Johnson carried these observations an essential step further—and proved the existence of clitoral stimulation by that hood during coital thrusting and other activities in which the clitoris is not directly touched.

In addition to these relatively large-scale gynecological observations, we also had sufficient data based on direct observation of sexual arousal, orgasm, and postorgasmic resolution in men and women to describe both the engorgement of blood vessels and the heightened muscular tensions which Dr. Masters and Mrs. Johnson have since traced in such precise detail.

Concerning engorgement, we wrote in 1953:

> Almost instantly, or within a matter of seconds or a minute or so after the initiation of a sexual contact, certain areas of the body may become swollen, enlarged, and stiff with an excess of blood. This is equally true of the human and lower mammalian species, both female and male. . . . The penis, clitoris, some of the tissues near to the entrance of the vagina, the nipples of the breast, and the side walls of the nose contain a spongy *erectile* tissue which makes those structures especially liable to enlargement during sexual arousal.

And concerning muscular tension we wrote similarly:

> One of the most striking aspects of . . . sexual performance is the development of neuromuscular tensions throughout the body of the responding individual, female or male. From head to toe, the muscles contract and relax involuntarily, in steady or more convulsive rhythms. The movements may vary at various times in the experience of each individual, but they may vary even more between different individuals. Sometimes the muscular action is sufficient to effect major movements of the limbs and of still other parts of the body. Sometimes the movements are violent. Sometimes they are so limited that they are hardly noticeable; but in even the most quiescent individuals, whenever there is sexual response there is likely to be some evidence that muscles are rhythmically tensing and relaxing, everywhere in the body.

Finally, let me quote from an overall description of orgasm which we published in 1953:

> In the most extreme types of sexual reaction, an individual

who has experienced orgasm may double and throw his whole body into continuous and violent motion, arch his back, throw his hips, twist his head, thrust out his arms and legs, verbalize, moan, groan, or scream in much the same way as a person who is suffering the extremes of torture. In all of these respects, human females and males may react in essentially the same way. In some individuals the whole body may be thrown, or tossed, or rolled over a distance of several feet or yards. On occasion the sexual partner may be crushed, pounded, violently punched, or kicked during the uncontrolled responses of an intensely reactive individual. The movements are obviously involuntary, and they are for the most part beyond voluntary control. Some persons whose responses are mild can control their movements if there is some social advantage in reacting without attracting attention; but for those whose responses are more extreme, any deliberate control is almost impossible.

In explaining the source of this information, we stated simply:

We have had access to a considerable body of observed data on the involvement of the entire body in the spasms following orgasm.

None of our preliminary spadework, of course, detracts in the slightest from the enormous achievement of Dr. Masters and Mrs. Johnson. They have shown that on some points we were simply wrong. They have recorded many observations which we missed. They made their observations under controlled laboratory conditions. And they have woven their observations together into a coherent pattern covering the entire cycle of female and male response. Readers interested in the details may compare their *Human Sexual Response* with Chapters Fourteen and Fifteen of our *Sexual Behavior in the Human Female*.

Masters and Kinsey are alike in another significant respect: their terrific drive to accomplish the task at hand. Masters is said to work eighty hours a week, including one whole night a week; Dr. Kinsey pushed himself in the same way. At the office he worked a twelve- to fourteen-hour day, and pushed his staff almost as hard. On field trips we could not keep up with him; he was always after "one more history" before knocking off for the day. He never took a vacation in his life.

I remember one field trip to Chicago on which Dr. Kinsey and I interviewed ordinary people all day, and at night worked in a homosexual community. One night about midnight we came to a sailor who proceeded to give an unusually long and involved history which went on hour after hour. Kinsey asked the questions while we both recorded the replies independently, as we sometimes did to check the reliability of our code-recording techniques. About 4 A.M. there was a lull. I looked up from my code sheet and saw that Dr. Kinsey had fallen asleep. I picked up the thread and asked questions until he woke up again to continue the interview. Following another all-night session of this kind, Dr. Kinsey fell asleep in the middle of one of his own Indiana University lectures.

This drive to accomplish all that could possibly be accomplished continued to the end. He literally and knowingly worked himself to death. In June, 1956, when he was sixty-two, he had several heart attacks—particularly ominous because of his childhood bout of rheumatic fever. His physician told him he could still work two to four hours a day, and predicted that if he limited his work to this maximum he might last another four years. Dr. Kinsey utterly rejected the instructions. He said he would cut down to an eight-hour day, but no less than that, regardless of the consequences. When his physician came visiting the campus to urge him again to cut down on his work, Dr. Kinsey's response was to take him on a strenuous two-hour tour of the Institute. Two months later he died.

The two men never met, but Dr. Kinsey would have been delighted, I am sure, to have known that at Washington University, 220 miles away, Dr. Masters was just then beginning the laboratory observations that he himself had so long planned but had never been able to launch.

FEMALE ORGASM AND SEXUAL INADEQUACY

Daniel G. Brown, Ph.D.

Editors' note: Prior to the researches of Masters and Johnson, many aspects of human sexual response were matters of speculation on which varying opinions could be expressed. What is the nature of female frigidity? Do some women have several orgasms in rapid succession? Are there two kinds of female orgasm—clitoral and vaginal—or only one? Dr. Daniel G. Brown, a psychologist, here reviews the medical and behavioral literature on these and related aspects of human female sexuality. Dr. Brown is a consultant on mental health services for the U.S. Public Health Service in Atlanta, Georgia. His study was first presented, in somewhat different form, at a 1964 conference sponsored by the American Association of Marriage Counselors.

Readers unfamiliar with the earlier professional literature concerned with female sexual experience will welcome the Masters-Johnson findings with interest. But to readers long confused and distressed by endless theoretical controversies that have characterized writings in this area, the Masters-Johnson research will come with particular welcome. In place of speculations and guesses, we at last have some facts.

This review is designed to survey the professional literature on eight major issues, all of which have been discussed in the past, and in relation to which the Masters-Johnson report casts a new light:

(1) Why has there been so little understanding of the female orgasm prior to the work of Masters and Johnson?
(2) What is the nature of female orgasm?
(3) What is the nature of frigidity?
(4) How common is frigidity? What percentage of women experience orgasm? How frequently?
(5) What is the nature and present status of the controversy over clitoral *vs.* vaginal orgasm?
(6) Is orgasm necessary to sexual satisfaction and marital happiness in women? Is failure to have orgasm related to neurotic symptoms or psychosomatic disturbances?
(7) What are the determinants of sexual inadequacy and frigidity in women?
(8) What approaches and procedures have been used in the treatment of frigidity and orgasmic inadequacy in women?

The references cited in this review have for the most part been published over the last sixty years, though there are a few older references. Nearly nine out of ten were published in the last twenty years. One reason for this, of course, is that the behavioral science field is quite young—and within this field the study of human sexual behavior is even younger.

This review is limited to *human* female sexual behavior and response; hence, the very significant work of men like Harlow on the sexual development and adjustment of monkeys is not covered. And among humans the coverage is primarily of American sources—except for some references from England and from psychoanalytic writers with European origins and backgrounds.

The task of securing references was greatly facilitated by access to the Menninger Foundation in Topeka, Kansas, which has one of the most complete psychiatric-psychological libraries in the country. The 167 sources cited are listed on pages 164–174.

WHY HAS THERE BEEN SO LITTLE UNDERSTANDING OF THE FEMALE ORGASM?

Until very recent years, the nature of the female's sexual adequacy and inadequacy was one of the most neglected and least understood subjects in the biological and psychological sciences. In general terms, Sigmund Freud (59),[1] toward the close of his life, acknowledged that the scientific understanding of the sexual nature of woman was admittedly incomplete and fragmentary: "If you want to know more about femininity, you must interrogate your own experience, or turn to the poets, or else wait until science can give you more profound and more coherent information." In 1937 Karl Menninger (121) pointed out the neglect that medical science has shown toward this area by citing a leading standard textbook of medicine that made no mention whatsoever of female sexual frigidity—yet references to the impairment of *walking* occupied more than a full page of the index. And Edmund Bergler (11) referred to sexual frigidity in women as the forgotten disease: "Its frequency is tragically high, still medicine has, in general, little or nothing to say about its causation and treatment." In a span of thirty-six years, from 1928 to 1963, the number of specific references to female orgasm in *Psychological Abstracts* was under thirty, an average of less than one per year, and the number of references to female frigidity was under forty, an average of about one per year.

This neglect is still evident. Within the past fifteen years, a number of books have been published, the titles of which would suggest a coverage of such subjects as female orgasm, sexual satisfaction, and frigidity. Some of these titles include: *Woman's Inside Story, The Seven Ages of Woman, What*

---

[1] For references, see pages 164–174.

Women Want To Know, Man and Woman, Psychosexual Functions in Women. These books were all written by professional workers in obstetrics and gynecology, psychiatry, psychoanalysis, psychology, or sociology. Nevertheless, they contain very little discussion, or none at all, in the area of female genital experience.

This same contemporary pattern of avoidance is also seen in the almost total lack of preparation in the sexual area afforded physicians, ministers, psychologists, sociologists, social workers, and members of related disciplines and professions.

This taboo on sex has been strong, has persisted for centuries, and has still not disappeared by any means. As recently as 1930 Theodoor H. Van de Velde (158), the Dutch physician and author of *Ideal Marriage,* one of the earlier classics on sexual adjustment, pointed out in an introductory statement that such a publication would have many unpleasant results for him because of the habit of human beings to condemn what is unusual and unconventional and, for this reason, he could not have written the book earlier because of the requirements of his medical practice. He wrote:

> So I must write down what I have learnt to be true and right; I could not face the evening of my life with a quiet conscience if I omitted to do so. There is need for this knowledge; there is too much suffering endured which might well be avoided, too much joy untasted which could enhance life's worth. . . . I could have escaped the unpleasantness referred to above by the use of a pseudonym . . . but, as a scientist, it is my duty to sign my own name to a serious medical and scientific work.

In addition to the agelong taboo on the study and understanding of sex, until recent times it was taken for granted, at least in most of the Western world, that *the majority of females had neither the desire nor the capacity for sexual gratification*—and in the minority who did, it was a defect that should be denied or somehow eliminated. There was no reason to study female sexuality because women either didn't or shouldn't have any capacity for sexual desire and pleasure. J. Duffy (39), for example, observes that the nineteenth century, while ushering in the scientific and industrial revolutions, was also the Victorian age of prudery in which it was unthinkable that any "decent" woman should derive pleasure from sex. According to Havelock Ellis (52), Acton, a leading authority on sexual matters in England during the latter part of the last century, condemned the idea that women have sexual feelings as a "vile aspersion." Related to this denial of sexuality in women has been the long-held notion that sexual relations in marriage should be only for the purpose of procreation. Ellis also cites an Anglican bishop who declared that intercourse in marriage for any reason other than procreation was a "degrading act of mere self-gratification." In this country, a physician in 1883, writing in a New Orleans medical journal, said that he did not believe one bride in a hundred accepted matrimony from any desire for sexual gratification. He conceded, however, that some women from the "lower elements" of society might admit to desiring sexual gratification. The modest woman, he believed, submitted to her husband only to please him, and except for the desire for children, would otherwise prefer to leave sex out of her life. Apparently there were still some "decent women" who found pleasure in sex, because about this same time an English surgeon by the name of Dr. Isaac Brown Baker performed numerous clitoridectomies on women in order to prevent sexual stimulation which, in turn, he was convinced would "cure" or prevent various "insanities," "epilepsy," "hysteria," "catalepsy," and other diseases.

Marie Robinson (138) points out that many authorities, up to World War I, agreed that sexual feeling in young women in love was pathological and abnormal. Mary Melendy (120) —a physician and Ph.D., whose book, *The Perfect Woman*, was published in 1903 as a "Complete Medical Guide for Women"—not only omitted any discussion of female sexual satisfaction, orgasm, or frigidity, but at the same time repeatedly cautioned about the dire consequences of "self-abuse," that is, autoerotic stimulation, which the author asserted "causes an undue amount of blood to flow to the (genital organs), thus depriving other parts of the body of its nourishment. . . . This produces a diseased condition . . . and lays the foundation for consumption, paralysis and heart disease . . . weakens the memory . . . makes many lose their minds; and, others, when grown, commit suicide." And as recently as 1957 P. D. Klingensmith (94) referred to a modern textbook in psychosomatic gynecology that implies that the majority of women derive little or no pleasure from the sex act.

It might be added that more recent writers on the subject of female sexuality are of the opinion that the Victorian era has passed and that increasing numbers of women are able to accept their sexual drives and fulfill their need for gratification and orgasm. While Havelock Ellis (52) points out that the sexual-erotic claims and rights of women have been the *last* of all human rights to be attained, these rights have become firmly established at least in part of the Western world. Eustice Chesser (29) in England refers to the important change that has taken place in the sex life of English women: "Before the first World War, it was shameful for a woman to admit to experiencing pleasure in sexual intercourse; today, many women feel ashamed to admit they do not experience orgasm." And, in this country, Maxine Davis (34) considers that, along with the social and economic emancipation of women, there has been a major discovery, an "astounding development," namely, the recognition and acceptance by both men and women of the fact that the human female is capable of sexual desire and can fully enjoy the sexual relationship.

In this connection, several recent books have dealt with the problem of the continuing emancipation of the contemporary American woman. Marion Bassett's *A New Sex Ethics and Marriage Structure* (5) is a plea for complete equality of the sexes and for a *single* standard of sexual conduct for men and women. Betty Friedan's *The Feminine Mystique* (61) is an indictment of the exclusive role of homemaker for women; Mrs. Friedan believes that those women who have emancipated themselves socially from their traditional confinement to the home have also, as a group, freed themselves sexually and are capable of full responsiveness and gratification. Pearl Buck (21), in a chapter contributed to the book *American Women: The Changing Image,* points out that the new realization that women enjoy sex as much as men has "revolutionized the relationship between men and women." In 1963, an entire book was published to emphasize that increasing numbers of American women from the higher socio-economic and educational levels have "sexually emancipated" themselves. Arthur Hirsch's *The Love Elite* (75) is based on the contents of thousands of personal letters, interviews, observations, and publications. Its theme is that more and more women have come to accept sexual intimacy in or out of wedlock as an ethically acceptable new source of happiness. Helen G. Brown's (20) *Sex and the Single Girl* has essentially the same theme.

Still another factor has retarded our understanding of female sexuality. Most of what has been recorded about sex in females has been written by males. Until recently, there has been a reluctance of women to explore and report on their sexual natures and experiences. Helena Wright (167), an English gynecologist, has commented on the slow progress in understanding orgasmic inadequacy in women as probably due mainly to the fact that

> the thinkers and writers on the subject have been predominantly male, and all they can do is to use their powers of observation and inquiry and interpret the results in comparison with their own experiences. *It is lamentable that women have done so little thinking and writing on their own behalf and have accepted so meekly the passive role which men in Western civilization have stamped upon female sexual interests.* (Italics added.)

WHAT IS THE NATURE OF FEMALE ORGASM?

Female sexual *dissatisfaction* has probably existed since the beginning of the human race. E. Elkan (44) points out that this problem has not been confined to a particular race. He believes that the question of human female orgasm began when females first became aware of the male's pleasure in sex and his orgasmic ability. At that point, women became dissatisfied with what seemed to them to be inequalities inherent in sexual activity. In other words, according to Elkan, the problem developed when woman first realized that man had an orgasm in intercourse while she did not.

Historically, Elkan mentions Vatsyayana's book, *Kama Sutra* (159), written in India some 1,500 years ago, which summarized the contents of many previous writings on sexual topics dating back more than three thousand years. This Hindu manual is the first reference on record exclusively devoted to the subject of human sexuality and man-woman relationships. It contains a long list of ways in which women can be stimulated to help them obtain sexual satisfaction.

The human race could have survived, of course, without a single female having an orgasm. But it could *not* have survived without orgasms in males, generation after generation. Elkan (44) proposes the hypothesis that, from a biological and evolutionary standpoint, the capacity of the human female for orgasm may still be emerging and that, therefore, many women are not yet fully capable of complete orgasmic responsiveness. This was also suggested by L. H. Terman (154) in his study of 792 married couples, after he failed to find what he considered to be sufficient reasons to account for the sizable percentage of wives (1 in 3) who only "sometimes" or "never" obtained orgasm. He comments on the inability of these wives to achieve orgasm as ". . . one of the most puzzling mysteries in the psychology and physiology of sex." Failing to find evidence of the influence of emotional conditioning and experience in the background of sexually inadequate wives, Terman raised the question whether the causes of orgasmic inadequacy might not be biological, perhaps of genetic origin, rather than psychological.

Various attempts have been made to specify the nature of female orgasm, what it is, and what it is not. Hardenbergh (68), on the basis of a study of the replies of thirty-nine married women to a questionnaire, summarizes the characteristics of orgasm in woman as follows:

General bodily excitement . . . perspiration, breathlessness. . . . Response to stimulation occurs at the clitoris, the vagina near the clitoris . . . (with) the walls of the vagina widening and becoming pliable; the clitoris becoming erect and pulsating; a pleasant feeling, increasing excitement . . . and the desire for intromission of the penis . . . (after which) spontaneous and involuntary contraction occurs in the pelvis and genital muscles. . . . There is a rising tension and then a sudden release; and less often there is no sudden change in experience but after a maximum is reached subsidence is gradual; or the tension mounts to a condition of rigidity and then there is cataclysmic release . . . characterized by the wall of the vagina contracting and relaxing slightly to violently.

The duration of the orgasm is estimated by Hardenbergh to be between twelve and fifteen seconds. Hannah and Abraham Stone (150) have pointed out that the term *orgasm* refers to the spasmodic contractions of the genital muscles occurring at the climax of the sex act. In the female, these rhythmic and involuntary contractions are concentrated in the regions of the vulva, vagina, and the clitoris. All this, of course, is now primarily of historic interest. Masters and Johnson, by actually observing more than 7,500 orgasms in hundreds of women under a broad range of conditions, have provided the first objective, scientific account of what the orgasm *is* from the physiological point of view. Their research not only stands unparalleled in the history of the science of sex, but has established the first and as yet the only demonstrable, confirmable scientific information on the subject.

WHAT IS THE NATURE
OF FRIGIDITY?

Frigidity, sometimes called hyposexuality or sexual anesthesia, refers broadly to disturbances in female sexuality ranging from lack of orgasm and dissatisfaction during coitus, to a relative absence of desire for heterosexual relations, or even an inability to participate in them at all.

Frigidity may involve one or more or some combination of deficits in female sexuality. For example, a woman may have little desire, find no satisfaction, and never experience an orgasm in sexual relations. Or she may have great sexual desire, find lovemaking quite pleasurable, but be unable to achieve orgasm. Other combinations are also possible.

In specifying *heterosexual* relations, it is implied that a woman may be more or less frigid in relation to the opposite sex but may have much desire and be capable of orgasm through such experiences as autoeroticism or homosexuality. A number of writers hold that the most common and most disturbing form of frigidity is that in which the woman has strong sexual drive, arousal, and desire, but is unable to reach orgasm (38, 83, 110, 126, 147, 151, 158).

Karl Menninger (121) and Sandor Lorand (108) consider frigidity a form of hysteria involving the functional impairment of genitality comparable to an hysterical paralysis of the leg from so-called shell shock. Frigidity, as understood by these writers, is a condition of sexual anesthesia, or paralysis, or both, based on psychic conflict and inhibition.

Some writers restrict the meaning of frigidity simply to the absence of orgasm; others limit it even more to the absence of vaginal orgasm. Typical in this regard is Eisenstein's view that there may be strong sexual excitement in many frigid women, particularly in the clitoris, but pleasurable vaginal sensations either do not arise or else end without orgasm. Georgene H. Seward (144) has emphasized the factor of desire and has suggested that in frigidity there is not an absence but rather a *blocking* of sexual desire; the sexually inadequate woman is frustrated rather than indifferent about sex.

E. Grafenberg (63) points out that a wife is not necessarily frigid just because she is unable to reach orgasm with her husband. She may respond freely and completely with another man. He mentions the case of one of his female patients who married an older man and bore him children, but never experienced orgasm with him. In therapy this patient repeatedly asked why she could not have an orgasm with her husband. Grafenberg describes the outcome of therapy as follows:

Bored by the repeated discussions with her, I finally asked her if she had tried sex relations with another male partner. No, was the answer, and reflectively she left my office. The next day, in the middle of the night, I was awakened by a telephone call and a familiar voice, who did not give her name asked: "Doctor, are you there? You are right," and hung up the receiver with a bang! I never had to answer any further sexual questions from her.

There is almost universal agreement that frigidity and lack of orgasm are based on psychogenic rather than organic or physiological factors. Most workers have been greatly impressed with the overwhelming role of conditioning, learning, and experience in determining female erotic responsiveness. Typical in this regard is the conclusion of Hamilton (67) from his study of sexual adjustment in marriage. The importance of psychological factors in determining orgasm inadequacy was so convincingly demonstrated, he stated, that a separate publication would be necessary to present all the findings.

WHAT IS THE INCIDENCE OF FRIGIDITY?
WHAT PERCENTAGE OF WOMEN EXPERIENCE ORGASM?
HOW OFTEN?

Since different criteria are used by different writers to define frigidity, the incidence varies in part because of the criteria selected. It is not surprising, therefore, that writers such as Bergler (10), who equate frigidity with failure to reach a *vaginal* orgasm, report that frigidity is a problem that "concerns from 70 to 80 percent of all women." Robert P. Knight (95) writes similarly: "Perhaps 75 percent of all married women derive little or no pleasure from the sexual act." The same estimate is made by W. S. Kroger and S. C. Freed (96). Other estimates of the percentage of women who report incomplete sexual satisfaction or who are usually unable to have orgasmic experience include: Weiss and English (162), more than 50 percent, Joan Malleson (111), 30 to 40 percent; and Marie Robinson (138), over 40 percent. Bassett (5) estimates that in this country some six million wives, about one in four, are not satisfied in their sexual relations; either they prefer to avoid sex altogether or else they desire relations but are not gratified.

An important consideration in the above estimates is the sample of women on which they are based. For the most part, the above percentages are applicable *only to women who have been seen by clinicians*—usually obstetricians, psychiatrists, psychoanalysts, psychologists, social workers, or marriage counselors. These women have requested help because of various somatic symptoms or emotional problems. The question then arises, what about women from the general population?

W. Stekel (147) points out that very few healthy women are sexually anesthetic, while most neurotics are frigid. Kinsey (92) concluded that such estimates as those cited above are exaggerated and lack substantiation.

A number of questionnaire studies over the past thirty years have been concerned with marital and sexual adjustment: Dickinson (38), Burgess and Wallin (22), Chesser (29),

Kinsey (92), Hamilton (67), Locke (106), Terman (154), and Thomason (156). Although differing in some respects, all of these studies specifically asked the frequency with which wives experienced orgasm or satisfaction in sex relations. By combining the Terman and Burgess-Wallin studies, data become available on some 2,500 married women. From these combined studies, the following estimates and generalizations may be made: between 60 and 70 percent of married women experience orgasm "usually or always," about 25 percent "some of the time," and between 5 and 10 percent "rarely or never." These findings are comparable with the findings of Chesser's (29) study of 3,705 married women in England: 59 percent "usually or always" had orgasms, 26 percent "sometimes," and 15 percent "rarely or never."

Kinsey's data on the incidence of orgasm is analyzed somewhat differently, which makes direct comparisons in some ways more difficult. In essence, however, based on about 2,500 wives, Kinsey found that about 75 percent of the women in his sample had some orgasmic experience by the end of the first year of marriage, 83 percent after five years of marriage, 87 percent after ten years of marriage, and 90 percent after fifteen or more years of marriage. One out of ten married women in Kinsey's group apparently rarely or never reached orgasm, which is consistent with the findings of other investigators noted above. On the other hand, Kinsey's data shows that 51, 55, 59, 61, and 64 percent of the females who have been married one, five, ten, fifteen, and twenty years respectively, achieve orgasm between 60 percent and 100 percent of the time. If "60 to 100 percent of the time" is a satisfactory criterion for defining "usually or always," the Kinsey figures are relatively consistent with the Terman, Burgess-Wallin, and Chesser figures.

Harvey J. Locke (106), in his study of 181 married females, found that nine out of ten wives reported that their sex relations with their husbands were: *enjoyable* (58 percent) or *very enjoyable* (32 percent). Specific data on orgasm were not presented.

Three other aspects of female orgasm may be briefly mentioned; these are: (1) multiple orgasms, (2) nocturnal sex dreams and orgasm, and (3) orgasm through the use of imagination and fantasy.

The occurrence of *multiple orgasms* during a single lovemaking episode has been discussed by a number of writers. Terman (154) found that about 13 percent of his sample of

792 married women reported having multiple orgasms. Kinsey (92) found that about 14 percent of all women in his study with twenty-five or more coital experiences, irrespective of marital status, experienced multiple orgasms. In his discussion of sexual adjustment in marriage, Robert Street (152) devotes considerable attention to the subject of multiple orgasms in women and suggests that most women have this capacity although many are not aware of it.

Some male workers in the field, probably influenced by male standards, have questioned the capacity of females for repeated orgasms in rapid succession. Hamilton (67), for example, referred to his "uncertainty" as to the validity of the report of some of his female subjects that they had experienced multiple orgasms. He concluded that they must have been referring to nonterminative "minor" climaxes rather than full-fledged orgasms. Bergler and Kroger (14) completely rejected the findings of Kinsey that a sizable percentage of his female subjects had experienced multiple orgasms. They state:

> One of the most fantastic tales the female volunteers told Kinsey (who believed it) was that of multiple orgasm. Allegedly 14 percent of these women claimed to have experienced it. . . . Multiple orgasm is an exceptional experience. The 14 percent of Kinsey's volunteers, all vaginally frigid, belonged obviously to the nymphomaniac type of frigidity where excitement mounts repeatedly *without* reaching a climax. . . . *Not being familiar with this medical fact . . . Kinsey was taken in by the near-misses which these women represented as multiple orgasm.*

If there ever was any basis for questioning the occurrence of multiple orgasm in women there is none now. Masters and Johnson (117, 119) have actually observed multiple orgasms, and have measured the accompanying physiological contractions. They have conclusively demonstrated not only the existence of the phenomenon but the relative ease with which it can be experienced in many women. They write:

> If a female who is capable of having regular orgasm is properly stimulated within a short period after her first climax, she will in most instances be capable of having a second, third, fourth, and even fifth and sixth orgasm before she is fully satiated. As contrasted with the male's usual inability to have more than one orgasm in a short period, many

females, especially when clitorally stimulated, can regularly have five or six full orgasms within a matter of a few minutes.

A second aspect of interest concerning female sexuality, though infrequently reported in the literature, is the incidence of nocturnal sex dreams, and of orgasm during dreams. Kinsey (92) found that more than 70 percent of his total female sample had experienced overtly sexual dreams in the course of their lives; about one in three females had reached orgasm in their nocturnal dreams. Hamilton (67) reported slightly more than one in three of his female subjects had nocturnal dreams leading to orgasm.

Tapia, Werboff, and Winokur (153), found the incidence of nocturnal orgasm among female outpatient neurotics markedly and significantly higher than among nonpsychiatric patients—47 percent compared to 8 percent. Winokur, Guze, and Pfeiffer (164) also found the occurrence of dream orgasm much more common in neurotic, psychotic, separated, or divorced females compared to presumably normal, married females. These studies seem to suggest some interesting relationships between the emotional and marital status of women and their experience of actual versus imagined sexual activity.

Kinsey (92), however, is skeptical of such hypothesized relationships. He doubts that there is any basis for assuming the women reporting nocturnal dream orgasm in his sample were any more neurotic or psychotic than the women who had not experienced them. He also presents data showing that about 90 percent of the females having the greatest frequency of nocturnal orgasm also had regular orgasm in coitus and about 40 percent had multiple orgasms in coitus; this compared to about 50 percent and 14 percent, respectively, for the overall sample of female cases.

A third related subject of interest is the occurrence of female orgasm in the waking state through the use of fantasy and imagination, without any manual stimulation. Kinsey found only about 2 percent of all females who had masturbated to orgasm had ever been able to use fantasy alone to reach orgasm. This is evidently a rare occurrence. Polatin and Douglas (132) report the case of a twenty-five-year-old female schizophrenic patient who had a number of "spontaneous" orgasms over a period of six months; these orgasms occurred without masturbation and without any known conscious fantasy; the authors hypothesize that the evoking stimuli were deeply rooted in the unconscious of this patient and hence were not perceived by her. Hilda O'Hare (125) mentions the case of a woman who was able to achieve complete vaginal orgasms solely through the use of her "own mental stimulation." And Rey Anthony (2), in writing her personal sexual history, mentions the fact that through the imaginative use of what she calls "sex pictures," involving highly erotic fantasy, she was able to reach a climax without any other stimulation.

WHAT IS THE NATURE AND PRESENT STATUS OF THE CONTROVERSY OVER CLITORAL VS. VAGINAL ORGASM?

In a journal review of five books dealing with female sexuality published in 1953–54, J. Shor (145) points out that the central question, the one about which there is greatest dispute, concerns the nature of sexual climax in women. He found that the authors of these books had basic disagreements regarding the conditions for and qualities of satisfactory sexual experience, both physically and psychologically. How did such disagreement and controversy about the female orgasm begin? Part of the answer to this goes back to the writings of Freud.

In 1910 Freud, in his *Three Essays on the Theory of Sexuality* (60), developed what was to become basic psychoanalytic doctrine concerning female sexuality. Briefly summarized, the most relevant parts of Freud's theory for the purpose of this review are as follows: (1) the female has two basic tasks in her psychosexual development; one is a shift in attachment from the mother to the father, and the other involves a shift in primary sexual pleasure from the clitoris to the vagina; and (2) the genital sexuality in young girls is of a "wholly masculine character. . . . With the onset of the phallic phase . . . we recognize that the little girl is a little man . . . (she obtains pleasure from her clitoris as a boy with the penis)." As the principal organ of female sexual feeling in childhood, the clitoris is the "true substitute for the penis."

This concept of Freud has come to be uncritically and enthusiastically accepted by many psychoanalytic writers up to the present time (13, 14, 15, 23, 36, 42, 43, 56, 77, 109, 138). Each of these writers insists that clitoral orgasm is an expression of immaturity, neuroticism, masculinity, or frigidity, or some combination, while vaginal orgasm denotes maturity, femininity, and normality. Marie Bonaparte (15) refers to the "most remarkable biological feat" of the mature woman in being able to deflect and displace the masculine libido of the clitoris to the "purely feminine channels" of the vagina. However, Bonaparte deviates just a little from the straight Freudian line when she acknowledges that "women who experience *both* clitorical and vaginal stimulation have an advantage over those who have only vaginal stimulation . . . since preliminaries can lead to end-pleasure."

Helene Deutsch (36), in her earlier writings, subscribed to Freud's view that clitoral activity is "masculine and immature," while vaginal responsiveness is "feminine and mature." She wrote that the sexual act for a woman may be "profoundly cathartic . . . [but] only under the condition that it is experienced in a feminine, dynamic way and is not transformed into an act of erotic play or sexual 'equality.' " [2]

Marynia Farnham (109) is another female analyst who goes right along with the Freudian thesis. She deplores the "enormously high" percentage of women today who find their main source of sexual satisfaction in clitoral stimulation—which is, according to Farnham, essentially an "infantile fixation" and probably represents a "denial of femininity."

Another psychoanalyst, Marie Robinson (138), devotes an entire chapter in her book, *The Power of Sexual Surrender,* to the elaboration of the view that the orgasm of the "truly mature woman" always takes place in the vagina, while the woman who has only clitoral orgasms is suffering from a form of frigidity: "We call a woman suffering from this form of frigidity a 'clitoridal' or 'masculine' type. . . ." Having said all of this, Robinson then paradoxically adds: "However, millions of women find this earlier method of gratification [clitoral orgasm] so satisfying that they are not motivated to move up to the mature level."

---

[2] Some years later, however, Deutsch raised some serious questions regarding the accuracy and adequacy of the traditional psychoanalytic interpretation of female orgasm. For references to her later thinking, see Burgess E. Moore (123).

G. Bychowski (23) considers the difference between vaginal and clitoral orgasm of major importance as a manifestation of feminine sexuality. He contends that for women who have only clitoral orgasms, "there is always a deep denial of the feminine role and a morbid masculine identification."

Perhaps the most outspoken advocate of the Freudian view is Bergler (11), who insists that every woman who cannot or does not have a *vaginal* orgasm is frigid, the absence of vaginal orgasm being the sole criterion of frigidity. The alternative view, held by a number of other workers, that the clitoris may be a primary or the principal source of sexual arousal and pleasure for many normal, mature women has evoked vehement protest from Bergler. In fact, following the second Kinsey volume, which emphasized the normality and universality of clitoral orgasm, Bergler and Kroger (14) felt compelled to write a book, *Kinsey's Myth of Female Sexuality,* in an effort to repudiate Kinsey's conclusions. Marie Robinson (138) states that the "great observers . . . in the field of psychiatry have been unanimous in their observation on the difference between clitoral and vaginal orgasm and its importance to personality development and to neurosis."

There have been several psychoanalysts, however, who have taken exception to the Freudian position. These include Therese Benedek (9), Marjorie Brierley (17), Karen Horney (79), Clara Thompson (157), J. Marmor (113), and S. Rado (134). They hold essentially that the clitoris remains a major source of *normal* eroticism in women throughout their lives.

Both Horney (79) and Brierley (17) vigorously deny the idea that vaginal eroticism is merely transferred from the clitoris and is characteristic only of adult maturity. These writers are convinced that many girls experience vaginal sexual response throughout childhood. In addition, Brierley is critical of the notion that the clitoris must "give up" or "transfer" primary sensitivity to the vagina. She writes:

There are many women in whom clitoral stimulation is a necessary precondition to vaginal orgasm. If then we find a considerable range of clitoral activity compatible with, or even necessary to, vaginal normality, perhaps we should do better to speak of normality as dependent upon a particular kind of coordination between the two functions rather than only supplanting of one by the other.

Clara Thompson (157) rejects the idea that the vagina is sexually responsive only in adult females since many girls know of it earlier and derive sexual pleasure from vaginal stimulation. She also rejects the idea that the "mature" woman gives up or transfers her interest in the clitoris; instead, it remains a principal source of natural sexual satisfaction throughout her life.

Therese Benedek (9) and Marmor (113) also doubt the validity of the clitoral-to-vaginal transfer as a prerequisite to normality and maturity. Marmor points out that while this conclusion of Freud has seldom been seriously questioned in the psychoanalytic literature, there is ample justification for questioning it. He presents his own conceptualization by postulating a *single* orgasmic mechanism, regardless of the source of stimulation, that varies with the degree of cortical inhibition or cortical facilitation of the individual woman—that is, varies with the absence of anxiety, degree of relaxation, concentration on erotic arousal, psychological responsiveness, etc. If the cortical inhibition is considerable, only a spinal-level orgasmic response may be possible, or no sexual response at all. An *absence* of inhibition (guilt feelings, fear, etc.) and maximum psychological facilitation results in a full-fledged consummatory orgasm.

Rado (134) has joined the apparently increasing number of psychoanalytic writers who do not go along with the Freudian interpretation of female genitality. He holds that *both* clitoral and vaginal stimulation facilitate sexual arousal and orgasm. He adds: "By suppressing her clitoral sensations, the female cannot possibly augment her vaginal responses; she can only reduce her capacity for sexual performance, health, and happiness."

The most recent critique of the psychoanalytic interpretation has been made by Hastings (69). He writes:

The present day reader acquainted with scientific method might, after reading the above (psychoanalytic account of clitoral versus vaginal orgasm), ask to see the experimental data or, lacking that, request the opportunity to review in some detail case material from which Freud drew his conclusions. Neither of these conditions can be met, and one is forced to regard the theory as the unsupported opinion of a very gifted man, but unsupported nevertheless. Another complication in this matter is that none of the proponents of the clitoral-vaginal transfer theory, Freud included, have stated signs or symptoms by which one may distinguish between these presumably different types of orgasms.

Hastings adds that the final demolition of the old transfer notion came with the research of Masters and Johnson.

Before examining alternate views of the orgasm controversy, the work of Kegel (88) deserves mention. In connection with his work in gynecology, particularly with cases of urinary stress incontinence, Kegel found that by having his patients exercise and strengthen their pelvic-vaginal muscles (specifically the pubococcygeus muscles that surround and are attached to the walls of the vagina), the urinary incontinence could be corrected without surgery.

In his work with hundreds of women with this problem, Kegel inadvertently discovered that a number of these women spontaneously mentioned that their sexual responsiveness and satisfaction had increased—some having orgasm for the first time in their marriage. This led him to the conclusion that the physiological basis of vaginal orgasm involved highly specialized nerve endings in the pubococcygeus muscle that are stimulated by penetration of the penis in intercourse, giving rise to a pressure or deep-touch response. Kegel reasons that women who have a weak and atrophic pubococcygeus muscle are unable to receive sexual satisfaction in coitus. He estimates that one-third of all women are so afflicted, another third have some weakness, and the other third have strong, responsive vaginal muscles.

As far as the treatment of frigidity is concerned, Kegel reports that strengthening these muscles through daily exercises is successful in more than six out of ten women. He mentions that the mere awareness of this muscle and its contractility sometimes enhances a woman's sexual responsiveness and pleasure. (It should be noted that while Kegel's name is associated with this emphasis on vaginal muscles, LeMon Clark (30) pointed to the importance of this factor a number of years earlier.)

Oliven (126) and Maxine Davis (34) have attached much importance to the findings of Kegel. Both of these writers strongly recommend vaginal muscle exercises in cases of hyposexuality." Davis points out that the existence of these "magic muscles," which function to enhance sexual pleasure, have only recently been discovered, and that it is not surprising very few women realize they have them. An example of her enthusiastic acceptance of Kegel's "muscle therapy" is evident in the following statement: "Psychiatrists have wasted endless hours of their own and their patients' time trying to probe into subconscious emotional factors in frigidity when all the patient needed was systematic exercise of her horrendously labeled 'pubococcygeus muscles.' "

Though consistent with the Freudian emphasis on vaginal orgasm, Kegel's work was done independently of a psychoanalytic setting or influence and involves an entirely different rationale. For Freud there is a change of libido from the clitoris to the vagina in the interest of femininity and psychosexual maturity; for Kegel the vaginal orgasm is simply a neuro-muscular, conditioned reflex response based on intact and healthy vaginal muscles.

In direct contrast to Freud and some of the other psychoanalytic writers cited previously, Kinsey (92), Kelly (90), Albert Ellis (46, 48, 51), Ruth Herschberger (73), and Street (152) in particular have emphasized the central and primary role of the clitoris and the secondary role of the vagina in the female orgasm. The main basis for the argument of these writers is the fact that the clitoris is richly endowed with sexual receptor cells, genital corpuscles, which are extremely sensitive to tactile stimulation; these neurons are largely absent in the vagina. This basic consideration has led to such statements as the following: "It is difficult . . . in the light of our present understanding of the anatomy and physiology of sexual response, to understand what can be meant by a 'vaginal orgasm.' The literature usually implies that the vagina itself should be the center of sensory stimulation, and this, as we have seen, is a physical and physiologic impossibility for nearly all females [92]." "[Orgasm] is in the clitoris . . . whether the subject localizes the sensation there or not [90]." "After carefully reviewing the recent literature on this subject and interviewing scores of sexually normal and disturbed women, I was forced to conclude that the so-called vaginal orgasm is largely a myth [51]."

Ruth Herschberger (73) has provided what is probably the most eloquent defense of the theory of clitoral primacy in female sexuality:

In the symphony of love, the lost chord is a small organ lying somewhat north of the vagina. This entire zone is called the vulva, and includes all external genitals, labia, entrance to the vagina, and the organ alluded to, the clitoris. . . . If any one assumption is agreed on by the sex booklets, it is the lamentable inferiority of the clitoris to the penis. . . . Has the clitoris any purpose at all? . . . The Germans have called the clitoris, *Wollustorgan*, the *ecstasy* organ; but it is more commonly frowned on as autoerotic, infantile (Freud) vestigial (like the tonsils) and in general the progenitor of no good. . . . Marriage manuals admit grudgingly that this organ is the most sexually sensitive organ in the female body but then inform women "that the fullest expression of their sexual nature is not reached until sensation is felt as acutely in the vagina as in the clitoris."

Herschberger mentions that while the clitoris is only a fraction of the size of the penis, it is demonstrably richer in nerves. She then adds:

It was quite a feat of nature to grant the small clitoris the same number of nerves as the penis. It was an even more incredible feat that society should actually have convinced the possessors of this organ that it was sexually inferior to the penis.

A number of writers (4, 17, 24, 34, 38, 58, 84, 130, 125, 145, 113, 126, 159, 157, 158), emphasize both the clitoris and the vagina as more or less equal and complementary in female sexual responsiveness. In addition, even advocates of the superiority of the clitoris over the vagina in female sexuality, such as Kinsey (92), Kelly (90), and Albert Ellis (49) acknowledge that some women regularly reach orgasm via the vagina.

More than thirty years ago Van de Velde wrote that female orgasm, whether by clitoral or vaginal stimulation, is the same, as far as the internal physiologic processes and relief are concerned. He added, however, that the stimulation of the clitoris and the vagina differ and uses an analogy of the "flavor and aroma of two fine kinds of wine or the chromatic glories and subtleties of two quite separate color schemes [158]."

Oliven (126) recognizes the existence and relative equality of clitoral as well as vaginal mechanisms in female orgasm. He discusses the fact that the clitoris and vagina each has its own *specific* sensory nerve endings each capable of bringing about orgasm, and he points out that genital orgasm can be obtained *without* stimulating the vagina and *without* stimulating the clitoris. Rado (159) and Baruch (4) specifically emphasize the *complementary* nature of clitoral and vaginal stimulation in female orgasm. For example, Baruch writes: "Some women enjoy having an orgasm first manually as part of the foreplay. . . . [This can] make for reaching a second orgasm more rapidly in coitus."

From the physiological point of view, contrasting inter-
pretations related to Freud's concepts of vaginal versus clitoral
orgasm have now been made unnecessary. Masters and
Johnson have shown, on the basis of direct observations and
laboratory measurements, that the same train of events,
including the same orgasmic responses, occur following
clitoral stimulation, vaginal stimulation, or (in some women)
stimulation of the breasts alone, without clitoral or vaginal
contact. They have also shown that the clitoris is stimulated
simultaneously with the vagina during ordinary coitus. Thus
the half-century-long controversy is now of primarily historical
interest. There remains, however, one major question: are
there differences in the *conscious experience* and *subjective
awareness* of orgasm following clitoral stimulation, vaginal
stimulation, or a combination of the two simultaneously?
Several women have written on this topic.

Sylvia Payne (130) holds that the vaginal orgasm can
be subjectively distinguished from the orgasm due to clitoral
stimulation. She writes: "One may and I think should be
merged into the other, but they are frequently easily distin-
guishable. Vaginal orgasm has a sucking characteristic . . .
clitoral orgasm is a discharging orgasm and is more like the
male orgasm."

Joan Malleson (111), on the one hand, states that the
clitoris is the source of greatest sexual feeling for the majority
of women; on the other hand, she refers to the "external"
clitoral orgasm as a pleasurable but less satisfying substitute
for the "complete fulfillment" that comes with the "internal"
vaginal orgasm.

Perhaps the most personal, revealing information regarding
the experience of clitoral in contrast to vaginal orgasm has
come from Hilda O'Hare (124, 125), who describes what
she considers an unmistakable difference between the two. She
reports sometimes having one kind of orgasm, sometimes the
other, and sometimes not having any at all. O'Hare refers to
her experience of clitoral orgasm as

> . . . more shallowly placed and seems to me to be localized
> in the anterior wall of the vagina not far from the clitoris itself,
> [while the vaginal orgasm] produces a pronounced and pro-
> longed tonic state of the deeper placed vaginal muscles. . . .
> [She continues] I now wish to add that I have experienced
> vaginal orgasms in which stimulation of the clitoris (by either
> penis or male pubic area) was a contributory factor. . . .
> Why clitoral stimulation during coitus should sometimes re-
> sult in its own characteristic orgasm but occasionally should

merge with other sensations to produce the greater vaginal orgasm, I do not know.

IS ORGASM NECESSARY TO SEXUAL SATISFACTION AND MARITAL HAPPINESS IN WOMEN?

IS FAILURE TO HAVE ORGASM RELATED TO NEUROTIC SYMPTOMS OR PSYCHOSOMATIC DISTURBANCES?

There is considerable confusion in the literature about these questions. While a number of writers are convinced that lack of female orgasm is a basic cause of chronic tension, frustration, and psychophysiological complaints as well as marital unhappiness, other writers insist that many women are sexually satisfied without orgasmic experience. Some writers seem to hold both views simultaneously.

For example, Kinsey (92), on the one hand, emphasizes that female orgasm should not be used as the sole criterion of the amount of satisfaction in sexual relations since "considerable pleasure may be found in sexual arousal . . . and in the social aspects of a sexual relationship." Yet practically all of Kinsey's data in this area are in terms of orgasm. Similarly, Chesser (29) suggests that a distinction is necessary in women between sexual satisfaction in general and orgasm in particular. He writes: "There are those married women whose sexual satisfaction consists essentially in giving pleasure to their husband without achieving a sexual climax themselves; others rarely obtain sexual pleasure on a genital level at all." Later on, however, he refers to the "outstandingly important influence" of female orgasm and sexual satisfaction on sexual intercourse and marital happiness.

C. R. Adams (1) studied the marital and sexual adjustment of 150 wives at Pennsylvania State University, divided into three groups, low, intermediate, and high in terms of sexual responsiveness. He concluded that marital happiness depends to a considerable extent on sexual adjustment, which, in turn, depends considerably on sexual responsiveness. "But, if most other factors are favorable," he adds, "a wife may be happy in marriage even though she is quite unresponsive sexually.

Conversely, if most other factors are not favorable, a wife may be unhappy in marriage even though she is very responsive sexually."

Hannah and Abraham Stone (150) mention that even if a woman does not attain an intense climax she may nevertheless derive a great deal of satisfaction in sex. They then add, however, that if orgasm is not reached, "the relief is not complete, and the woman may remain for some time in an unsatisfied and restless condition. Repeated experiences of this kind may eventually lead to various physical or emotional disturbances."

Joan Malleson (111) rejects the idea that orgasm in the wife is essential to sexual satisfaction. She describes the "joys" in sex that many women experience without ever having orgasm, and refers to the large number of women who live their lives in harmony and health without orgasm. Yet she also states that, ideally, the woman should achieve an internal vaginal orgasm for complete fulfillment, and adds that unless clitoral stimulation of the wife is provided by the husband, "extraordinary suffering can be caused in some cases."

Wallin's conclusions (161), from his study of 540 wives, are similarly ambiguous. On the one hand, he interprets his findings as consistent with those from Terman's (154) study of 750 wives, namely, that for many women intercourse can be a satisfying and enjoyable experience without orgasm; yet, at the same time he concludes that frequency of orgasm in wives is clearly associated with completeness of relief in intercourse and that intercourse without orgasm is associated with frustration and unsatisfied desire.

Other workers (36, 45, 57, 84, 103, 70, 63, 98, 110), state quite unequivocally that female orgasm may be unrelated to sexual satisfaction or marital happiness. Mace (110), describes wives who never experience orgasm and are not at all bothered by this lack unless they are told that something is wrong with them. He writes:

It is a mistake to think that these women are cold and unresponsive by nature. On the contrary, they are often deeply affectionate and capable of giving and receiving tender love. It is just that, for them, the mechanism of orgasm doesn't work. This does not necessarily deter them, however, from enjoying sex relations with their husbands. In their quiet way they respond to the warmth and intimacy and closeness of the sexual embrace.

Elkan (45) simply states that orgasm has nothing to do with a woman's health or normality. Although it may enrich her life, she "may also be very happy without it." Grafenberg (63) says essentially the same thing: "Numerous women have satisfactory enjoyment in normal heterosexual intercourse, even if they do not reach the orgasm." "Many women never have orgasm," says Haveman (70) "yet greatly enjoy every act of sexual intercourse which gives them profound sensual and psychological satisfaction."

In sharp contrast, still other researchers (19, 40, 83, 34, 126, 136, 158) are convinced either that: (1) lack of orgasm in women is associated with neurotic and psychosomatic disturbances; or (2) female orgasm is necessary for sexual fulfillment. Several held both of these views and perhaps the most outspoken of these is Reich. In his book *The Function of the Orgasm,* he develops the thesis that all kinds of psychological disturbances and somatic symptoms result from "the damming up of biological energy and undischarged sexual energy." For Reich, the failure to reach orgasm was the basic cause of psychophysiological and behavioral disorders in human beings.

Van de Velde (158), in his classic *Ideal Marriage,* is another worker who insists on the importance of orgasm in the female; he refers to the harmful effects of unrelieved tension by stating: "It is at the present time impossible to estimate how much unbalance of mind and nerves, and misery in marriage, are due to this check and deprivation of complete relaxation in coitus. But I am profoundly convinced of its frequency and importance as of the under-estimate (or neglect) of this factor by doctors and laymen alike." Brown and Kempton (19) refer to lack of orgasm as one of the central and widespread problems of female sexual frustration: "The mounting tension and excitement of intercourse would be intolerable were it not for the promise that orgasm will provide an outlet for this accumulation of nervous energy in waves of pleasurable sensation. When this expectation is not fulfilled, the wife remains bitterly disappointed. . . . Most often she is tense and resentful. . . ."

Isabel Hutton (83), a physician, points out that when a woman is unable to reach an orgasm her sexual organs may remain in a more or less chronic state of congestion, for a period of hours, with harmful effects. Oliven (126) says essentially the same thing and also feels that a sizable percentage of complaints of insomnia by women otherwise free from illness or disease may be due to lack of orgasm—even though

the women themselves may not be aware of this. Sophia
Kleegman (93), a gynecologist, is convinced that the woman
who experiences arousal repeatedly without orgasm "is a
candidate for many gynecological problems." [3]

Lack of orgasm may be related to marital maladjustment.
Hamilton (67) found that 73 percent of the women whose
marriages terminated in divorce did not have orgasms during
the first year of their marriage. He writes:

Unless the sex act ends in a fully releasing, fully terminative
climax, in at least 20% of copulations, there is likely to be
trouble ahead. The least serious consequence is a chronic sense
of tense, restless unsatisfaction. It is, I think, one of the most
suggestive findings of my research that, of the 46 women who
are inadequate as to orgasm capacity, 20 had been diagnosed
at one time or another in their lives as more or less seriously
psychoneurotic . . . [while] only one of the 54 women who
could have orgasm with reasonable frequency had ever been
regarded as psychoneurotic.

Florence Hollis (78), Locke (106), and Appel (3) have
also reported studies that indicate the importance of sex in
marital adjustment. Hollis reports on a study of thirty-four
couples who were seen for marriage counseling. Eight of the
wives reported a satisfying sexual adjustment, while twenty-six
wives had an unsatisfactory sexual adjustment and of these,
nineteen said they were more or less unable to respond
sexually. Locke studied 181 wives who were happily married and 210 who were divorced, relative to various factors
including the enjoyment of sex. He found that 90 percent of the former compared to 53 percent of the latter
enjoyed sex relations. Appel reports that out of 222 married clients seen at the Marriage Council of Philadelphia,
72 percent showed significant concern about sexual problems.

[3] Obviously, the way to settle this particular question was by laboratory
study—and this is precisely what Masters and Johnson have done. They
actually observed the physiological responses of women following orgasm and of women following intense erotic stimulation that did not
terminate in orgasm. A description of their findings appears above,
pages 75–79.

WHAT ARE THE DETERMINANTS OF SEXUAL INADEQUACY AND FRIGIDITY IN WOMEN?

In the broadest sense, the causative factors in determining lack of sexual responsiveness in females may be classified as *psychogenic* or *biogenic*. The overwhelming consensus of most investigators in the field is that frigidity and related female sexual difficulties are the result of pyschological development and social conditioning (1, 13, 38, 67, 113, 122, 126, 147). Most other workers simply accept as a fact that frigidity is a psychological rather than biological problem. A few writers, however, have taken exception to this exclusive emphasis on behavioral determinants. They agree that organic disease or physiological processes as such are responsible only in rare instances; but they suggest that there may be innate, constitutional differences in women as far as sex drive, arousal threshold, and orgasmic capacity are concerned.

Elkan (44) hypothesizes that female orgasmic ability may still be an emerging development from an evolutionary standpoint and hence many women may lack or have only a feebly endowed capacity for sexual arousal and gratification. Terman (154), Kinsey (92), and Levine (102) have all expressed a similar view in suggesting that individual differences among women may be a significant factor in accounting for limited sexuality in some. Kinsey suggests that the 30 percent of women in his sample who are relatively unresponsive sexually may have a "basically low" capacity for orgasmic experience. He writes:

> Our understanding of individual variation in morphologic and physiologic characters, among all plant and animal species, makes it probable that differences in the physical and physiologic capacities of the structures which are concerned in sexual response may account for some of the individual variation which we observe in human sexual behavior. . . . For instance, the exceedingly rapid responses of certain females who are able to reach orgasm within a matter of seconds from the time they are first stimulated . . . of some females [who are able] to reach orgasm repeatedly within a

short period of time, are capacities which most other individuals could not conceivably acquire through training, childhood experience, or any sort of psychiatric therapy.[4]

There is considerable agreement in the literature that one overall factor characterizes hyposexual women as a group. That factor is *psychological inhibition*. Such women have learned consciously or unconsciously to inhibit, by means of suppression, repression, or denial, one or more of the following components of their sexual nature: (1) drive and desire; (2) excitability and passion; and (3) orgasm and gratification. Whatever the original circumstances in the background of a particular woman, or whatever the precise nature of the inhibition, this restraint interferes with the complete sexual response cycle. Ruth Herschberger (73) describes this in an interesting way:

> Women are bewildered because their first response to sex is so prompt, spontaneous, and rewarding. Up to a point excitement prevails. But suddenly something in them stops climbing, pleasure retreats. They feel tired, exhausted, they don't want any more. . . . When a woman begins to speed toward a climax, she is likely to hear a siren in her ears and her mother's voice saying, "pull over to the curb, dear, you are driving too fast." It is the woman, who is not required to "do anything" in the sex act, who usually suffers the most from fatigue. Women do nothing and get tired doing it. . . . It is precisely because women do nothing that they get so tired doing it. The cure is not rest and sedatives but freedom to participate. Sexual excitement does not tire women. It is their fight against it that proves so wearying.

What is the basis of this inhibition? There is a consensus in the literature that the answer in the majority of cases is *fear-anxiety, hostility-aggression, conflict-guilt* or some combination of these emotional states. Writer after writer, regardless of discipline or theoretical background, stresses the fundamental importance of these conditions. Thus Dickinson (38)

---

[4] Unpublished clinical findings by Dr. Masters and Mrs. Johnson cast some doubt on this view. At a meeting of psychoanalysts in May 1966 they reported that some married women who had never before had orgasms, despite psychotherapy or other forms of treatment, not only experienced orgasms but experienced multiple orgasms following effective short-term treatment.

concludes that *fear* is the root of the difficulty that prevents some women from freely entering into the sexual relationship and life of another person. Menninger (121) asks what it is in the normal sexual act that assumes for so many people "the terror and danger of a battle field, so much so as to induce the voluntary surrender of the power and pleasure of the act? What great and irrational fear can be harbored in the unconscious to make necessary this automatic defense reaction in the face of such powerful conscious wishes to the contrary?" And Rado (134) observes that sexual activity for many women is not a promise of pleasure but a threat of damage and punishment. He adds that the sexual motivating system of such a woman is dominated by fears and by rages beneath the fears. "These inappropriate emergency emotions culminate in her fears of conscience and her guilty fears. Sexual pathology is in essence a pathology of conscience."

Menninger (121) has proposed a threefold classification of emotional barriers in female sexuality as follows:

(1) Strong fears, such as fear of punishment, fear of submission to a man, fear of being hurt by the man, fear of pregnancy. For example, some women feel that sex as such is evil and wrong, hence punishable. In some cases this fear reaction is conscious. Menninger mentions a woman patient who could not respond to her husband because each time during intercourse she would have a picture of her stern, disapproving parents.

(2) Strong hostility and aggression toward the male, based on hate, envy, resentment, masculine protest, revenge. Oswald Schwarz (142), for example, holds that the largest proportion of frigid women are the "fighting ones," who are unable to release themselves in sexual pleasure because to do so is interpreted by such women as "dependency on a man," and the idea is intolerable to them.

(3) Strong conflicting loves. Inhibition may be based on divided or opposing emotional attachments, or fixations on a parental figure, on some other man, on members of her own sex, or on herself.

Summing up, a woman who is consciously or unconsciously too fearful, too hostile, too guilty, or in too much conflict is likely to be too frigid to experience sexual love. This becomes all the more likely when such fears, hostilities, and conflicts directly relate to the sexual area.

In emphasizing the factor of fear as a major condition in the frigidity of one hundred married women, Dickinson (38) recorded a total of 219 expressed fears and classified them as follows: sex repulsion, 146; pregnancy, 63; and venereal disease, 10. Some women reported they were "shocked for life" by such intense fear experiences as the first account of menstruation and birth, the first "ugly" news about sex, by hearing the first story of coitus, by having a boy expose his genitals, or by the first attempt at coitus. From such experiences a woman comes to feel that the sex impulse is wicked and vile, that her sex life is concerned with the "lowest part" of herself and that "down there," a standard phrase for referring to the vulva, is something below and outside herself.

Another pattern is the fear of loss of ego-control or self-identity in the sexual relationship. Several writers (42, 56, 89, 107, 123) have stressed this factor. Keiser, for example, describes a syndrome in some women with weakly developed egos and poorly differentiated body images that is characterized by manifest narcissistic preoccupation with, devotion to, and care of their own bodies, together with inner feelings of hollowness, inadequacy, and little sense of identity. For these women, if there is any enjoyment in the sexual relationship at all, it lasts only up to the point approaching orgasm. They are unable to "let go" because of the fear of bodily disintegration and loss of ego control.

In addition to primary complaints of frigidity as such, other forms of female sexual dysfunction, such as actual pain in intercourse or painful spasms of the vaginal muscles, may also occur. Klingensmith (94) reports that these conditions seen in gynecologic practice are commonly based on sexual fear, inhibition, and related emotional states.

A second psychogenic source of impaired female sexuality involves *parental attachments* and *incestuous fixations*. It is surprising how frequently these factors are cited in the literature. Lorand (107) states there is a consensus among psychoanalytic investigators that incestuous attachment is one of several major factors in the development of frigidity. A number of nonpsychoanalytic writers also stress this factor along with other irrational notions about sex carried over from childhood.

Based on his study of one hundred wives, Hamilton (67) suggests that the fear of incestuous impulses or aggressions may be the essential determinant of frigidity and lack of orgasm in women. Overattachment to the mother in infancy and childhood may impair a girl's orgasmic ability in adulthood. Lorand (107) comments on this as follows:

> The inability to cope with the reality of sexual functioning has its deepest roots in the earliest mother fixation. . . . I feel strongly that the success of therapy of neurotic difficulties in women depends on the solution of this decisive infantile attachment. Especially is this so when the fears and aggressions resulting from early frustration by the mother are carried over to the field of adult sexual function. As a result the entire sexual life of these patients is disrupted. Their flight from sexual pleasures is caused by fear of repeated frustrations as in the early mother attachment.

Much more common than the mother-daughter attachment in female sexual disturbances, however, is the father-daughter incestuous relationship, which is specified by a number of investigators (13, 42, 56, 67, 86, 107, 121, 123, 134, 136, 140, 147). Stekel's comments (147) may be taken as illustrative. In discussing the dynamics of frigidity, he refers to the fixation of the woman on her father as the *most common occurrence*.

> That daughters fall in love with their father, sacrificing their lives to him, that actual incestuous relations sometimes take place is so common a fact of observation that I do not think it necessary to dwell further on this. Such incestuous wishes are shared by all children. The fact that the neurotic has not rid himself of such wishes shows that he is still a child.

Three interrelated factors may be grouped together as a third determinant of female hyposexuality. These are: (1) *envy of the male,* either in the form of penis envy or masculine protest or both; (2) *masculine identification;* and (3) *rejection of femininity.* These factors, all of which have to do with disturbances in feminine role development, are stressed by practically all psychoanalytic writers and a number of other clinicians as well (7, 9, 56, 78, 79, 86, 95, 96, 107, 121, 123, 140).

The fourth determinant reported in the literature may

be described as *specific conditioning against sexuality* in general, and against heterosexuality in particular. Some females are deliberately trained and educated to be frigid by their parents or other people. Helene Deutsch (36) writes: "In many women, bourgeois morality or their mother's malicious frigidity has created the idea that coitus is a sacrifice they must make to the dirty needs of man, and they must dutifully let it happen to them." Kinsey (91) puts it this way: "The female who has lived for 20 or more years without learning that any ethically or socially decent male has ever touched a female breast, and the female who has no comprehension of the fact that sexual contacts may involve a great deal more than genital union, find it difficult to give up their ideas about the right and wrong of these matters and accept sexual relations with any abandon after marriage." Weiss and English (162) write: "When a human being has been taught to hate or fear some idea or act long enough and intensely enough, it is with great difficulty that he can change his point of view." Cameron (25) has very effectively described the process whereby the mother prepares her daughter for frigidity, so that in effect the daughter socially "inherits" frigidity from her mother, who "has been rejected because of this by her husband. . . ."

A typical situation is one in which the wife, from the onset of marriage, has been unable to gain sexual satisfaction, usually because of anxieties concerning sex instilled during her own childhood. . . . The wife then raises the age-old cry that the husband does not care for her for her own sake, but simply wants to use her as a means of sexual satisfaction, and then, by illogical but very human extension declares: "All men are brutes; every one of them wants only to make use of women." The marriage becomes a battleground, with the mother turning to the girls as her allies, and at the same time indoctrinating them with this fear of sex and, therefore, of men: "I never want you to go through what I have had to endure." In this way, sex fear, with accompanying hostility, frigidity, and other neurotic mechanisms, may be perpetuated down through several generations.

A fifth determinant is that of *situational conditions* or *temporary psychological states* in the development of frigidity. Such factors include:

(1) Adverse environmental conditions, such as a lack of privacy, lack of comfortable surroundings, freedom from

distraction, etc. (2) Fatigue, preoccupation, or too many competing attractions (31, 70, 73, 74, 85); and (3) Ignorance of what to expect, or wrong ideas as to the nature of female sex arousal and orgasm (5, 93, 167).

A final determinant is *inadequacies in the husband.* Writers have called attention to the fact that some husbands are essentially "marital morons." They are said to be so clumsy, crude, or inept that they are incapable of providing the normal stimulation necessary for their wives to experience sexual satisfaction (29, 38, 67, 152, 162). Someone has observed that certain husbands in their marital relations resemble an orangutan trying to play the violin.

The overly inhibited husband is also a source of difficulty for some wives. Just as psychological inhibition is a determining factor in many frigid women, it may function in the same way in some men. Dickinson (38) found this kind of inadequacy in husbands to be a contributing factor in fifteen out of one hundred frigid women that he studied. These women described some of the inhibitions in their husbands in the following ways: "He will not touch my vulva"; "He thinks it wrong to make clitoris friction"; "He thinks coitus is carnal"; "He fears pregnancy"; "He thinks no decent woman asks for it"; "He will never dress or undress before me."

WHAT APPROACHES AND PROCEDURES HAVE BEEN USED IN THE TREATMENT OF FRIGIDITY AND ORGASM INADEQUACY IN FEMALES?

Since the overwhelming majority of workers in the field are convinced of the *psychological* basis of most cases of female sexual inadequacy, treatment usually involves marriage counseling, re-education, or psychotherapy. Weiss and English (162) have commented on the unfortunate practice of some physicians who assume an organic basis for frigidity in many women and, hence, take a medical rather than a psychological approach in treatment. These writers refer to the "abuse of surgery" in some cases. They point out that while surgeons hesitate to remove testes in males, they "castrate" women by the hundred. An illustrative case is cited of a woman who marries early and soon afterward develops abdominal pains; this is followed by an appendectomy. At short intervals, other abdominal operations are performed. Finally the ovaries, tubes, and uterus are removed. Attention to the *emotional* life of such a woman unfortunately comes only after irreparable damage has been done. Menninger (121) effectively sums up this point:

Many [patients] do not know that there is efficacious treatment, while others become the easy prey of quacks and charlatans. Still others are treated by well-meaning but, in my opinion, mistaken physicians who ascribe all impotence and frigidity to physical or chemical factors and use corresponding methods of treatment. It is, as Crookshank has put it in another connection, as if a doctor, seeing a woman weeping should label it "paroxysmal lacrimation" and recommend treatment with belladonna and astringents, local applications, restriction of fluids, a salt-free diet and the avoidance of sexual excess, tea, tobacco, and alcohol with a further reservation that in the event of failure of these measures, the surgical removal of the tear glands might be imperative.

Relative to psychological treatment methods, Bergler (11, 13), Fenichel (56), Stekel (147), and other psychoanalytic therapists recommend psychoanalysis or psychoanalytic therapy. This, of course, reflects their assumption that most cases of frigidity are based on early childhood fixations, unresolved Oedipal conflicts, bisexuality, masculine identification, repudiation of femininity, etc. Their recommendation is also based on the assumption that *only* through the psychoanalytic approach can such factors be dealt with satisfactorily. This view has been expressed by Bergler as follows:

The greatest majority of neurotic women never experience vaginal orgasm. The fact that Freudian psychoanalysis is so successful in restoring the orgasmic capacity proves conclusively that a neurotic inhibition is involved, and nothing else. Every other form of therapy is a waste of time [11].
Cure is possible with Freudian psychoanalysis, but the amount of time that one must give to the individual patient (an appointment several times a week for a minimum of eight months and a maximum of two years) is so enormous and the knowledge of the physician in treating this disease is so specialized, requiring a period of years for acquisition, that

mass treatment is out of the question. As a mass problem, the question of frigidity is unfortunately not to be solved [13].

Fortunately, other clinicians do not share the pessimistic view of Bergler that the problem of frigidity "is not to be solved"; nor do they agree with him that every other form of therapy, except Freudian psychoanalysis, is a "waste of time." In fact, some psychoanalysts themselves have expressed disappointment over the lack of success of analytic therapy in many cases. For example, Lorand (101) has pointed out that psychoanalytic therapy in cases of women with psychosexual difficulties is frequently not quite satisfactory. He adds: "Although analysts have long attempted to formulate causes of these difficulties, their therapeutic results have not kept pace with their theoretic formulations." Moore (123) refers to the disappointment that Helene Deutsch has expressed in the results of psychoanalytic treatment of frigidity.

In general, psychological approaches to the treatment of female sexual inadequacy may be divided into those that involve a *depth-oriented*, probing, interpretative, past-reliving, insight-producing, reconstructive type of therapy in contrast to those that involve an emphasis on the *here-and-now*, present-life situation, desensitizing, reconditioning, advice-giving, re-educative, rational type of therapy. These two contrasting therapeutic approaches reflect contrasting conceptions as to the nature of female hyposexuality. Psychoanalysis and psychoanalytic therapy have traditionally treated frigidity as a symptom of immaturity, neuroticism, or maladjustment requiring intensive, long-term analytic therapy. The assumption is that since unresolved, unconscious sexual conflicts are involved, the patient can really be helped only by working back and working through these early conflicts and fixations.

Various nonpsychoanalytic approaches have in general assumed that frigidity is not necessarily a symptom of some other difficulty or illness but may rather constitute a central problem in itself. In other words, *regardless of what factors have contributed to a woman's frigidity,* including those emphasized by psychoanalysts, the effort in therapy is largely present-oriented, supportive, explanatory, and re-educative. Utilizing this general orientation, some workers have reported considerable improvement in a number of cases with only a relatively few counseling or therapy sessions. Dickinson (38), Bassett (5), Sophia Kleegman (93), and Helena Wright

(167), all report that by providing simple explanations of female sexual physiology and adequate sex instruction, many women are able to obtain orgasm for the first time. In referring to their experience in group marriage-counseling with wives having sexual problems and inadequacies, Stone and Levine (149) write:

> We have observed with a great deal of interest how these discussions profoundly influenced the attitudes of some of the participants. After only a few sessions, some members of the group would report marked changes in their sexual responses and a resort to sex techniques which they had formerly regarded as entirely unacceptable and out of accord with their sexual mores and values.

Hastings (69) describes a technique that some of his married female patients reported using to increase their responsiveness and facilitate orgasm. Under suitable circumstances, the woman initiates arousal by reading sexually stimulating literature or some comparable activity and then proceeds to stimulate her genitals to orgasm even if a prolonged period is necessary. Hastings elaborates this procedure as follows:

> On the next occasion she repeats the stimulation, attempting by concentration to shorten the stimulus time to orgasm (i.e., to lower the threshold of excitability). Having accomplished the desired threshold lowering by self-stimulation, she may then enlist the husband's cooperation to accomplish the same end through manual stimulation by him, subsequently attempting to achieve the same results with coitus. Apparently once the desired response pattern has been achieved, it tends to remain a stable one.

Mary Calderone (24) has addressed herself to females with sexual inadequacy along the lines described by Hastings. She writes: "You, yourself, must reawaken your body, rediscover it, re-educate it . . . find out for yourself how it feels to touch yourself in certain places. Find out which places arouse the most pleasure in you when touched. Communicate these discoveries to your husband." Albert Ellis (49) has also referred to the wife's self-initiated, manual stimulation leading to orgasm as a valuable aid in helping sexually unresponsive wives.

A variation of this approach involves the use of an electric vibrator, particularly in women who have never experienced orgasm; this has been recommended by Clark (30), Kelly (90), and Albert Ellis (49). What often happens is that the continuous, rhythmic stimulation provided by the vibrator will eventuate in orgasm and, once this occurs, future experiences through manual stimulation by the woman herself or by her husband will be facilitated. Kelly has summarized this procedure as follows:

> In stubborn cases in which the patient does not respond to any treatment, the [ice] can be broken by use of an electric vibrator. The technic is to apply a good lubricant to the clitoris and upper part of the vulva, and also to the surface of the soft sponge rubber applicator of the vibrator. Contact of the applicator to this region during vibrations will usually bring on a climax very quickly, sometimes in a minute or less. When the patient has learned what to expect, it is much easier for the orgasm to be repeated, either by gentle finger stimulation during intercourse or later by penile contact in normal intercourse.

The effectiveness of self-stimulation in the treatment of female hyposexuality is indirectly supported by studies reporting the percentage of women who have sexually stimulated themselves. The research of Dickinson (38), Katherine Davis (33), Hamilton (67), and Kinsey (92) shows that between about two-thirds and three-fourths of the female population have practiced self-stimulation, and that *orgasm is reached about 95 percent of the time*. As Geddes (62) has observed, this is a higher rate of orgasm than for any other kind of female sexual activity, and clearly indicates the human female's capacity for sexual arousal and orgasm.

Another factor that has been found helpful for unresponsive wives is *learning to focus attention on erotic stimulation and sexual imagery*. Since so many females are conditioned in childhood *not* to acknowledge sexual desires and *not* to think about sexual activity, the problem in counseling becomes one of re-educating them as adult women to accept and express their sexual desires, to focus their minds on erotic stimuli. Hilda O'Hare (124) describes the experience of having her first orgasm after reading a sexually stimulating book, and suggests that many women may need to have their sexual imaginations awakened. She points out that there are countless stimulants of the sexual urge for males but nothing comparable for women in our society. Related to O'Hare's observations are those of Albert Ellis (49), Clark (31), and Johnson and Masters (85), who refer to *distractions, fatigue,* and *preoccupation* as basic barriers to satisfying sexual experience in women. Albert Ellis (49) has particularly stressed the importance of what he calls "sexual focusing," which he uses extensively in his marriage-counseling practice. He tells his patients: "If you have any difficulty, then, in becoming sexually aroused or reaching a climax, focus, and keep focusing, on something sexually exciting whatever that may be . . . anything, as long as it gets you more interested in your current relations."

The use of "systematic desensitization" in counseling with cases of frigidity has been reported by Wolpe (165) and Lazarus (100). This approach is based on the assumption that frigidity is often the result of anxiety connected with sexual desire and activity. It involves several aspects including teaching the patient progressive relaxation; listing the anxieties of the patient from most intense to least intense; verbally presenting the weakest anxiety-evoking items to the deeply relaxed patient followed by progressively stronger anxiety-producing items. Lazarus reports success with this approach in nine out of sixteen women whose primary complaint was persistent, recalcitrant frigidity.

The use of hypnosis in removing specific blocks to sexual expression has been reported. This technique is somewhat similar to the systematic desensitization method, but differs in that it is usually more concerned with uncovering repressed sexual experiences and conflicts. Highly successful results have been reported by Caprio and Berger (26). These writers discuss a married female patient who became frigid with her husband after he tried some "unorthodox techniques" in love-making with her; this reactivated deeply repressed incestuous relations she had in childhood with her father. Through hypnosis she was able to recall and verbalize these earlier experiences, and with several posthypnotic suggestions was able to re-establish satisfying sexual relations with her husband. Caprio and Berger emphasize the decided advantages of this approach over the method of a long, time-consuming analysis. Richardson (137) reports on his use of hypnosis with seventy-six patients treated for frigidity either by direct hypnotic suggestions and symptom removal (sixty-one cases) or, in cases with underlying problems or which did not respond to direct suggestions, by hypnoanalysis (fifteen cases). He reports that about 95 percent of these women were "rather dramatically improved" with only a few sessions of hypnosis.

Another recommendation has been reported by Robinson (139) and Marion Hilliard (74) who instructed their female patients to *simulate sexual arousal and orgasms*. Marion Hilliard, a woman obstetrician and gynecologist, writes:

> I am making a fundamental distinction between loving and making love. A wife loves, therefore, she woos a tired mate when she knows he needs her. The pretense is only in her physical reaction to the act itself. There is no greater gift and it should be treasured. It's the worthiest duplicity on the face of the earth; I heartily recommend it to discontented wives. . . . Thousands of women who have begun this sort of benign sham have discovered that their pretended delight rapidly became real.

A suggestion that has been advocated by a number of workers, including Mary Calderone (24), Clark (31), and Mace (110) is that of helping establish or re-establish effective channels of communication with the husband or wife. In a sense, this factor seems so obvious that it hardly deserves mention; yet many couples seen in marriage counseling, even though they may be able to talk about practically anything else that concerns them, are unable to talk to each other about their most intimate relations.

Since 1959, Masters and Johnson have been engaging in the clinical treatment of female frigidity and other types of male and female sexual inadequacies. Unlike most of their predecessors and contemporaries, they treat husband and wife together, so that the marriage itself is the patient. They also have the important advantage of being able to make use of their laboratory findings in their clinical practice. Their latest progress report appears on pages 203–218, below; a comprehensive report, summarizing the development of their treatment approach and the results of their clinical work over a period of years is scheduled for publication in 1967.

REFERENCES

1. Adams, C. R., *Some Factors Relating to Sexual Responsiveness of Certain College Wives*. Pennsylvania State University, Mimeographed, 1953.
2. Anthony, Rey, *The Housewife's Handbook of Promiscuity*. Tucson, Arizona: Seymour Press, 1960.
3. Appel, K. E., "Problems with Which People Want Help in Sex and Marriage," in Emily H. Mudd and A. Krich, eds., *Man and Wife*. New York: Norton, 1957.
4. Baruch, Dorothy W. and Miller, H., *Sex in Marriage*. New York: Harper, 1962.
5. Bassett, Marion, *A New Sex Ethics and Marriage Structure*. New York: Philosophical Library, 1961.
6. Beauvoir, Simone de, *The Second Sex*. New York: Knopf, 1953.
7. Benedek, Therese, "Psychosexual Functions in Women," in P. Harriman, ed., *The Encyclopedia of Psychology*. New York: Philosophical Library, 1946.
8. Benedek, Therese, *Studies in Psychosomatic Medicine: Psychosexual Functions in Women*. New York: Ronald Press, 1952.
9. Benedek, Therese. "Sexual Functions in Women and

Their Disturbance," in S. Arieti, ed., *American Handbook of Psychiatry,* Vol. I. New York: Basic Books, 1959.

10. Bergler, E., "The Problem of Frigidity." *Psychiatric Quarterly,* Vol. 18, 1944, pp. 374–390.

11. Bergler, E., "Frigidity in the Female: Misconceptions and Facts." *Marriage Hygiene,* Vol. 1, 1947, pp. 16–21.

12. Bergler, E., "Newer Genetic Investigations on Impotence and Frigidity." *Bulletin of the Menninger Clinic,* Vol. 11, 1947, pp. 50–59.

13. Bergler, E., *Neurotic Counterfeit-Sex.* New York: Grune and Stratton, 1951.

14. Bergler, E. and Kroger, W. S., *Kinsey's Myth of Female Sexuality.* New York: Grune and Stratton, 1954.

15. Bonaparte, Marie, *Female Sexuality.* New York: International Universities Press, 1953.

16. Bowman, C. C., "Social Factors Opposed to the Extension of Heterosexuality." *American Journal of Psychiatry,* Vol. 106, 1949, pp. 441–447.

17. Brierley, Marjorie, "Some Problems of Integration in Women." *International Journal of Psychoanalysis,* Vol. 13, 1932, pp. 433–448.

18. Brothers, Joyce, *Woman.* New York: Doubleday, 1961.

19. Brown, F. and Kempton, R. T., *Sex Questions and Answers.* New York: McGraw-Hill, 1950.

20. Brown, Helen G., *Sex and the Single Girl.* New York: Bernard Geis, 1962.

21. Buck, Pearl S., "Changing Relationships between Men and Women," in Beverly B. Cassara, ed., *American Women: The Changing Image.* Boston: Beacon, 1962.

22. Burgess, E. W. and Wallin P., *Engagement and Marriage.* New York: Lippincott, 1953.

23. Bychowski, G., "Some Aspects of Psychosexuality in Psychoanalytic Experience," in P. H. Hoch and J. Zubin, eds., *Psychosexual Development in Health and Disease.* New York: Grune and Stratton, 1949.

24. Calderone, Mary S., *Release from Sexual Tensions.* New York: Random House, 1960.

25. Cameron, D. E., "Sexuality and the Sexual Disorders," in J. R. Rees, ed., *Modern Practice in Psychological Medicine.* New York: Hoeber, 1949.

26. Caprio, F. and Berger, J. R., "Hypnosis in the Treatment of Frigidity," in *The X Report.* New York: Belmont Books, 1962.

27. Castallo, M. A. and Schulz, Cecilia L., *Woman's Inside Story*. New York: Macmillan, 1948.

28. Cervantes, L. F., *And God Made Man and Woman*. Chicago: Henry Regnery, 1959.

29. Chesser, E., *The Sexual, Marital, and Family Relationships of the English Woman*. New York: Roy Publishers, 1956.

30. Clark, L., *The Enjoyment of Love in Marriage*. New York: Crest Books, 1949.

31. Clark, L., "Sexual Adjustment in Marriage," in Albert Ellis and Albert Abarbanel, eds., *The Encyclopedia of Sexual Behavior*. New York: Hawthorn, 1961.

32. Damon, V. G. and Taves, Isabella, *I Learned about Women from Them*. New York: David McKay, 1960.

33. Davis, Katharine B., *Factors in the Sex Life of Twenty-two Hundred Women*. New York: Harper, 1929.

34. Davis, Maxine, *The Sexual Responsibility of Woman*. New York: Dial Press, 1956.

35. Dengrove, E., "Techniques for Heightening Sex Response," in *The X Report*. New York: Belmont Books, 1962.

36. Deutsch, Helene, *The Psychology of Women*, Vols. I and II. New York: Grune and Stratton, 1945.

37. Devereux, G., "The Significance of the External Female Genitalia and of Female Orgasm for the Male." *American Psychoanalytic Association Journal*, Vol. 6, 1958, pp. 278–286.

38. Dickinson, R. L. and Beam, L., *A Thousand Marriages*. Baltimore: Williams and Wilkins, 1932.

39. Duffy, J., "Masturbation and Clitoridectomy." *Journal of the American Medical Association*, Vol. 19, 1963, pp. 246–248.

40. Eeman, P. D., "Physiology of the Orgasm and of Psychoanalysis." *International Journal of Sexology*, Vol. 3, 1949, pp. 92–98.

41. Ehrmann, W., "Some Knowns and Unknowns in Research into Human Sex Behavior." *Marriage and Family Living*, Vol. 19, 1957, pp. 16–24.

42. Eisenstein, V. W., ed., *Neurotic Interaction in Marriage*. New York: Basic Books, 1956.

43. Eissler, K., "On Certain Problems of Female Sexual Development." *Psychoanalytic Quarterly*, Vol. 8, 1939, pp. 191–210.

44. Elkan, E., "Evolution of Female Orgastic Ability—A

Biological Survey." *International Journal of Sexology,* Vol. 2, 1948, pp 1–13; 84–93.

45. Elkan, E., "Orgasm Inability in Women." *International Journal of Sexology,* Vol. 4, 1951, p. 243.

46. Ellis, A., "Is the Vaginal Orgasm a Myth?", in A. P. Pillay and Albert Ellis, eds., *Sex, Society and the Individual.* Bombay, India: International Journal of Sexology Publ., 1953.

47. Ellis, A., "Marriage Counseling with Couples Indicating Sexual Incompatibility." *Marriage and Family Living,* Vol. 15, 1953, pp. 53–59.

48. Ellis, A., ed., *Sex Life of the American Woman and the Kinsey Report.* New York: Greenberg, 1954.

49. Ellis, A., *The Art and Science of Love.* New York: Lyle Stuart, 1960.

50. Ellis, A., "Frigidity," in Albert Ellis and Albert Abarbanel, eds., *The Encyclopedia of Sexual Behavior.* New York: Hawthorn, 1960.

51. Ellis, A., *The American Sexual Tragedy,* 2nd ed. New York: Lyle Stuart, 1962.

52. Ellis, H., *Little Essays of Love and Virtue.* New York: Doran, 1922.

53. Ellis, H., *Psychology of Sex,* 2nd ed. New York: Emerson, 1954.

54. English, O. S., and Pearson, G. H. J., *Emotional Problems of Living.* New York: Norton, 1945.

55. Feldman, S. S., "Anxiety and Orgasm." *Psychoanalytic Quarterly,* Vol. 20, 1951, pp. 528–549.

56. Fenichel, O., *The Psychoanalytic Theory of Neurosis.* New York: Norton, 1945.

57. Ferguson, L. W., "Correlates of Woman's Orgasm." *Journal of Psychology,* Vol, 6, 1938, pp. 295–302.

58. Ford, C. S. and Beach, F. A., *Patterns of Sexual Behavior.* New York: Harper, 1951.

59. Freud, S., *New Introductory Lectures on Psychoanalysis.* New York: Norton, 1933.

60. Freud, S., *Three Essays on the Theory of Sexuality,* ed. and tr. by James Strachey. New York: Basic Books, 1963.

61. Friedan, Betty, *The Feminine Mystique.* New York: Norton, 1963.

62. Geddes, D. P., ed., *An Analysis of the Kinsey Reports on Sexual Behavior in the Human Male and Female.* New York: Dutton, 1954.

63. Grafenberg, E., "The Role of Urethra in Female

Orgasm." *International Journal of Sexology,* Vol. 3, 1950, pp 145–148.

64. Graham, S. R., "The Effects of Psychoanalytically Oriented Psychotherapy on Levels of Frequency and Satisfaction in Sexual Activity." *Journal of Clinical Psychology,* Vol. 16, 1960, pp. 94–95.

65. Grant, V. W., *The Psychology of Sexual Emotion.* New York: Longmans, Green, 1957.

66. Greenacre, Phyllis, "Sexual Problems of Early Female Sexual Development," in *The Psychoanalytic Study of the Child,* Vol. 5, 1950, pp. 122–138.

67. Hamilton, G. V., *Research in Marriage.* New York: Albert and Charles Boni, 1929.

68. Hardenbergh, E. W., "The Psychology of Feminine Sex Experience," in A. P. Pillay and Albert Ellis, eds., *Sex, Society and the Individual.* Bombay, India: International Journal of Sexology Publ., 1953.

69. Hastings, D. W., *Impotence and Frigidity.* Boston: Little, Brown, 1963.

70. Havemann, E., *Men, Women and Marriage.* Garden City: Doubleday, 1962.

71. Heiman, M., "Sexual Response in Women." *Journal of the American Psychoanalytic Association,* Vol. 11, 1963, pp. 360–385.

72. Hendrick, I., "Psychosexuality," in A. M. Krich, ed., *The Anatomy of Love.* New York: Dell, 1960.

73. Herschberger, Ruth, *Adam's Rib.* New York: Pellegrini and Cudahy, 1948.

74. Hilliard, Marion, *A Woman Doctor Looks at Love and Life.* New York: Permabook, 1960.

75. Hirsch, A. H., *The Love Elite.* (The Story of Woman's Emancipation and Her Drive for Sexual Fulfillment.) New York: Julian Press, 1963.

76. Hirsch, E. W., "Coital and Non-Coital Sex Techniques," in Albert Ellis, ed., *Sex Life of the American Woman and the Kinsey Report.* New York: Greenberg, 1954, pp. 161–174.

77. Hitschmann, E. and Bergler, E., "Frigidity in Women—Restatement and Renewed Experiences." *Psychoanalytic Review,* Vol. 36, 1949, pp. 45–53.

78. Hollis, Florence, *Women in Marital Conflict.* New York: Family Service Association of America, 1949.

79. Horney, Karen, "The Denial of the Vagina." *International Journal of Psychoanalysis,* Vol. 14, 1933, pp. 57–70.

80. Huffman, J. W., "The Effect of Gynecologic Surgery on Sexual Reactions." *American Journal of Obstetrics and Gynecology*, Vol. 59, 1950, pp. 915–917.

81. Hunt, M. M., *The Natural History of Love*. New York: Knopf, 1959.

82. Hunt, M. M., *Her Infinite Variety*. New York: Harper, 1962.

83. Hutton, Isabel E., *The Sex Technique in Marriage*, rev. ed. New York: Emerson Books, 1961.

84. Imerman, H. M. and Dewey, I. B., *What Women Want to Know*. New York: Crown, 1958.

85. Johnson, Virginia E. and Masters, W. H., "Treatment of the Sexually Incompatible Family Unit." *Minnesota Medicine*. Nov. 1961, pp. 466–471.

86. Kaplan, L., "Father and Daughter: Fragment of an Analysis." *International Journal of Sexology*, Vol. 4, 1951, pp. 232–235.

87. Kamiat, A. H., *Feminine Superiority*. New York: Bookman, 1960.

88. Kegel, A. H., "Letter to the Editor." *Journal of the American Medical Association*, Vol. 153, 1953, pp. 1303–1304.

89. Keiser, S., "Body Ego during Orgasm." *Psychoanalytic Quarterly*, Vol. 21, 1952, pp. 153–166.

90. Kelly, G. L., *Sex Manual*, 8th ed. Augusta, Georgia: Southern Medical Supply Co., 1959.

91. Kinsey, A. C., Pomeroy, W. B. and Martin, C. E., *Sexual Behavior in the Human Male*. Philadelphia: Saunders, 1949.

92. Kinsey, A. C., Pomeroy, W. B., Martin, C. E. and Gebhard, P. H., *Sexual Behavior in the Human Female*. Philadelphia: Saunders, 1953.

93. Kleegman, Sophia J., "Frigidity in Women." *Quarterly Review of Surgery, Obstetrics, and Gynecology*, Vol. 16, 1959, pp. 243–248.

94. Klingensmith, P. O., "Sexual Adjustment as Seen by the Gynecologist and Obstetrician," in Emily H. Mudd and A. Krich, eds., *Man and Wife*. New York: Norton, 1957.

95. Knight, R. P., "Functional Disturbances in the Sexual Life of Women." *Bulletin of the Menninger Clinic*, Vol. 7, 1943, pp. 25–35.

96. Kroger, W. S. and Freed, S. C., "Psychosomatic Aspects of Frigidity." *Journal of the American Medical Association*, 1943, 1950, pp. 526–532.

97. Kubie, L. S., "Psychiatric Implications of the Kinsey Report," in Jerome Himelhoch and Sylvia Fava, eds., *Sexual Behavior in American Society*. New York: Norton, 1955.

98. Lamson, H. D., "Are American Women Frigid?" *International Journal of Sexology*, Vol. 3, 1950, pp. 162–167.

99. Lanval, M., "General Anesthesia and Female Frigidity." *Marriage Hygiene*, Vol. 1, 1948, pp. 236–237.

100. Lazarus, A. A., "The Treatment of Chronic Frigidity by Systematic Desensitization." *Journal of Nervous and Mental Disorders*, Vol. 136, 1963, pp. 272–278.

101. Levie, L. H., "Vaginal Orgasm." *International Journal of Sexology*, Vol. 3, 1949, p. 122.

102. Levine, Lena, "Orgasm Capacity of Women." *Marriage Hygiene*, Vol. 1, 1948, pp. 172–173.

103. Levine, Lena, "A Criterion for Orgasm in the Female." *Marriage Hygiene*, Vol. 1, 1948, pp. 173–174.

104. Lewis, C. S., "Courtly Love," in A. M. Krich, ed., *The Anatomy of Love*. New York: Dell, 1960.

105. Lief, H. I., "What Medical Schools Teach about Sex." *Bulletin of Tulane University Medical Faculty*, Vol. 22, 1963, pp. 161–168.

106. Locke, H. J., *Predicting Adjustment in Marriage*. New York: Holt, 1951.

107. Lorand, S., "Contribution to the Problem of Vaginal Orgasm." *International Journal of Psychoanalysis*, Vol. 20, 1939, pp. 432–438.

108. Lorand, S., "Unsuccessful Sex Adjustment in Marriage." *American Journal of Psychiatry*, Vol. 19, 1940, pp. 1413–1427.

109. Lundberg, F. and Farnham, Marynia F., *Modern Woman, The Lost Sex*. New York: Harper, 1947.

110. Mace, D. R., *Success in Marriage*. New York: Abingdon Press, 1958.

111. Malleson, Joan, *Any Wife or Any Husband*. New York: Random House, 1952.

112. Mandy, A. J., "Frigidity," in Albert Ellis, ed., *Sex Life of the American Woman and the Kinsey Report*. New York: Greenberg, 1954.

113. Marmor, J., "Some Considerations Concerning Orgasm in the Female." *Psychosomatic Medicine*, Vol. 16, 1954, pp. 240–245.

114. Masters, W. H., "The Sexual Response Cycle of the Human Female: Vaginal Lubrication." *Annual of the*

New York Academy of Science, Vol. 83, 1959, pp. 301–317.

115. Masters, W. H. and Johnson, Virginia, "The Sexual Response Cycle of the Human Female. I. Gross Anatomic Considerations." *Western Journal of Surgery, Obstetrics, and Gynecology,* Vol. 68, 1960, pp. 57–72.

116. Masters, W. H. and Johnson, Virginia, "The Artificial Vagina: Anatomic, Physiologic, Psychosexual Function." *Western Journal of Surgery, Obstetrics, and Gynecology,* Vol. 69, 1961, pp. 192–212.

117. Masters, W. H. and Johnson, Virginia, "Anatomy of the Female Orgasm," in Albert Ellis and Albert Abarbanel, eds., *The Encyclopedia of Sexual Behavior.* New York: Hawthorn, 1961.

118. Masters, W. H. and Johnson, Virginia, "Intravaginal Contraceptive Study." *Western Journal of Surgery, Obstetrics, and Gynecology,* Vol. 70, 1962, pp. 202–207.

119. Masters, W. H. and Johnson, Virginia, "The Sexual Response Cycle of the Human Female. III. The Clitoris: Anatomic and Clinical Considerations." *Western Journal of Surgery, Obstetrics, and Gynecology,* Vol. 70, 1962, pp. 248–257.

120. Melendy, Mary R., *Perfect Womanhood: A Complete Medical Guide for Women,* 1903.

121. Menninger, K. A., "Impotence and Frigidity." *Bulletin of the Menninger Clinic,* Vol. 1, 1937, pp. 251–260.

122. Mittlemann, Bela, "Psychosomatics," in P. Harriman, ed., *The Encyclopedia of Psychology.* New York: Philosophical Library, 1946.

123. Moore, Burness E., "Frigidity in Women." *American Psychoanalytic Association Journal,* Vol. 9, 1961, pp. 571–584.

124. O'Hare, Hilda, "The Normal Woman." *International Journal of Sexology,* Vol. 4, 1950, pp. 117–118.

125. O'Hare, Hilda, "Vaginal Versus Clitoral Orgasm." *International Journal of Sexology,* Vol. 4, 1951, pp. 243–246.

126. Oliven, J. F., *Sexual Hygiene and Pathology.* Philadelphia: Lippincott, 1955.

127. Oltman, Jane E. and Friedman, S., "Acute Heterosexual Inadequacy: II. In the Female." *Psychiatric Quarterly,* Vol. 14, 1940, pp. 194–204.

128. Niederland, W. G., "Some Psychological Disorders of

Femininity and Masculinity," in J. E. Fairchild, ed., *The Way of Woman*. New York: Fawcett, 1956.

129. Parker, Elizabeth, *The Seven Ages of Woman*. Baltimore: The Johns Hopkins Press, 1960.

130. Payne, Sylvia M., "A Concept of Femininity." *British Journal of Medicine and Psychology,* Vol. 15, 1936, pp. 18–33.

131. Pillay, A. P. and Ellis, A., eds., *Sex, Society and the Individual*. Bombay, India: The International Journal of Sexology Publ., 1953.

132. Polatin, P. and Douglas, D. E., "Spontaneous Orgasm in a Case of Schizophrenia." *Psychoanalytic Review,* Vol. 40, 1953, pp. 17–26.

133. Rado, S., "An Adaptational View of Sexual Behavior," in P. H. Hoch and J. Zubin, eds., *Psychosexual Development in Health and Disease*. New York: Grune and Stratton, 1949.

134. Rado, S., "Sexual Anesthesia in the Female." *Quarterly Review of Surgery, Obstetrics, and Gynecology,* Vol. 16, 1959, pp. 249–253.

135. Rainer, J. and Rainer, Julia, *Sexual Pleasure in Marriage*. New York: Messner, 1959.

136. Reich, W., *The Function of the Orgasm*. New York: Orgone Institute Press, 1942.

137. Richardson, T. A., "Hypnotherapy in Frigidity." *American Journal of Clinical Hypnosis,* Vol. 5, 1963, pp. 194–199.

138. Robinson, Marie N., *The Power of Sexual Surrender*. Garden City: Doubleday, 1959.

139. Robinson, W. J., *Woman: Her Sex and Love Life*. New York: Eugenics Publ., 1939.

140. Reusch, J., *Chronic Disease and Psychological Invalidism*. New York: The American Society for Research in Psychosomatic Problems, 1946.

141. Rutherford, R. N., et al., "Psychometric Testings in Frigidity and Infertility." *Psychosomatics,* Vol. 1, 1960, pp. 3–7.

142. Schwarz, O., *The Psychology of Love*. Baltimore: Penguin, 1949.

143. Sentnor, M. and Hult, S., "Woman's Erotic Cycle," in *The X Report*. New York: Belmont Books, 1962.

144. Seward, Georgene H., *Sex and the Social Order*. New York: McGraw-Hill, 1946.

145. Shor, J., "Female Sexuality: Aspects and Prospects." *Psychoanalysis,* Vol. 2, (3), 1954, pp. 47–76.

146. Shuttleworth, F. K., "A Biosocial and Developmental Theory of Male and Female Sexuality." *Marriage and Family Living,* Vol. 21, 1959, pp. 163–176.

147. Stekel, W., *Frigidity in Women,* Vols. I and II. New York: Boni and Liveright, 1926.

148. Stokes, W. R., *Married Love in Today's World.* New York: Citadel, 1962.

149. Stone, A. and Levine, Lena, "Group Therapy in Sexual Maladjustment." *American Journal of Psychiatry,* Vol. 107, 1950, pp. 195–202.

150. Stone, Hannah M. and Stone, A., *A Marriage Manual.* New York: Simon and Schuster, 1952.

151. Stone, A., "The Kinsey Studies and Marriage Counseling," in Jerome Himelhoch and Sylvia Fava, eds., *Sexual Behavior in American Society.* New York: Norton, 1955.

152. Street, R., *Modern Sex Techniques.* New York: Archer House, 1959.

153. Tapia, F., Werboff, J., and Winokur, G., "Recall of Some Phenomena of Sleep." *Journal of Nervous and Mental Disorders,* Vol. 127, 1958, pp. 119–123.

154. Terman, L. M., *Psychological Factors in Marital Happiness.* New York: McGraw-Hill, 1938.

155. Terman, L. M., "Correlates of Orgasm Adequacy in a Group of 556 Wives." *Journal of Psychology,* Vol. 32, 1951, pp. 115–172.

156. Thomason, B., "Marital Sexual Behavior and Total Marital Adjustment: A Research Report," in Jerome Himelhoch and Sylvia Fava, eds., *Sexual Behavior in American Society.* New York: Norton, 1955.

157. Thompson, Clara, *Psychoanalysis: Evolution and Development.* New York: Hermitage, 1950.

158. Van de Velde, T. H., *Ideal Marriage.* New York: Random House, 1930.

159. Vatsyayana, *Kama Sutra.* New York: Lancer Books, 1964.

160. Vincent, C. E., "Social and Interpersonal Sources of Symptomatic Frigidity." *Marriage and Family Living,* Vol. 18, 1956, pp. 355–360.

161. Wallin, P., "A Study of Orgasm as a Condition of Women's Enjoyment of Intercourse." *Journal of Social Psychology,* Vol. 51, 1960, pp. 191–198.

162. Weiss, E. and English, O. S., *Psychosomatic Medicine.* Philadelphia: Saunders, 1949.

163. West, Jessamyn, *Love Is Not What You Think*. New York: Harcourt, Brace, 1959.
164. Winokur, G., Guze, S. B. and Pfeiffer, E., "Nocturnal Orgasm in Women." *Archives of General Psychiatry*, Vol. 1, 1959, pp. 180–184.
165. Wolpe, J., *Psychotherapy by Reciprocal Inhibition*. Stanford: Stanford University Press, 1958.
166. Woodside, Moya, "Orgasm Capacity among Two Hundred English Working-class Wives." *Marriage Hygiene*, Vol. 1, 1948, pp. 133–137.
167. Wright, Helena, "A Contribution to the Orgasm Problem in Women." In A. P. Pillay and Albert Ellis, eds., *Sex, Society and the Individual*. Bombay, India: International Journal of Sexology Publ., 1953.

SEXUAL PATTERNS IN A SOUTHWEST PACIFIC SOCIETY

William Davenport, Ph.D.

Editors' note: One of the criticisms sometimes made of the Masters-Johnson research is that its description of human sexual responses is based on observations of Middle-Western Americans only. Similar studies made on populations as different as possible would provide a fascinating opportunity to distinguish responses that are common throughout the human species from those that are more variable.

No study comparable to the Masters-Johnson project has been published outside the United States. Beginnings have been made, however, in the study of sexual behavior and sexual response in other cultures. The following report by Dr. Davenport is presented here as an outstanding example of recent anthropological sex-research field studies.

Dr. Davenport is associate professor of anthropology at the University of Pennsylvania and associate curator for Oceania of the University Museum in Philadelphia. He and Mrs. Davenport are currently on the third of their prolonged field trips to study South Pacific communities in the British Solomon Islands Protectorate, under a grant from the National Institute of Mental Health.

Dr. Davenport's paper was initially presented at a Conference on Sex and Behavior, sponsored at the University of California at Berkeley by the Committee for Research in Problems of Sex, National Academy of Sciences–National Research Council. It was published at somewhat greater length in the report on that conference, *Sex & Behavior,* edited by Frank A. Beach.

INTRODUCTION

It is my purpose to discuss certain aspects of the patterning of sexual and associated behavior in an isolated but rapidly changing South Sea community.[1] In this society, as in all others that we know of, what people say should be done is one thing; what they do is often another. The data I shall present represent only verbal reports and attitudes about sexual behavior.

The information reported here is from a group of Melanesian Islands that will be called the "X Group."[2] In this group live several thousand people of different racial back-

[1] The field work involved in the study here reported was sponsored by the Tri-Institutional Pacific Program (University of Hawaii, B. P. Bishop Museum, Yale University), which was supported by a grant from the Carnegie Corporation of New York. The investigation of sex was supported by a grant from the Committee for Research in Problems of Sex, National Academy of Sciences–National Research Council.

[2] Because the author obtained and here reports information unavailable to the local administrative personnel, and because of the possibility that publication of certain data might result in embarrassment of informants *vis-à-vis* this personnel, the precise time and locus of the field study have been withheld. Suffice it to say that the work is accurately described as "recent," and that it was carried out in Melanesia [Frank Beach].

grounds, speaking several languages, and having a number of different subcultures; yet in their entirety they comprise a unitary economic system based on mutual interdependencies among districts and islands as well as complex networks of intra- and interisland trade and exchange. The data on sex pertain only to East Bay, a large district of one island in the group. They must not be generalized to other districts nor to islands where marked differences are known to exist.

East Bay consists of a number of small coastal villages, each with its inland areas of garden, orchard, and foraging lands, and has a total population of 636 persons. It is one of the most prosperous districts in all the "X Group" and the hub of trade relations that extend both inland to other districts of the same island and across the open Pacific to other islands which lie from twenty-five to ninety miles distant. Cultivated lands at East Bay are far in excess of local needs and surplus foods are a significant item of export to oversea communities that are less well endowed with agricultural resources. Consequent to the relative wealth that East Bay enjoys, feasts, ceremonies, entertainments, and political activities have been, and still are, somewhat more lavish and elaborated than elsewhere in the "X Group."

Some of the wealth East Bay amasses is spent to pay bride prices for women brought from the outside. These women come as wives to East Bay from the northern islands, and, until it was forbidden by the colonial government that now administers the "X Group," some came as concubines. Wealth moving out for bride prices and women moving in constitute vital links in the chain of economic transactions that keep the intricate economic system of the "X Group" operating. Wealth accumulated in and around East Bay communities is drawn off by bride-price payments. Much of this wealth is eventually returned to East Bay in exchange for food and various manufactured products, only to be redistributed again for women.

The population of the East Bay area is highly masculine. Men of marriageable age outnumber women of corresponding maturity by a ratio of as much as one hundred and twenty to one hundred. Excessively masculine populations of this sort are known elsewhere in Melanesia, but the causes of the disparity are not understood.

The material to follow was obtained in the following manner. For the first eighteen months of field work the writer and his wife made little deliberate attempt to elicit direct evidence pertaining to sexual behavior, although a great deal was accumulated through observations and conversations during this time. At the end of this initial period all of the sex data were assembled and carefully reviewed with a few key men informants so that the most obvious errors, omissions, and inconsistencies could be corrected. Out of this body of data a schedule of fifty-four items was prepared, and all the males of one village over the age of about six years (except one senile old gentleman), thirty-four in all, were informally interviewed and scored or rated on each item. This limited survey of one village was intended to provide a check on biases in the data obtained by less standardized procedures. At the same time it was intended to help us identify those topics which might most fruitfully be pursued further through subsequent surveys in some future study.

GENERAL CONCEPTS OF
SEXUAL PROPRIETY

At East Bay sex is an ordinary topic of conversation except with certain types of kin in whose presence sexual and other personal matters may not be mentioned. Sex can be joked about or treated in a completely matter-of-fact manner; there are no such things as sexual swear words, except very insulting ones imputing incest (e.g., "copulate with your mother . . . with your sister . . . with your sister's daughter"). Sexual intercourse between husband and wife is assumed to be natural, highly pleasurable, and, for men at least, almost a physical necessity. There is no concept of "excessive" sexual intercourse, and no permanently harmful physical or mental effects to adults are believed to follow from normal coitus. Conversely, deprivation is believed to be harmful.

Yet, despite this somewhat unconcerned attitude toward intercourse with a legitimate spouse, and formerly with a concubine as well, there is great concern for sexual propriety. Severe sanctions of several kinds are imposed on individuals who engage in what in English must be distinguished as forni-cation (intercourse between unmarried persons) and adultery (extramarital intercourse). Social efforts to forestall, to dis-cover, and to punish proven sex offenders are far more vigor-ous than any that occur even among the most Puritanical segments of our own society.

Insofar as the legal system is concerned, fornication and adultery are classed as larcenies and are punished in the same manner as serious mayhem. Only murder carries a more severe punishment. Incest, on the other hand, is regarded not so much as a serious crime as an indication of moral inca-pacity closely akin to insanity.

To the East Bay people nakedness and lack of genital modesty is a sign of either immaturity or insanity. Although there is very little contact between them, the people of East Bay consider Europeans to be sexually proper because of their extreme modesty and their discretion about sexual matters. They are not aware of the fact that Europeans do not discuss sexual matters as openly as they do, and the former are equally ignorant of all aspects of sex in East Bay, for the language barrier prevents much communication. In spite of their gen-erally favorable impression of the discretion of Europeans, East Bay people are generally scandalized by the informal way European men and women behave toward each other in public. Men and women in East Bay may never touch each other or directly exchange personal articles or food, although in the presence of special kinsmen they may talk about sexual matters. In contrast, Europeans pay little heed to physical proximity between sexes, even though they are very sensitive to sexual topics of conversation.

The sexual impulse or drive in adult males is, like hunger, sleep, and fatigue, considered to be almost irrepressible once it has been aroused. In this respect sexual desire differs from aggressive tendencies, which are thought to be highly modifi-able. The sex drive in adults is assumed to increase with deprivation, and men are considered to be more easily aroused than women. For men, high erotic value is attached to women's breasts. Women go about naked from the waist up and it is not forbidden, as in some societies, for men to look at women's breasts. Therefore, these erotic organs are always available for comparison and admiration.

Women, of course, are aware of this, and consequently take pride in their breasts. Successive stages of female maturation and aging are described by the condition of the breasts as they swell, come into full roundness, begin to droop, fall, and ultimately flatten. Despite these seemingly indifferent references to normal mammary development, it is clear from the habitual conversations about breasts that men are being continually aroused by the sight of what to them are very erotic organs.

SOCIAL CONTROL OF HETEROSEXUAL CONTACTS

Regulation of socially undesirable sexual relations is achieved in other ways besides imposing serious punishments on illicit acts. This involves an extensive system for separating the sexes by what amounts to a general social avoidance between men and women in all but a few situations.

For example, the village is laid out so that along the front are located one or more men's houses where unmarried men and boys sleep and eat, and married men spend much of their time during the day. Ranged behind the men's house or row of men's houses, sometimes at a considerable distance, are the family dwellings in which women and girls spend most of their time while they are in the village. Leading away from the dwelling side of the village are paths to the gardens, so that women may come and go between their houses and subsistence plots without passing the men's side of the village. Men's houses are normally located close to the sea, or, in inland villages, at the outskirts where the main path leads off to other villages. Hence men may come and go to the sea to fish, or travel from village to village with few encounters with women.

Within the village, men's latrine areas are adjacent to the men's houses alongside the canoe passages and landings. Women's latrine areas are always located some distance away behind a high stone wall that screens the entire area from view. Paths to these screened women's areas are never traversed by men. A man caught anywhere near these paths or areas is assumed to be a Peeping Tom, a not infrequent offense, and is treated exactly as if he had been apprehended in illicit intercourse. In addition, women are allotted a portion of each beach area, in full sight of the men's part of the beach, where they may go to prepare roots and tubers for cooking and to dump household trash. Men avoid these areas as studiously as women avoid the men's beach area. Young children, however, are allowed to play freely on the women's or the men's part of the beach so they may be kept under constant surveillance.

Within the village each dwelling is oriented with respect to the sex-designated areas and directions. Each house has at least two doors, one opens toward the men's house and is used only by men, another opens toward the back of the village and the gardens and is used only by women and children. Inside the house the floor space nearest to the men's door is a kind of men's area where the husband, the head of the household, eats, sleeps, and, when he has visitors, talks with his men friends. Opposite or adjacent to the men's floor space, in the direction of the women's door, is the area where women sit, eat, and sleep. Here the earth oven and other cooking facilities are located. The short connecting pathways between houses, hardly perceptible to a stranger's eye, are also reserved for exclusive use by women or men. With working and living areas, as well as access paths and daily tasks allocated in this manner, men and women may go about their everyday activities with a minimum of face-to-face encounters.

Not all community facilities, however, are clearly set aside for use by one sex or the other. Wells, for example, are frequently located next to the men's house so that men may go to drink whenever they wish. Women and young children drink from containers of water kept in their dwellings. These containers are refilled each day at a particular time set aside for this task. Just before sunset each evening young girls go to the well and fill the household water containers, and the men in the men's houses next to them stay away from the well for this brief period.

At East Bay the separation of sexes is not reinforced by strict taboos or fear of ritual contamination as it is in some Melanesian communities. Women and men avoid mixing socially for the same reasons that women in our society avoid places like men's locker rooms, billiard rooms, and men's bars. Failure to comply with these restrictions is a transgression of sex-gender roles, and when these are thoroughly internalized a member of either sex is greatly embarrassed in any situation that prevents their observance.

Obviously the activities of men and women are not so

completely separated that all contacts can be avoided. Among
adults of opposite sex husbands and wives are permitted the
freedom of being seen together and talking freely with each
other. But even between spouses there is great reserve when
they are in public. Only in their own dwelling or in the privacy
of their own garden are married couples free to behave completely informally, intimately, and affectionately. To act in
these ways in public is embarrassing for all those around
them.

When a woman, alone or with a child, meets a man alone
she must move well out of his way, turn her back to him,
and not resume her travel until he is well past. Under no circumstances are they to speak to each other at close range or
to look into each other's eyes. If communication is necessary,
they must shout to each other from a distance. This restriction
is lessened only when one person is aged. When men are
traveling along garden paths or near villages alone or in
groups, they are expected to make as much noise as possible
by talking, singing, or shaking and banging trees. This is to
serve as a warning to all women in the vicinity. Women who
hear men approaching move off the path and hide, allowing
them to pass, and often the men do not know the women are
nearby.

In summary, it is the woman's duty always to avoid a man
as discreetly and completely as possible when a casual encounter is made or appears imminent. When other people are
present, the avoidance may be less pronounced than if the
couple were alone, for under these circumstances the encounter is witnessed and, in a sense, chaperoned.

From this brief description of the interpersonal behavior
patterns between men and women it can be seen that situations that might lead to erotic arousal and provide opportunities for sexual intimacy are greatly minimized for all
pairs except husband and wife. For persons in whom these
behavior rules are thoroughly internalized, deviation is reported to cause great uneasiness and intense shame. Against
temptations to transgress these rules of etiquette stands the
fear of extreme punishment for sexual offenses of all kinds,
and as will be elaborated later, these are much stronger against
offending men than against offending women.

ARRANGING MARRIAGE

When it is time for them to be married, young, single adults are never consulted. They are not even permitted to express their wishes about marriage until negotiations are well under way. The kin of the groom usually initiate the proceedings among themselves by taking stock of their financial resources and putting together what they are able to offer as a bride price. The bride price is made up in local currency or money that is made of feathers and is of great value.

The mother of the groom, in consultation with women of her husband's family, usually designates which of the available girls would make good wives, and together with their husbands and married sons they decide on one of these. Negotiations are then commenced with this girl's father, who in turn consults with his close kin, among whom, if the marriage is consummated, the bride price will be distributed. If the girl's kin are in favor of the marriage, a betrothal agreement is made between the two families. After this the girl's kin will not accept offers from or enter into negotiations with any other suitors without first notifying the kin of the betrothed man.

Betrothals may be made almost at any time during a boy's or girl's life, and frequently they are made during infancy. In the latter case the betrothed children are brought up under conditions of rigid avoidance of each other, and under no circumstances are they permitted to have premarital sex relations. When betrothal is made after the bride and groom have reached marriageable ages, they are informed of it, and are also required to observe strict avoidance of each other until they are actually married. At the time of betrothal, parents usually, but not invariably, make sure whether their children wish to marry the spouse who has been selected. If for some reason either of the betrothed flatly refuses to marry the other, the whole affair may be called off.

Even though children are not allowed the initial freedom of selecting their own mates, there are no, or at least very few, marriages enforced by the parents against their children's consent. Young adults seem always to feel that their parents are the best judges of a spouse for them, insofar as considerations of morality, ability to bear children, and willingness to work are concerned. Parents, on the other hand, believe that their children are the only judges as to whether or not the spouse selected will be physically and sexually attractive. Sexual attractiveness and compatibility are regarded as important considerations in marriage, just as are morality, fertility, and industry. It is firmly believed that no marriage can be happy and stable unless the couple are sexually attractive to each other.

THE MARITAL RELATIONSHIP

For girls, consummation of marriage is possible any time after their breasts are fully developed and have begun to drop slightly. This seems to be at about eighteen or nineteen years for most young women. Boys are considered mature enough for marriage somewhat later, at about twenty or older, when they behave like fully adult men. That is, social rather than physiological factors are the stressed criteria for manhood. First marriages normally are between young persons of about this age difference. But, as mentioned above, at East Bay there is an acute shortage of women as compared with men in the fifteen-to-twenty-five-year age range, and a suitable bride of the desired age cannot always be found. When this is the case, marriage with an older widow may be arranged. Widows of an elder brother or of a maternal uncle are considered to be eminently suitable. Conversely, older widowers often seek remarriage with women much younger than themselves, thus aggravating the shortage of young marriageable girls. If the family of the young man can afford it, a bride may be sought from the islands just to the north. Under no circumstances, however, do East Bay families ever permit their daughters to become brides of men of these northern islands.

As part of the actual marriage ceremony, the bride is conducted to her husband's father's house, or husband's elder brother's house where she immediately takes up residence as a wife. For most young persons this initiates one of the most excruciating adjustment periods of their entire lives.

Having been strenuously trained all their lives to avoid all persons of the opposite sex except for their parents, siblings, and spouses of a few close kin, it is impossible for a young married couple to be at ease with each other at the start of their marital career. Months sometimes pass before a young husband is able to speak to his wife without shame and embarrassment. She, on the other hand, must work closely with her mother-in-law and her sisters-in-law, for she has become a new daughter to their household. Much of her husband's time will be spent in the men's house avoiding her.

Elders are very considerate of newly married couples who find themselves in these painful circumstances, and in some ways the adjustment difficulty is considered a mark of a proper upbringing—something to be proud of and admired. However, the husband's parents consider it their responsibility to smooth things over so the couple can learn to grow fond of each other and to develop an easy intimacy. The first move toward this end is to assign separate garden land to the newly married couple, and to urge the son to build a comfortable garden shed there. Ostensibly the shed is for storing garden implements and seed, a place to get in out of the rain, and a subsidiary dwelling where the wife can prepare an oven during her working hours away from the house in the village. However, it is also the only place where a couple has the privacy to work out their sexual and other personal relations. To concerned parents, the first sign of a successful marriage adjustment comes when a couple begins to go regularly and easily together to their garden, even though they may still be embarrassed and shy in the village in the presence of others.

As soon as the new daughter-in-law shows unmistakable signs of pregnancy, or she and her husband are more or less at ease with one another all the time, this fact is announced officially to all the village by a small presentation of food to each household of the village by the parents of the husband. This public announcement, usually coming anywhere from one to two years after the marriage, signifies that the couple has made their adjustment to each other successfully and marks the beginning of another transitional period during which the young husband builds a separate house in the village for himself, his wife, and the children that are expected to follow. This may take another year or two, and even then he may build only a little hovel in the village, a place just big enough to cook and to sleep. Young men are careful not to build large houses at first, for that would be considered somewhat ostentatious.

At her first marriage, a bride is expected to be a virgin and a husband is delighted when he finds his wife's hymen to be unperforated. However, lack of bleeding after first intercourse is not considered absolute evidence of previous intercourse. All male informants we interviewed agreed that many a virgin does not have a hymen and, therefore, does not bleed as a result of first intercourse. During the early months of married life a bride is expected to suffer from vaginal irritation caused by frequent intercourse, and again this is viewed as a kind of proof of her earlier chastity.

Despite the apparent value placed on early sexual continence, it is not virginity as such that is valued, instead it is that indications of chastity before marriage reveal a girl to be morally sound and reliable; hence as a wife she is less likely to be an adulteress and a worry to her husband.

Moral blame for sex offenses falls most heavily upon the man. This is a patriarchal society in the sense that women, although enjoying very high status, are always not only represented by men, but are also obliged to serve and be obedient to the men who exercise legitimate authority over them. Because women are trained to be so obedient to men, they are not expected to be able to refuse the sexual advances of a man, particularly when he offers enticing presents. Whether or not she accedes to him, the woman is morally bound to report these advances to her brother, father, or husband. This is the only training in sex restraint and morality that is emphasized as girls reach sexual maturity and become sexually attractive.

In spite of the precautions taken against illicit affairs, the severity and consequences of such offenses, and the fears of disgrace and legal retaliation they entail, clandestine affairs do occur. Just how frequently is impossible to know. As long as there is opportunity, desire, complicity of the couple, and care to avoid discovery, an affair can go on undetected for a long time. Several male informants gave complete histories of lengthy affairs they had had with single and with married women. In addition, a surprising number of affairs came to light just during our period on the island.

The pattern of these affairs is very clear. The man is expected to give frequent and sizable presents to the woman. In such a small society, presents are not easy to conceal, and it is frequently their notice that leads to discovery of the affair. Usually the gift is money to buy cloth, soap, and trinkets, which women desire greatly, but for which they rarely have the purchase price. The rendezvous is most always in the forests, the only place where detection is well nigh impossible. Usually the time is during the day, and the place is the deserted bush behind the garden area, well away from all connecting paths. Sometimes it is more convenient to meet late at night, in which case the couple may rendezvous near the village among the groves of fruit trees.

Returning to sex in marriage, during the first months of coresidence, despite public bashfulness, sexual intercourse with orgasm at least twice a day is considered probable and normal. It is expected that sexual excitement will remain high during the early years of marriage, and when a couple finally gets established with their own dwelling, they may continue for many months to have intercourse once a day while they are in the garden and again at night after going to bed. Daytime intercourse in one's own dwelling in the village is never attempted, because villagers are continually coming in and out, and one never closes a house unless he leaves it.

Intercourse frequencies of three times in a twenty-four-hour period were reported, and in one well-attested case, three times with orgasm during a night was recorded for a man involved in a particularly passionate illicit affair. Such frequencies, however, are thought to be beyond the capacities of the majority of virile men. Most men report that women seem to have orgasms synchronous with their own, but a few women are noted for brief intervals between orgasm, and one informant reported that in her youth his wife sometimes had as many as twenty orgasms to his one.[3]

---

[3] For further discussion of multiple orgasm, see pages 84–89, 136–138

While a couple is still living with the husband's father most acts of intercourse are likely to take place in their garden hut, and also the older people may curtail their own nocturnal intercourse because of the embarrassment of being observed by the young couple. However, not all men worry about being observed during intercourse by their close, coresident kin. If the coresidence is continued for long periods, a partition usually is built across the interior of the house to partially screen off the bed of one of the women, for all intercourse in the dwelling occurs where the wife sleeps. Sleeping arrangements, as indicated earlier, are according to the male and female orientations of the house. Husband and wife each have their own sleeping mats and coverlets, which are rolled up and stored away during the day. At night they are brought out and arranged on the appropriate sides of the house, and if the man wishes intercourse, he goes to the wife's bed. Rarely does he sleep there through the night, but returns to his own mat shortly after intercourse is completed.

Infants sleep next to their mothers for the first year or a little longer, but rarely after they begin to toddle. An infant of this age, sleeping alongside the mother, is never considered to be a hindrance to intercourse, for coitus can usually be completed without disturbing the child. Older children have their own mats, and they are apt to sleep almost anywhere in the house. They are not discouraged altogether from sleeping near their mother or father until they are about four or five years old. Parents are somewhat constrained in their intercourse when older children are about, and they attempt to copulate mostly while the youngsters are sleeping. When real privacy is wanted, they leave the children at home and go to their garden house.

Despite these precautions, there is no concerted attempt to conceal parental sex relations from the children, and indeed children of five and six years are already knowledgeable about adult intercourse. Nevertheless, a certain amount of privacy is considered desirable, and children's curiosity to observe the act can be a nuisance. When a child becomes too curious and bold it is told sharply to mind its own business and is instructed not to look. By early adolescence boys and girls have learned to ignore or to conceal their curiosity about the intercourse of their parents when they are aware of it, and from this time on sexual matters can be discussed within the family with perfect frankness.

Intercourse occurs in complete nudity, or with all clothing removed except for a belt. In fact, this is the only occasion when either person exposes his genitals to another individual. After early adolescence, by which time genital modesty is well learned, neither man or woman ever undresses before another person, even of the same sex.

Criteria of modesty differ considerably between men and women. It is not immodest for a man to expose his buttocks to other men or even to women who are sufficiently distant, and it is a frequent sight to see a man emerge from his bath wearing a wet clout or a wraparound garment, turn his back on everyone present, remove it entirely, and then don another. When men wear their traditional-style clouts, which cover only the penis and scrotum, the groins, the thighs, and some pubic hair frequently are visible. Genital modesty for men, then, is confined mainly to the sex organs.

Women, on the other hand, never expose their groins, and carefully cover their thighs half-way down to the knees. The lower part of the buttocks must always be covered, but the upper buttocks as well as part of the cleft between them may be exposed. Women secure their wraparound skirts by tucking them in under their belts in the front, allowing the back part to ride low and thus expose the upper portion of the buttocks.

These sex differences in modesty requirements also affect sitting postures. Men may sit cross-legged or with one knee up, thus exposing their thighs right up to the groin; but mature women always sit with their legs straight out in front, thighs pressed tightly together, and skirts pulled down to cover the legs.

Foreplay and Coitus [4]

Foreplay, as one informant described it, is the indispensable source, "the root" of intercourse.

FORMS OF PRECOITAL STIMULATION. Foreplay begins usually as the man fondles and mouths the woman's breasts and nipples. The woman manipulates her partner's penis and scrotum and may also tickle or mouth his nipples. This may be interspersed with what is sometimes called the oceanic kiss, pressing the nose lightly to the face, the cheek, or neck, and quickly drawing in a breath. The man also masturbates his

---

[4] For comparative descriptions of other societies, see C. S. Ford and F. A. Beach, *Patterns of Sexual Behavior*, New York: Harper and Brothers, 1951.

partner, at first lightly around the labia, feeling the pubic hair, and finally by full insertion of one or more fingers. Neither partner conceals his mounting passion, and hearing and feeling the other pant and strain is considered a stimulating part of the sexual preliminaries. Foreplay usually occurs with both the man and woman lying on their sides so that both hands are free.

Body odors are erotic stimulants, particularly the emanations from the woman's genitalia. There is a form of love magic based upon the similarity of vaginal odors to that of fish. Men use a red ground cherry attached to the leader of a trolling line to attract fish. After having caught a fish in this way, the ground cherry is believed to have power to attract women in the same way that it attracted fish. Their vaginas, like the elusive fish, will be attracted to the possessor of the ground cherry. Other odors are also thought to be seductive. Most potent of these is a very musky aromatic leaf worn only by men when they dance, and another is the somewhat astringent odor of coconut oil mixed with turmeric. Women rub this mixture into their hair on festive occasions. Nowadays, scented talcum and pomade are thought to have mildly erotic qualities as well.

COITAL TECHNIQUES. During coitus the woman lies on her back, spreads her legs, and tucks up her knees. Usually, she inserts the penis as the man reclines upon her. Men seem to vary some in their preference of coital position; some prefer to lie fully on the woman so as to feel her breasts against their chests as they embrace her; some prefer to hold themselves off the woman by placing their palms on the mat; and others like to continue fondling the breasts until orgasm is reached. Likewise, some women lie with their knees barely flexed, others bend their knees sharply, keeping the feet on the mat, while others lift their legs up entirely and lock them around the man, tightening them strongly during climax.

The only variant coital position occurs when both persons lie on their sides, with the woman's leg thrown over the man. This is used only during late pregnancy or when the couple wishes to be extremely quiet so as not to wake someone sleeping near them. Novel or experimental coital positions were not reported, nor was any erotic interest shown in them when such were described.

Men state a definite preference for a very moist and a loose vagina, and they may ask a woman to position her legs so as to favor this condition. There is a strong dislike for both a dry and a tight vagina, and occasionally coconut oil may be used as a lubricant when the woman's secretions are not copious.

Men enjoy intercourse most when women are very active, but they assume that some women are more passive than others and they accept this as a difference among individuals. Although gentle biting of the nipples during foreplay is accepted, hard biting, scratching, or other rough behavior during coitus is unheard of. Likewise, mouth-genital contacts were universally denied, and in most instances with a shudder of disgust accompanying the denial.

As most frequently described, intercourse consists of a prolonged period of foreplay, ceasing only when both partners are very close to or absolutely sure of orgasm, insertion with immediate and vigorous thrusting movements, a short period of actual copulation culminating in synchronous orgasm before the man gets winded and tired. There seems to be no dalliance during copulation; no attempt to prolong arousal while delaying orgasm. Fifteen to thirty seconds seems to be the modal duration for optimal satisfaction, although several men admitted that many times it took much longer before they reached their climax.[5]

Aside from the feeling of responsibility to provide sufficient foreplay to stimulate a woman before insertion, men feel no necessity to time their orgasms with their partner's. No one had ever heard of a woman who was at the same time passionate and unable to reach orgasm. In fact there is a firm belief that once engaged in foreplay, there is really nothing to prevent a woman from achieving orgasm if intercourse follows. *Ejaculatio praecox* is recognized in young men as a sign of inexperience only, and it is assumed that in time it will disappear. No women were ever heard to complain of early orgasm by mature men.

Frequency and Its Relationship to Marital Adjustment and Divorce

Most sexual maladjustment in marriage seems to result

---

[5] Measurement of duration was obtained by counting aloud at intervals of about one second and asking the respondent to call for a stop at the number that seemed roughly equivalent to the time from insertion to orgasm. Admittedly, this was not an accurate device, but it demonstrates that the ideal is to reach orgasm as quickly as possible.

from loss of interest on the part of either or both husband and wife. Erotic responsiveness to other potential partners need not be reduced. In fact, it is assumed that after a few years of marriage, the husband's interest in his wife will begin to pale, and the frequency of intercourse will drop to once a day or perhaps even to once every five or ten days. Some wives complain bitterly about insufficient sexual attention, and it is regarded as justifiable for a woman to leave her husband when she is not attended at least once every ten days or so.

Men, on the other hand, feel it is the wife's duty to accept them whenever they ask, no matter how often, unless there is some physical reason why she cannot comply. When a wife repeatedly refuses her husband's sexual advances, he is justified in beating her into compliance, as long as he does not inflict severe wounds. If he can demonstrate that she has not accommodated him sufficiently, he can abandon her and have his kinsmen seek another wife for him. Most divorces, in fact, seem to involve some sexual dissatisfaction.

If a man is strongly attracted to another woman and he can persuade his relatives to assist him to accumulate the bride price, he may go ahead and marry her, if her kin agree, without consulting his original wife or even bothering to ask her to leave his house. In other words, while adultery by a husband is an offense against his wife, the wife has no rights over her husband with regard to another marriage. If she wishes to remain as a second wife, she may; if not, she can leave. In spite of such provisions polygamy is infrequent in this society, but when it occurs, it most often comes about because the husband takes a new wife and his old one does not leave. Plural marriages are not closely associated with high social status of the husband as they are in some societies.

If a woman wishes to leave her husband, she must first prove that she has been neglected or mistreated in some vile way. Even then her kin will bring to bear all the pressure they can muster to make her remain with her husband.

When a couple's marital difficulties are known to be sexual, the kin of both partners may attempt to correct the matter by employing sex magic. There are numerous kinds, but they all follow a single magical formula. A leaf or scraping of bark from a plant believed to have aphrodisiac qualities is surreptitiously inserted in the food, or, better, in the betel lime which will be chewed by the spouse whose ardor has cooled. After a time, and especially if the couple is rejoined, they are informed that this was done to them. These magical devices are believed to have great power and must be used with discretion because the excessive desire created by their overuse can lead to over-stimulation and trouble of a different kind.

Marriages at East Bay are remarkably stable in spite of the high frequency of marital disputes, accusations of infidelity, and suspicions of adultery. Less than 5 percent result in divorce, yet there seems to be no long-standing marriage that has not had a stormy history and at least one period of separation. Even though the husband is almost the lord and master of his wife and is expected to beat her from time to time when she irritates him, husbands and wives often reveal their deep respect and affection for each other in many ways. At the sudden death of either, the surviving spouse may be genuinely and completely incapacitated by grief for a long period.

The sexual intimacy of marriage is overtly symbolized by one activity: husband and wife eating together. Actually, however, in the home husband and wife rarely take their meals simultaneously. Out of respect to his position as head of the household the man is served first, and his wife and young children eat together after he has finished. Only a man and his wife may eat in each other's presence. All other men and women must carefully avoid the sight of each other when they eat. Similarly, giving food or the ingredients for betel or tobacco are considered intimate acts, and as far as men and women are concerned, only a man and his wife (or lovers) may exchange these items.

CONCUBINAGE

Until colonial law forbade it, there was an institutionalized means by which well-established older men could acquire young girls, not as secondary wives, but as concubines. Concubines were always imported from the island immediately to the north at bride prices that were at least ten times the amount paid for a wife. These were beyond the financial resources of most individuals, hence a group of five to ten men collectively purchased a concubine in a sort of polyandrous arrangement. Every group purchasing a concubine included one man who was senior to the others and exercised absolute authority over the concubine and the sharing of her sexual favors. A group sharing one concubine was always composed of individuals belonging to the same men's house association. The men's house was her home, and she slept there with each of her owners more or less in rotation. Children born to a concubine were classified as legitimate offspring of the senior owner, and his wife was considered to be their sociological mother.

The concubine was never permitted to work in the gardens or to prepare food, the two domestic occupations intimately associated with wives. She always wore the finest clothing obtainable, she kept herself adorned and made up as though she were going to a festive occasion each day. On the night that she slept with one of her owners, she served him his food, but in the men's house instead of in his dwelling. The food, however, was prepared by the man's legitimate wife and given to the concubine to serve and to share with him. When the concubine was indisposed and could not sleep with a man, she stayed in the principal owner's house with his wife. This woman and the wives of her other owners regarded the concubine as if she were a special kind of adopted daughter. She was pampered, spoiled, and held up as a very precious thing. To own or to share in the ownership of one or more concubines was the highest mark of prestige a man could obtain in this society. Wives of men possessing concubines were as proud of them as were their husbands.

The expression of jealousy over a concubine was not permitted, nor does it seem to have been often felt by the wives of the men sharing them. The clear-cut differences in status between a wife and a concubine reduced or prevented social conflict. A wife was mistress of her home, manager of her gardens, and mother of her children. A concubine was an object of sexual pleasure, a plaything of the men, and a status object. Even though all the niceties of life were showered upon her, the concubine's social status was really that of a domestic slave.

The concubine was also a prostitute and, sometimes, could represent a sound economic investment. If she was attractive, men from other men's houses would pay her owners for her services on a night-by-night basis. Frequently, too, some concubines gained exceptional reputations and were sold by one group to another for a profit. When the joint owners of a concubine tired of her, they might sell her to another group, and then begin to negotiate for a new one. As concubines grew old and less attractive, they were sold into the southern and less prosperous districts of the island. Finally, they were given over as wives to other men who paid for them by the usual transfer of normal bride price. Thus each concubine ended her career as a wife and mistress of her own household.

The concubines served still another important purpose. Some of her owners usually had young unmarried sons of their own, and occasionally the concubine was turned over to the latter to satisfy their growing needs for sexual outlet. This practice was believed to reduce a youth's temptation to enter into illicit affairs with single or married women and thus become involved in serious legal tangles.

Older people, men and women alike, agree that the outlawing and eradication of concubinage is the greatest tragedy and source of bitterness in their recent history; greater even than the importation of new diseases that has reduced the population to a fraction of what it once was.

Older men often comment today that without young women to excite them and without the variety once provided by changing concubines, they have become sexually inactive long before their time. To them a wife is sexually exciting only for a few years after marriage. After the birth of several children she loses interest in sex generally and in her husband in particular. The sexual spice of life is then gone, and this, many informants agreed, is why there are so many marital problems, fights, and squabbles. In earlier days, working hard to amass wealth for a concubine was worthwhile, and the rewards were great. Nowadays, there is no comparable incentive. The best that an aging man can hope for, provided he survives his wife, is to secure a young wife in her place, but the excitement of variety in youthful concubines is gone altogether. Clearly, one of the most important social motivations for the men of this society has been removed.

In talking about their former concubines, men reveal an important part of their personalities. Only to a concubine could a man be tender, protective, and at the same time sexually intimate. In support of this, former concubines recall with nostalgia the considerate and loving ways in which they were treated, not only by their owners, but by their owners' wives as well. In contrast, a wife is a hard-working partner, and although admired and respected—even loved—there was or is rarely the degree of tenderness and heated sexual excitement between a husband and wife that there was between a man and his concubine. In brief, men with social positions of consequence and past their physical prime did, and still do, desire to have women over whom they could exercise absolute authority; on whom they could heap material favors—young women who would remain uncalloused by hard work, and whom they could possess sexually, yet cast off when passion declined or when an opportunity for profit appeared.

EFFECTS OF AGING

We have already noted that the frequency of coitus declines after several years of marriage, and this is commonly attributed to loss of responsiveness to the spouse. It is also assumed that the ability to perform sexually declines with age. A middle-aged man (e.g., about thirty years) is thought to be fully capable of one orgasm each day provided he can be erotically aroused. This level of sexual outlet is considered normal and reasonable until he reaches approximately the age of fifty, after which, for unaccountable reasons, a man usually "dries up." This means he can no longer produce semen. The ability to produce semen is believed to be perfectly correlated with a man's ability to have erections. Thus, older men are sometimes sexually aroused, but because they have no or little semen, so the theory goes, they cannot achieve an erection or orgasm.

The same kind of reasoning is applied to women. Those who can produce vaginal secretions can be aroused and are capable of intercourse; those who are too old to do this are no longer sexually responsive.[6] In a small sample of older married men surveyed, whose ages ran from about thirty to

[6] For a discussion of vaginal secretion and sexual arousal, see pages 22–23, 260.

well over sixty, not one had ceased having intercourse with his wife, but the frequencies they mentioned do decrease from about once a day among the younger to about once a month among the eldest respondents. Each man, however, felt, or perhaps boasted, that were concubines still permitted, his sexual life would be much more active than it was now.

COITUS AS RELATED TO PREGNANCY

East Bay people believe that conception resembles the planting of seeds in the ground. The semen is the seed containing all of the material that eventually will grow into a fetus. The womb is the soil from which the developing organism draws nourishment. A child is influenced before birth by both parents. It "inherits" some qualities from the father's seed, and since it "feeds" upon substances of the mother's body, the fetus is affected by the quality and quantity of the nutrients thus obtained.

In order to secure successful impregnation, the man should allow his semen to accumulate for some time; and this calls for complete abstinence for several days before intercourse if conception is desired. Once successful impregnation has been achieved, further introduction of semen must be avoided, or else a second fetus may be started, and twins be the result. Twins are considered very undesirable.

There is no postpartum taboo on intercourse, but a husband is supposed to allow his wife at least a month to recover fully from giving birth before he attempts coitus. Some men believe that every precaution should be taken to prevent conception from occurring for at least two years, by which time the child is fully weaned and able to walk. Failure to allow the woman this interval between births is to endanger her life. Many men swear they abide by this precaution, and the spacings between their children seem to indicate they do. Abstinence from marital sex was no problem when there were concubines, but now such denial is more difficult for some men. Elder people insist that today young couples resume intercourse as soon as the wife is recovered from her brief lying-in period; and it is true that for a number of young couples with several children their successive births have occurred at almost minimal physiological intervals. These are duly noted by the group and singled out as the result of ill-advised sexual behavior.

Reviewing the evidence as it relates to the regulation of sexual behavior, it is clear that the pressures of restraint are not all directed at intercourse itself, but are equally centered upon the prevention of conception. On the one hand, sex is desired, enjoyed, and regarded as a fine and necessary activity. On the other, fear of twins and danger to the wife's health exert a temporary, negative effect on the sexual behavior of many individuals.

One solution to this conflict is prevention of conception without discontinuing sexual relations. For this purpose East Bay couples employ *coitus interruptus*. All of the men with whom sex was discussed and who had been married or who had entered into prolonged extramarital affairs had frequently practiced *coitus interruptus*. It is discussed openly along with other sexual matters. Children learn of the technique informally, just as they learn about the details of intercourse and the theory of reproduction. Both men and women are held to be morally obliged to practice *interruptus* or else suffer the consequences of unwanted pregnancies. There are, in addition, a number of magical treatments designed to prevent conception, to produce abortion, and even to produce complete sterility in women. The latter was used only on concubines in the hope that they would always be available for intercourse.

OUTLETS OTHER THAN HETEROSEXUAL COITUS

In East Bay society, young single men living in the men's house are the pride of the community, and the best of everything is reserved for them. They are pampered individually by their fathers, mothers, and sisters, and collectively by all the women and the married men. A personal offense against a man of this set is far more serious than one against a girl of the same age. Young women of this age have heavy domestic responsibilities, but a young man has very few. If he wishes to help in the family garden he can do so—and he usually does—but such useful activities are purely voluntary.

In many ways this period of late adolescence and early adulthood is a golden interval, during which young males are treated as special and privileged adults, but are not required to assume the duties and responsibilities the society places upon the head of a household. It is realized they are sexually mature in many ways, but heterosexual intercourse is considered harmful to a young man until his beard is fully grown. At the same time there is general recognition of the increasing strength of erotic desire during these years and of the need for some source of sexual satisfaction. Masturbation is seen as an ideal, socially acceptable solution to this problem.

Masturbation

Young men are urged to masturbate to orgasm as a substitute for heterosexual intercourse. This practice is considered healthy and proper, subject only to the restriction that it should be carried out in reasonable privacy, preferably in the men's house while in bed at night. Under these conditions young men masturbate when they wish, not always bothering to conceal their activities from their housemates. The housemates ignore such behavior just as intercourse between husband and wife in the house is ignored by other occupants of the dwelling.

Young single women are encouraged to engage in masturbation in the privacy of the dwelling where they sleep. As far as we could determine, women always use their fingers for masturbation, never employing any other penis substitute. It is impossible to overstress the fact that in this society masturbation to orgasm is not only accepted, but approved and encouraged as the proper sex behavior for young, unmarried adults of both sexes. It is regarded as a safe and normal sexual outlet for young unmarried persons.

Homosexual Behavior

For men, homosexual relations constitute another important and socially approved substitute for heterosexual intercourse. At some time during his life, very nearly every male engages in extensive homosexual activities. Such experiences are readily and openly discussed for they are considered to be as normal as masturbation and marital intercourse. Homosexual activity usually begins with foreplay which consists of mutual or unilateral masturbation and ends with anal intercourse culminating in orgasm.

Transvestitism does not occur at East Bay, and no one could recall ever hearing of a very masculine woman or a very feminine man.

Our information pertaining to the sexual behavior of young, single women is less satisfactory than is that for the men, but it seems reasonably certain that neither adolescent girls nor young adult women engage in homosexual activities. If such relationships do occur, which we doubt, they must be conducted with extreme secrecy. The only female substitute for heterosexual intercourse seems to be self-masturbation.

It is expected that after marriage a man will desire and value intercourse with his wife above all other sex relations, and that he will give up onanism. However, he need not forego pederasty as long as this does not prevent him from giving sexual satisfaction to his wife. In other words, this is a society that quite frankly expects and accepts some bisexual behavior in most men, although there is nothing odd or deviant about an exclusively heterosexual male. As a result these people have no concept to compare with our commonly accepted stereotype of the "psychological homosexual."

When adults alone were asked to compare homo- and heterosexual intercourse, ten reported they definitely preferred hetero- to homosexual intercourse, two reported them equally satisfying, and one stated a preference for homo- to heterosexual intercourse.

Asked to describe the most frequent content of ordinary erotic dreams (those without great anxiety), ten reported both male and female sex partners, four reported female partners alone, none reported male partners alone, and twenty were unable to recall or were too young to fully understand.

Inconclusive and tentative as these data on the manifest content of sexual fantasies are, they are congruent with the already stated notion that East Bay is a society that permits men to be either exclusively heterosexual or bisexual in their behavior, but denies the possibility of the exclusively homosexual man.

Part III

PRACTICAL

APPLICATIONS

OF SEX RESEARCH

COUNSELING WITH SEXUALLY INCOMPATIBLE MARRIAGE PARTNERS

William H. Masters, M.D., and
Virginia E. Johnson

Editors' note: In January 1959, in addition to their laboratory research, Dr. Masters and Mrs. Johnson began a program for treating married couples complaining of sexual incompatibility or of sexual inadequacy. This therapeutic program, now in its eighth year, has given them an opportunity to try out in clinical practice a number of procedures for enhancing sexual responses suggested by their laboratory observations. In addition, it has given them experience with a segment of the population deliberately excluded from their laboratory study—men and women unable to achieve satisfactory sexual response. Most of the patients were men who were unable to achieve or maintain erection or who ejaculated prematurely, and women unable to experience orgasm. In all cases, the husbands or wives of the patients were included in the therapeutic program.

Most of the patients were referred to Dr. Masters by physicians in other parts of the country; only about 10 percent came from St. Louis. The visitors spent ten days to three weeks in St. Louis in a "crash program" of treatment, during which they received from twenty-five to fifty hours of therapy. Specific training in sexual techniques was included in the treatment program along with psychological and educational procedures.

How successful is this approach to therapy? Many evaluations of therapeutic success are based on observations made at the time the therapy is completed and the patient says good-bye. Dr. Masters and Mrs. Johnson take the view that no claim for success should be made until patients have been followed up for at least five years to ensure that therapeutic benefits are in fact long-lasting. As a condition of being accepted for therapy, the Masters-Johnson patients agreed to remain available for follow-up studies. Five-year follow-ups are currently under way, and a full report on the program is scheduled for publication by Little, Brown and Company in 1967.

Meanwhile, Dr. Masters and Mrs. Johnson have made several preliminary reports at medical meetings and have published preliminary accounts in the medical literature (see Bibliography, page 311). The most recent is reprinted below, from *Counseling in Sexual and Marital Problems* (*A Physician's Handbook*), edited by Dr. R. H. Klemer.

At least one result of the cultural relaxation of sexual taboos has been of major consequence. Today, more—many more—marital partners are seeking professional assistance when sexual incompatibility threatens their marriage. Anyone exposed professionally to the emotional anguish and disrupted marriages caused by such clinical problems as impotence and frigidity will look upon this help-seeking trend with considerable satisfaction.

Most of the sexually distressed people are bringing their problems to their family physicians. Although the individual or combined efforts of psychiatrists, psychologists, marriage counselors, social workers, and/or clergymen may be needed in addition to those of the chosen physician to solve some problems of sexual inadequacy, it is the family physician, taking advantage of initial rapport and established confidence, who ordinarily overcomes any patient reluctance or embarrassment and builds motivation for further treatment.

Unfortunately, until recently the physician has been hampered in treatment by three major stumbling blocks:

First, there has been a long-standing and widespread medical misconception that a patient will not reveal sex history background with sufficient accuracy and in adequate detail for effective therapy.

Second, in the past the physician has been provided with very little basic information in sexual physiology upon which to develop any effective treatment of sexual inadequacy.

Third, many physicians have been convinced that since most sexual problems are psychogenic in origin, only a specialized psychopathologist can treat them effectively.

Increasingly large numbers of physicians are demonstrating clinically that none of these obstacles now has much substance in fact.

Almost ten years of investigation in the broad areas of human sexual response has brought conviction to the writers that if the interviewing physician can project sincere interest in the patient's problem and, even more important, exhibit no personal embarrassment in an open sexual discussion, almost any individual's sexual history will be reported with sufficient accuracy and in adequate detail for treatment purposes. Others, such as Eisenbud,[1] who have worked with human sexual problems, also believe that patients are usually very ready to talk freely about their disturbed sexual behavior patterns once they have gathered their courage to a degree sufficient to seek professional guidance.

While it is true that the amount of research in sexual physiology has in the past been meager indeed, this situation is rapidly being corrected.[2-6] Some of this recent material is synthesized in the latter part of this chapter and quite possibly may provide a minimal baseline for the more adequate clinical treatment of frigidity or impotence.

With regard to the third stumbling block—that of requisite referral to the psychopathologist of problems of sexual incompatibility—two things should be noted. First, there is ample clinical evidence for the observation that sexual imbalance or inadequacy is not confined to individuals who have been identified with major psychoses or even severe neuroses. Secondly, long-maintained individually oriented psychotherapy for sexual inadequacy frequently places irreversible strains on the marital state. While the psychopathologist is working with one marriage partner or the other

[1] For references, see page 219.

toward the resolution of his or her individual sexual inadequacy, the marriage itself may be deteriorating. One or two years of therapy directed specifically toward the impotent male or frigid female frequently leaves the unsupported marital partner in a state of severe frustration. Not only are unresolved sexual tensions of the nontreated spouse of major moment, but frequently no significant attempt is made by the therapist to keep the supposedly adequate partner apprised of his or her mate's fundamental problems and/or the specifics of therapeutic progress. Such situations of spouse neglect not only are sure to increase the performance pressures on the sexually inadequate partner, but obviously may lead to many other areas of marital strife and, for that matter, stimulate extramarital interests.

As the result of these observations, the conviction has grown that the most effective treatment of sexual incompatibility involves the technique of working with both members of the family unit. The major factor in effective diagnosis and subsequent productive counseling in sexual problems lies in gaining access to and rapport with both members of the family unit. This approach not only provides direct therapy for the sexually inadequate partner, but provides something more. An indirect therapeutic gain results from enlisting the complete cooperation and active participation of the adequate spouse (the husband of the frigid woman or the wife of the impotent male). It is virtually impossible for the mate of the sexually distressed partner to remain isolated from or uninvolved in his or her partner's concern for adequate sexual performance. Therefore, most of these individuals can and will be most cooperative in absorbing the necessary material of both physiologic and psychologic background necessary to convert them into active members of the therapy team.

As in so many other areas of medical practice, treating sexual incompatibility involves, first, recognizing the nature of the patient's problem; second, determining the type and degree of the incompatibliity and third, developing and activating the therapeutic approaches applicable to the particular clinical involvement.

RECOGNIZING THE
SEXUAL PROBLEM

The patient with sexual distress defines the problem directly with increasing frequency during this era of marked change in our cultural attitudes toward sexual material. However, many women initially may discuss such symptoms as fatigue, "nerves," pelvic pain, headaches, or any other complaint for which specific pathology cannot be established. The physician-interviewer must anticipate conscious vocal misdirection when Victorian concepts of sexual taboos still exist, or where there is a personal demand to fix blame on the marital partner.

If, for example, the female is the partner experiencing major dissatisfaction with her marriage, for any one of a number of reasons, she purposely may obscure her basic personal antipathies by describing gross sexual irregularities on the part of her marital partner. Sometimes when it is the husband who wishes to end the marriage, he often employs the pressure of partial sexual withdrawal, or even complete sexual refusal. At this point, medical consultation is sought solely to justify condemnation of what is termed the mate's unfair, inadequate, or perverted sexual behavior.

Actually, the marital incompatibility that brings the couple to the physician usually is not primarily of sexual origin. Sexual incompatibility may well be the secondary result of marital disagreement over such problems as money, relatives, or child care. Such areas of dispute easily may undermine any poorly established pattern of sexual adjustment. Frequently, withholding of sexual privileges is used as punishment in retaliation for true or fancied misdeeds in other areas. If the preliminary history reveals such a situation of secondary sexual incompatibility, the physician must decide whether he wishes to carry the full, time-consuming burden of total marriage counseling or if referral is in order. In the latter case, he still may wish to retain an active clinical role in the psychosexual aspects of the problems involved.

However, once the problem is established as primarily sexual in nature and as the cause and not the effect of the marital incompatibility, the complaint should be attacked directly and with the same sense of medical urgency with which clinical complaints of either a medical or a surgical background are investigated. Otherwise, permanent impairment of the marital relationship may be inevitable.

THE SEXUAL HISTORY

The need to acquire accurate and detailed sexual histories is basic to determining the type and the degree of the incompatibility of the members of the distressed family unit.

Sex histories must reflect accurately details of early sexual training and experience, family attitudes toward sex, the degree of the family's demonstrated affection, personal attitude toward sex and its significance within the marriage, and the degree of personal regard for the marital partner. While the actual nature of the existing sex difficulty may be revealed during an early stage of history-taking, the total history, as it discloses causation and subsequent effect, provides the basis for the most effective means of therapy.

The first step in the team approach to diagnosis and treatment has been to see the husband and wife together as a complaining unit during the initial interview.[7-9] Procedures and philosophies are explained to them. If the couple desires to continue after the investigative concepts have been outlined, they are separated for individual interrogation but only after each partner is assured that similar background material will be covered simultaneously by the two interviewers.

The knowledge that both unit members are undergoing

similar interrogative procedures, that essentially the same background material will be investigated, and that all areas of professed concern will be probed in depth, produces an atmosphere that encourages honest reporting and an unusual amount of patient attention to detail.

Finite details of past and present sexual behavior may be obtained during the initial interview with the facility and integrity anticipated for the recording of a detailed medical history. Encouraged by a receptive climate, controlled, brief questioning, and a nonjudgmental attitude, the patient is just as free to discuss the multiple facets of, for example, a homosexual background, as he might be to present the specific details of a chronic illness in a medical history.

It should be noted particularly that in the process of acquiring a detailed sexual history, the usual basic physical and social histories of medical and behavioral significance also are recorded.

For the rapid diagnosis and treatment of sexual incompatibility, a male-female therapy team approach has been developed as reported elsewhere.[9] This approach involves the male marriage partner being interviewed first by the male member of the therapy team. Simultaneously, material from the female partner of the involved marital unit is acquired by the female member of the therapy team. Prior to the second investigative session, members of the therapy team exchange pertinent details of the marital unit's reported sexual distress. During the second session the female partner of the complaining couple is reinterviewed by the male member of the therapy team. Meanwhile, the husband is evaluated by the female therapist. At the third interview, the therapy team and the marital couple meet to review the positive features of the earlier interrogative sessions and to discuss in detail the active degree of the sexual incompatibility.

While the male-female therapy approach has been found to be eminently satisfactory, obviously this technique usually is not possible in the typical physician's practice. However, the broad general steps toward diagnosis and evaluation that are outlined here can be adapted by the individual physician. For instance, the advantage of honest reporting obtained by simultaneous interviews of members of the marital unit can be retained by interrogating them consecutively.

THE THERAPEUTIC PROCESS

Once the background of the individual couple's sexual imbalance has been defined, and the clinical picture explained to their satisfaction and understanding, a discussion of therapeutic procedure takes place.

In general terms, the psychotherapeutic concepts and physiologic techniques employed to attack the problems of frigidity and impotence are explained without reservation. Specific plans are outlined for the therapeutic immediacies and a pattern for long-range support is described. With this specific information available, a decision must be reached as to whether the couple has sufficient need or interest for active participation in the therapeutic program. The decision obviously is based not only on a joint evaluation of the quality of the marriage and the severity of the sexual distress, but also on a review of the individual abilities to cooperate fully with the program. If doubt exists, on the part of either member of the investigative team or either partner of the sexually incompatible marital unit, as to real interest in remedial techniques or ability to cooperate fully as a unit, the couple is directed toward other sources of clinical support.

Since the two major sexual incompatibilities are frigidity and impotence, treatment for these problems will be discussed in detail.

IMPOTENCE

Three major types of impotence ordinarily are encountered in the human male. They are:

(1) *Failed erection.* Penile erection cannot be achieved.
(2) *Inadequate erection.* Full penile erection either cannot be achieved or, if accomplished, is maintained fleetingly and lost, usually without ejaculation.
(3) *Nonemissive erection.* Full penile erection is achieved, but ejaculation cannot be accomplished with the penis contained within the vagina.

Note. Premature ejaculation—ejaculation before, during, or immediately after mounting is accomplished—while not considered a form of impotence, is discussed in this chapter due to the similarity of therapeutic approach.

Impotence is rarely, if ever, the result of lesions of the posterior urethra. Once the possibility of spinal cord disease or certain endocrinopathies, such as hypogonadism or diabetes insipidus, has been eliminated, the total history should be scrutinized for the omnipresent signs of psychogenic origin for the specific type of male impotence reported.

In the case of the male with failed or inadequate erection, history-taking should stress the timetable of symptom onset. Has there always been difficulty, or is loss of erective power of recent origin? If recent in origin, what specific events inside or outside the marriage have been associated with onset of symptoms? Are there any masturbatory difficulties? Is there a homosexual background of significance?

Further questioning should define the male's attitude toward his sexual partner. Is there rejection not only of the marriage partner, but also of other women? Are the female partner's sexual demands in excess of his levels of sexual interest or ability to comply? Is there a sexual disinterest that may have resulted from the partner's physical or personal traits, such as excessive body odor or chronic alcoholism?

In the case of a patient with premature ejaculation, questions should be concentrated in a different area. Does this rapid ejaculatory pattern date from the beginning of his sexual activity? Has he been exposed to prostitute demand for rapid performance during his teen-age years? Does he come from a level of society where the female sexual role is considered to be purely one of service to male demand?

When working with the male with a nonemissive erection still other questions are more appropriate. Has the male always been unable to ejaculate during intercourse or has this difficulty been confined to exposure to his marital partner? Are nocturnal emissions frequent, especially after heterosexual encounters? Is there an active homosexual history?

Actually, the fundamental therapeutic approach to all problems of impotence is one of creating and sustaining self-confidence in the patient. This factor emphasizes the great advantage in training the wife to be an active member of the therapeutic team. All pertinent details of the anatomy, physiology, and psychology of male impotence should be explained to her satisfaction. The rationale of treatment, together with an explanation of the specific stimulative techniques most effective in dealing with the specific type of impotence distressing her husband must be made clear to her.

In the early stages of treating failed or nonerective impotence, it is wise to avoid emphasizing the demand that intercourse be the end of all sexual play. Frequently, the male's inability to meet just such a repetitive female demand is already one of the primary factors in his impotence. Some males find release from fear of performance when they are given to understand that sexual play need not necessarily terminate in intercourse. They are then able to relax, enjoy, and participate freely in the sexually stimulative situations created by their clinically oriented wives to a point where erection does occur. After several such occasions of demand-free spontaneous erections, the males may even initiate the mounting procedure and complete the sexual act. This casual mating may well be the beginning of release from their chronic or acute failed or nonerective impotence.

In most cases, manual penile manipulation varying in degree of intensity and duration probably will be necessary. This controlled penile stimulation must be provided by his previously trained female partner. The male with inadequate erection syndrome should be exposed to long and regularly recurrent periods of manual stimulation in a sensitive, sexually restrained, but firmly demanding fashion.

In the opposite vein, the male with the difficult problem of premature ejaculation should be manually stimulated for short, controlled periods with stimulation withheld at his own direction as he feels ejaculation is imminent. The shaft of the penis should be well lubricated to reduce cutaneous sensation. This technique will fail frequently and ejaculation will occur. However, the couple should be encouraged to return to the technique repetitively until the male's obviously improved control leads to the next therapeutic step. This will be a female superior mounting, which can later be converted to a nondemanding lateral resting position. These progressive control techniques emphasize the unit approach to the problem of sexual inadequacy and from here on psychogenic support and the cooperation of the wife certainly will reclaim many of those males who were formerly inadequate sexually.

The problem of the male with nonemissive erection is somewhat different. His is largely an infertility problem rather than one of sexual incompatibility. In these cases, reassuring both husband and wife that the problem is of little clinical consequence provides the basic therapy. Sometimes the infertility concern connected with this variant can be overcome by artificially inseminating the wife with her husband's seminal fluid obtained by manipulation. Since psychotherapy has produced so few positive results with this type of impotence, providing clinical reassurance and conceptive information may have to suffice in these cases.

FRIGIDITY

There is a great deal of misunderstanding over the connotation of the word "frigidity." It is often used in a context that presumes an irrevocable lack of sexuality on the part of a female sexual partner. Misconceptions are likely to occur when this word is used too freely as a diagnostic term.

From a therapeutic point of view, the maximal meaning of the word should indicate no more than a prevailing inability or subconscious refusal to respond sexually to effective stimulation. A woman is not necessarily lacking in sexual responsiveness when she does not experience an orgasm. Therefore, the achievement of orgasmic response should not be considered the end-all of sexual gratification for the responding female. Unhappily, many women, unable to achieve an orgasmic level of sexual response in the past, have been labeled frigid not only by their marital partner but also by the physician they may have consulted.

The free use of this term frequently does great psychologic damage. Frigidity is a term that should rarely be employed in the presence of the sexually inadequate female for it may well add shame, and/or fear of inadequate performance to whatever other psychologic problems she may have.

It is true that there are a number of women who experience a persistently high degree of sexual tension, but, for unidentified reasons, are not able to achieve a satisfactory means of tension release. In evaluating this problem, initial exploration should be concentrated in two areas of psychosexual withdrawal. The first is to determine the presence or absence of psychologic inability to respond to effective sexual stimulation. The second is to define the possible existence of sexual incompatibility caused by misunderstandings resulting from a difference in the sex tension demands of the marital partners.

As described elsewhere,[7] three positive indications of female psychosexual inadequacy can be developed by careful history-taking:

(1) Attitude toward sex and its significance within the marriage.
(2) Degree of personal regard for the marital partner.
(3) Fear of pregnancy.

In investigating the attitude toward sex, existing negative concepts should be pursued by careful interrogation. Questioning should explore early sexual training and experience, exposure to lack of demonstrated parental affection, history of homosexual experience, if any, and/or any traumatic sex-oriented incidents that might have affected natural sexual responsiveness.

When exploring the area of personal regard for the marital partner, the female partner's disinterest or lack of cooperation with the consulting physician may be an interesting clinical symptom of itself. When essential indifference toward a marital partner has been exposed, the existence of a basically unwanted marriage or marriage undertaken without intelligent preparation or emotional maturity is a real possibility. Perhaps, in these cases, referral to a marriage counselor or undertaking marriage counseling in the more general frame of reference is in order, rather than concentrating on the sexual aspects of the problem.

When there is any indication of fear of pregnancy the therapeutic approach is obvious to the counseling physician. Actually, satisfactory results are ordinarily more easily achieved in pregnancy-phobia situations than in either of the other two areas of psychosexual withdrawal.

After the background of the female's sexual unresponsiveness has been established, and the marital unit has accepted the conclusions presented during the diagnostic sessions, therapy may begin. Female sexual responsiveness may well depend upon the successful orientation to the following framework of therapeutic approach:

(1) The possibility of anatomic or physiologic abnormalities that can contribute to varying shades of discomfort during intercourse should be eliminated. Orientation to male and female sexual anatomy, directly if necessary, should be accomplished.

(2) Affirmation that sexual expression represents an integral basis for sharing within the marriage should be emphasized.

(3) A mutually stimulative sexual pattern should be developed and adapted to the individual psychosocial backgrounds of the marriage partners.

(4) Gentleness, sensitivity, and technical effectiveness in the male partner's approach to sexual encounter should be encouraged.

(5) Emphasis should be placed on the fact that female orgasm is not necessarily the end-all of every sexual encounter.

With regard to pelvic abnormalities, it might be noted that a history indicating actual pain or any other physical displeasure during sex play or coition certainly suggests the need for an adequate physical examination. If physiologic variants, such as pelvic endometriosis, causing severe, recurrent discomfort during intercourse with deep penile penetration are revealed, subsequent medical and/or surgical adjustments may be indicated. However, it should be noted that sometimes the simple clinical expedient of teaching the couple proper positioning for coital activity may remove the female partner's distress despite existing pelvic pathology.

A high percentage of psychologically based problems of inadequate female response begin as the result of rejection of, or ignorance of effective sex techniques by either or both marital partners. The physician may also be called upon to provide reassurance as to the propriety of variants of stimulative sexual behavior. Although the number of patients who are sexually incompatible as the result of the wife's or husband's total lack of sexual experience before marriage may well be declining, patients with this type of problem are seen occasionally. Moreover, many women have been taught that only certain specifics of sexual stimulation or certain coital positions are acceptable. These women do not readily accept any deviation from what they consider "right and proper," regardless of the interests of their marital partners. Victorianism, although vanishing from the American social scene, left a residual influence that may well require attention for at least another fifty years.

Teaching the sexually inadequate woman and her partner the basic rudiments of sexual anatomy may be extremely important. Many males, however experienced in coition, are unaware of the importance of adequate techniques for clitoral area stimulation. Few are aware that it is the gentle friction of the mons area or of the clitoral shaft rather than the clitoral glans that provides the most effective stimulation for the female partner. Moreover, many females as well as males are not aware of the basic physiology of sexual response and of the fact that physiologic orgasm takes place within the vagina and in the clitoris, regardless of where sensation is perceived by the female or initiated by the male.

In the development of a mutually stimulative sexual pattern it is important that the marital unit's move toward maximal female sexual responsiveness should be accompanied by the female's vocalizing such things as: specific sexual preferences, desired zones of erogenous stimulation, choice of coital positioning and, particularly, the fact of her approaching orgasm. The couple must be taught to consider moments of individual preference for sexual encounter. Experimentation with varieties of time, place, and sexual techniques should be made in order to achieve the necessary mood conducive to the female's successful sexual response. It is well to bear in mind that the two basic deterrents to female sexual responsiveness are *fatigue* and *preoccupation*.

The item in the therapeutic framework emphasizing gentleness and sensitivity needs little elaboration. But it should be noted that the male's approach—his ability to project both security and affection to the female—may be an absolute essential to any improvement in the female's sexual responsiveness. A re-evaluation of the male's attitudes toward sex and toward women may be as important to the progress of therapy as the attention paid to his education in specific sexual techniques.

The second major area to be explored with the couple is the possible difference in the degree of basic sexual tension demonstrated by the wife as opposed to that indicated by the husband. In analyzing this area, it should be emphasized that an impression of low-level female sexual demand should only be established in relative comparison to a higher-tension partner. A lower level of demand does not necessarily connote either inability to respond adequately to effective heterosexual stimulation or homosexual tendency. Yet, when such a divergence in sexual interest is encountered, there are inevitable misunderstandings between the marital partners. In some cases there may be a conscious sexual withdrawing by the lower-response partner, developing from a sense of personal inadequacy or from a wish to punish what is considered as excessive demand. Conscious sexual withdrawal also may develop from a deep resentment or a sense of rejection felt by the partner wishing a higher degree of sexual participation.

The marital unit's understanding and acceptance of a difference in sexual tension demand is far more important than its causation and the determination of a specific spouse role-playing. A higher level of demand may well belong to either partner. This is evident in marriages between younger partners as well as in many marriages between older individuals. Feelings of sexual inadequacy, distrust, or withdrawal may be corrected by education of each mate to the other partner's individual, highly personal, sexual requirements. Thereafter, the problem becomes one of adjusting acknowledged differences in sexual tension to a mutually accepted plan for effective release of the higher level of demand. It has been noted frequently that the relief of inhibitions of the lower-tension partner (once the marital unit problem is understood) may be marked by a more receptive, or even increased willingness to participate in sexual activity, even though there is no permanent elevation of the lower-level partner's own sexual tensions.[9]

As emphasized many times previously, the individual or combined interests of psychiatrists, psychologists, medical specialists, marriage counselors, social workers, and clergymen may be needed to solve severe problems of sexual incompatibility. However, the advice of the initially consulted family physician frequently will be the most important step in relief of marital sexual maladjustments. The physician's forthright guidance and initial reassurance, whether he refers his patients to other professionals or treats them himself, provide the best foundation for the solution of problems of sexually incompatible marriages.

REFERENCES

1. Eisenbud, J., "A Psychiatrist Looks at the Report," in *Problems of Social Behavior,* New York: Social Hygiene Association, 1948, pp. 20–27.
2. Masters, W. H., "The Sexual Response Cycle of the Human Female: I. Gross Anatomic Considerations." *West. J. Surg.,* 68: 57–72, 1960.
3. Masters, W. H., "The Sexual Response Cycle of the Human Female: II. Vaginal Lubrication." *Ann. New York Acad. Sc.,* 83: 301–317, 1959.
4. Masters, W. H., and Johnson, V. E., "The Physiology of Vaginal Reproductive Function." *West J. Surg.,* 69: 105–120, 1961.
5. Masters, W. H., and Johnson, V. E., "The Sexual Response Cycle of the Human Female: III. The Clitoris: Anatomic and Clinical Considerations." *West. J. Surg.,* 70: 248–257, 1962.
6. Masters, W. H., and Johnson, V. E., "The Sexual Response Cycle of the Human Male: I. Gross Anatomic Considerations." *West J. Surg.,* 71: 85–95, 1963.
7. Johnson, V. E., and Masters, W. H., "Treatment of the Sexually Incompatible Family Unit." *Minnesota Med.,* 44: 466–471, 1961.
8. Johnson, V. E., and Masters, W. H., "Sexual Incompatibility: Diagnosis and Treatment," in Charles W. Lloyd, ed., *Human Reproduction and Sexual Behavior.* Philadelphia: Lea & Febiger, 1964, pp. 474–489.
9. Johnson, V. E., and Masters, W. H., "A Team Approach to the Rapid Diagnosis and Treatment of Sexual Incompatibility." *Pac. Med. & Surg.* (formerly *West. J. Surg.*), 72: 371–375, 1964.

CAN SPECIFIC TRAINING PROCEDURES OVERCOME SEXUAL INADEQUACY?

Donald W. Hastings, M.D.

Editors' note: Only a line, not a wall, separates the psychological from the physiological. The notion that there are some purely physical diseases that physicians can treat by purely physical means, and some psychiatric conditions that psychiatrists must treat by purely psychological means, is slowly breaking down. In the following chapter Dr. Hastings presents the view that forms of sexual inadequacy that are primarily psychological in origin need not be treated solely by traditional methods of psychotherapy; he describes specific training procedures for three common forms of sexual inadequacy—frigidity, premature ejaculation, and vaginismus (spasmic contraction of the vagina).

Dr. Hastings is professor of psychiatry and chairman of the Department of Psychiatry and Neurology, University of Minnesota Medical School—posts he has held since 1946. He is the author of a book for physicians,

Impotence and Frigidity (1963) and a book for lay readers, *A Doctor Speaks on Sexual Expression in Marriage* (1966), both published by Little, Brown and Company.

It is a strange fact, unique to humans, that at the height of adult vigor a person may be unable to respond sexually. This does not happen, in the absence of physical disease or unnatural environment, in any other species we know of. Then why should humans be affected in this way?

The answer lies, I believe, in the *learning* process. We fail to respond because we have learned not to.

Consider the little girl brought up in a strife-ridden family in which her mother and father often fight and disagree, and never show affection to each other. The little girl thus learns how a woman "should" respond to a man. In her anger the mother frequently remarks that all men are beasts, interested in only one thing from women. The little girl learns that lesson, too. Though she may later think she has grown beyond these early influences, and may be determined *not* to repeat in her marriage the mistakes her parents made, she finds to her surprise that she cannot respond sexually. She feels frustrated herself, and disappoints her husband by her coldness.

At first glance, this girl, with her deep-seated emotional problem, would seem to be a case for the psychotherapist alone. Yet Masters and Johnson would treat her and her husband with specific training techniques (see page 203). How, if the barrier to sexual response lies in the wife's conscious or unconscious attitudes toward men, can such procedures help her? Won't they merely mobilize further hostility and thus make matters worse?

These are questions I propose to explore in this chapter. It is my belief that even though, as Freud taught and as the above oversimplified example illustrates, the roots of frigidity and impotence may lie deep in the past, and deep in the unconscious, quite specific training procedures may play a useful role in the treatment of these conditions.

IMPOTENCE AND FRIGIDITY

Some cases of impotence and frigidity, let me agree at once, have a clear physiological basis. Impotence is a fairly common symptom of diabetes, for example, and is sometimes the first symptom to make its appearance. Thus a test for diabetes should be part of the study of a patient who is continuously impotent under all conditions. The reason why diabetes and impotence occur together is not known—but the impotence usually ends when the diabetes is brought under control.

Morphine, sedative drugs including the barbiturates, excessive alcohol intake, and some of the tranquilizers affect sexual response unfavorably; and some authorities hold that cigarette smoking harms potency. Numerous men have reported an upsurge in sexual interest after they stop smoking.

But in the vast majority of cases, it is quite easy to prove that the roots of impotence are psychological. The hallmark of psychological impotence is a man's inability to attain an erection under some circumstances—but to demonstrate full potency under others. He may be sexually quite capable with prostitutes, for example, but not with women he considers respectable, including his wife. Or he may be quite capable with his wife, but find himself impotent when attempting to consummate an extramarital affair. He may attain erection during masturbation but not when he attempts relations with a woman.

There are many variations around this theme; but the diagnostic lesson is always the same: if a man is capable of attaining erection under *any* circumstance, whatever it may be, it follows logically that there is nothing wrong with his erectile apparatus, and that the roots of his problem are inherently psychological.

A few of the psychological causes for impotence and frigidity are so common that general statements about them are possible.

Impotence of Inexperience

It is common for the healthy young male at the outset of his sexual life to be troubled with temporary impotence or premature ejaculation until he has gained experience. One frequently hears the adult patient describe the difficulty he had during the first month or two of marriage or during premarital attempts. With the gathering of experience, the problem gradually diminishes and finally disappears. In effect, he has embarked on a period of self-training, and it has proved successful.

Frequently the young man will have a firm erection just before and just after attempting intercourse but not during the attempt. If there is a ready explanation, it is most likely a feeling of ineptness, a fear of hurting the girl, an inability to reconcile the loved female with sexual passion, feelings of guilt or wrongdoing, a fear of pregnancy, or any combination of these. For a while it may induce the "fear of fear" phenomenon. If the male has a few failures, he may come to have serious misgivings about his potency; subsequent sexual trials may be approached with a dread of failure. The determination to prove his masculinity, combined with inner doubts that he can, does not provide the ideal setting for sexual success.

Impotence Only with a Wife

Although there can be numerous emotional causes behind this phenomenon, the most frequent in my clinical experience has been deep-seated feelings of hostility and resentment toward his wife on the part of a moderately passive husband. In this setting impotence is a symptom of a troubled marriage, and the treatment focus has to be on the marriage and the relationship between the partners.

Sexual withholding is a frequent hostile act in a disrupted marriage. It is a particularly powerful weapon against the husband or wife who has relatively high sexual drives and equally high moral or ethical bars to extramarital contacts, masturbation, or other sexual outlets. This person is "trapped." Mounting resentment and anger often result in symptoms ranging from insomnia, bitterness and irritability, and mild depression to psychosomatic disturbance. Often it gives rise to fantasied death wishes against the withholder, which in turn can produce feelings of guilt for entertaining such violent ideas.

An interesting and tragic variation of this type was described in 1912 by Freud. As is characteristic of this group, the man loves his wife dearly and yet is impotent with her but not with certain other females. Freud pointed out that in the emotional development of the boy, the affectionate (love) feelings toward the female figure (mother) are much older than the sensual feelings of sexuality arising at puberty. If the newer sensual feelings become attached to incestuous fantasies, the result will always be total impotence, Freud felt. In other words, male sexual maturity requires that the older affectionate (love) feelings be freed from the (forbidden) mother and fused with the newer sensual feelings and that both then be attached to the new love object (wife). Freud felt that the degree of fusion determined the degree of potency in the male. Referring to degrees of incomplete fusion, he said, "Where such men love, they have no desire and when they desire, they cannot love. They seek out objects (i.e., women) they need not love. As soon as the sexual object fulfills the condition of being degraded, sensual feeling can have free play."

This particular condition of impotence is relatively common. In the face of an affectionate attachment to his wife, the husband is often capable of erections before and after the attempt. Genital union with her is forbidden by forces of which he is unaware. On the other hand, he is not at all impotent with downgraded women to whom he need form no affectionate attachment, for example, prostitutes. This condition—impotence in the face of a love relation between husband and wife—is a cruel tragedy for both. It is almost the rule in these situations that the wife comes to feel that she does not have the power to arouse her husband and regards herself at fault. If it becomes known to her that her husband is potent with a prostitute, it creates a condition beyond her understanding; nor does the husband understand it any better. Wives caught in this web may attempt, in the privacy of the home, to imitate their concepts of a prostitute (in dress, speech, coarse actions, and the like) in the hope of arousing their husbands. As a rule none of this helps as long as the husband retains his affectionate attachment to her. Treatment of this kind of impotence invariably requires intensive psychiatric help.

Other Forms of Psychological Impotence

In some situations the erection may disappear before orgasm and ejaculation due to various reasons. In its simplest form, it may occur because the vagina is too "loose" as a result of child bearing and does not furnish sufficient "grip" on the penis. (A relatively simple vaginal repair procedure can usually correct this condition.) At the psychological level, this type of impotence may relate to feelings of guilt, fear of discovery, fear of pregnancy, and the like. For example, it is a common observation that the male, engaged in intercourse, may quickly lose his erection if he hears noises that indicate a possible invasion of privacy. Another cause of this type of failure occurs if the male feels that his partner is unresponsive and uninterested. A casual remark on the part of the wife during coitus—for example about a household problem—often will cause erection to vanish by making the male aware that his wife's mind is elsewhere. Consistently felt attitudes of this sort may cause a male either to cease making approaches to his wife, or to be impotent when he does.

When it is apparent that impotence (and frigidity, too) is the symptom of a disturbed relationship between husband and wife, *little if anything will be gained unless an attempt is made to treat this marriage by helping both partners toward a better adjustment to each other.* Here, an attempt to treat one partner would be as futile as attempting to treat the pain of appendicitis without removing the appendix, the seat of the trouble.

Frigidity

By and large, frigidity is to the female what impotence is to the male; most of the things said about impotence are basically no different when applied to the female. In particular, it is nonsense to look for a physiological cause of frigidity if it occurs under one set of circumstances but not under others.

A wife, like a husband, may be frigid with a spouse but

not with other partners—or with another man but not with
her husband. She may be frigid with men but may attain
orgasm with masturbation or during sexual dreaming, and
so on.

The establishment of the circumstances under which a
specific instance occurs is of critical importance, and such
questions as the following must therefore be tactfully but
precisely asked:

(1) Has the woman achieved orgasm? Under what circumstances?

(2) Can she achieve orgasm by means of masturbation?

(3) Under what circumstances does she experience sexual
arousal?

(4) Has she achieved orgasm with a sexual partner other
than her husband?

(5) Does she notice sexual arousal in dreams or fantasy
during the day? Upon reading erotic literature? On
seeing suggestive movies? Etc.

(6) Do arousal and orgasm occur under any other circumstances?

(7) What are her usual responses during arousal and
genital union?

In the event that a "frigid" woman achieves arousal and
orgasm under any of the circumstances mentioned, it follows
that she possesses the physical potential for orgasmic response.

Typical is the case of the woman who before marriage was
able to achieve orgasm fairly easily during masturbation but
who has rarely, if ever, achieved orgasm with marital coitus.
Another fairly frequent pattern (in my patient group) is
demonstrated by the woman who had fairly consistent orgasmic response with her fiancé during their engagement, but
who lost this ability in the months or years after marriage.
This situation almost invariably points to nonsexual marital
problems which have arisen between the partners subsequent
to marriage.

The solution for such problems is clearly marriage counseling or psychotherapy or both. In its simplest terms, this means
that the physician and the patient propose to explore together

the psychological factors and attitudes that have entered into the formation of the symptoms.

Intellectual understanding of the causes, although an essential first step, is not enough. After reaching an *understanding* of why he is impotent, for example, it still remains for the male patient to tackle the larger task of applying this new-found knowledge to his feelings, attitudes, and conduct—a longer, harder job, and one which often involves knotty decisions.

TRAINING PROCEDURES

While I, in common with other psychiatrists, believe in psychotherapy, use it in my psychiatric practice, and teach it to medical and psychiatric students, this does not mean that I or other psychiatrists must reject other types of treatment—even for conditions that are clearly psychological in origin.

A simple example is a training procedure that some women find helpful in overcoming frigidity. Its purpose is to lower the threshold of erotic response. The woman initiates her arousal pattern in her own home by reading stimulating literature or by some other arousing activity, and then proceeds to stimulate her genital area manually in her own way to the point of orgasm (even though at first this may require a prolonged period of stimulation). On the next occasion she repeats the procedure, attempting, by close concentration, to shorten the stimulus time to orgasm. Having accomplished the desired lowering of her threshold response by repeated sessions of self-stimulation, she may then enlist her husband's cooperation to accomplish the same end by supplying her with the manual stimulation himself. The final step is the attempt, once mutual confidence has been established, to achieve the same result with coitus. Once the desired response pattern has been achieved through this technique of progressive training, it apparently tends to remain stable. This training procedure appears to be of material help to some women suffering from frigidity—*even though the roots of the frigidity may lie far back in the psychological experiences of childhood.*[1]

By similar methods some women who have previously experienced only a single orgasm report the ability to "train" themselves to multiple orgasms, first by self-stimulation and subsequently by coitus. As soon as clitoral sensitivity following the first orgasm has faded, the woman promptly resumes genital stimulation to the second orgasm, and so on.

Training has also helped in overcoming another barrier to sexual satisfaction in coitus—a condition called *vaginismus,* which is a spasm of the muscles surrounding the vagina and its entrance. This is not a conscious female response but a reflex response—much like the tight blink of the eyelids at a threatening motion toward the eyes. There are many degrees of vaginismus, including an extremely painful spasm so tight that even the lubricated tip of the physician's finger cannot be introduced into the vagina.

Regardless of the causes of vaginismus—at least some of them no doubt psychological—there is a very simple treatment. The woman is taught to dilate her own vaginal orifice gently and repeatedly, either with her fingers or with a lubricated cylinder.[2]

A useful training procedure for men who experience premature ejaculation was reported in 1955 by Dr. James H. Semans of the Duke University School of Medicine. It is the most successful therapy known for overcoming this form of sexual inadequacy. In brief, the man (or his wife) stimulates the penis until the first warning feelings of impending orgasm are noticed. Every adult male is familiar with these sensations a few seconds before ejaculation starts. When the first sensation is noticed, stimulation of the penis is stopped immediately and abruptly. The sensation disappears and the ejaculation does not occur. The erection may or may not go down; it doesn't matter. Ten or fifteen minutes later the same procedure is repeated. Repetitions three or four times a night (or day) for three or four days running have proved highly

---

[1] I take no credit for discovering this kind of training. I learned it from married women patients who had discovered it for themselves.
[2] For details, see J. F. Oliven's *Sexual Hygiene and Pathology.* Philadelphia: J. P. Lippincott, 1955.

successful in abolishing the premature ejaculation pattern. The patient and his wife can be assured that no harm will result if the stimulation is not stopped quite in time so that ejaculation occurs; they simply wait until the man is able to have an erection again—perhaps a few hours later—and then try again.

Against this background, it seems to me, the therapeutic methods of Masters and Johnson in treating various forms of frigidity and impotence can be more readily understood and accepted. They use a number of training procedures—including their own modification of the Semans procedure for premature ejaculation described above.

No training procedure, so far as I know, has as yet been published for the treatment of impotence—the inability of a man to achieve or to maintain an erection. Masters and Johnson, however, are said to have such a procedure, which is to be described in their next book.

OBJECTIONS TO THE TRAINING PROCEDURES

Some of my psychiatric colleagues, I am sure—and many lay readers as well—will be shocked and contemptuous of this seemingly superficial, do-it-yourself approach to such deep-seated conditions as frigidity and premature ejaculation. And there is some validity in the objections that can be raised to it. Let me review them briefly.

First, it is said that such a training procedure does not get to the root of the problem; it only succeeds in "charming away the symptoms."

One answer to this objection can best be stated in the form of a counter-question: Would you rather be a neurotic wife who is left frustrated and "hanging in the air" following coitus, or a neurotic wife who experiences orgasm in coitus with her husband? Would you rather be a neurotic husband who ejaculates prematurely or a neurotic one who has freed himself of that particular problem?

But there is another answer of greater weight, both theoretically and practically. The typical adult who comes to psychotherapy is not suffering from one traumatic early experience from which all his subsequent problems stem directly. Rather, a series of emotional stresses evokes distressing symptoms, which in turn add to his emotional pressure, evoking further symptoms or further exacerbating his initial symptoms, and so on. The vicious cycle is familiar to every psychotherapist. Frigidity, impotence, and premature ejaculation are three of the most crushing symptoms, producing the most widespread distress and contributing enormously to the viciousness of the cycle. Relieving these symptoms can thus be a significant contribution toward curbing the basic neurotic pattern.

A second objection to retraining procedures such as the ones I have described is raised both by psychiatrists and by laymen. The purpose and effect of the procedure to overcome some forms of frigidity is to teach a woman to attain orgasm. But orgasm is not the goal of life, nor the goal of interpersonal relationships. It should not, according to this view, be the goal of therapy.

Let me agree at once that it should not be the only goal, and that in many cases it should not be the major goal. But surely orgasm is one of the joys of life. The man or woman who learns to experience orgasm is to that extent better off than he was before. I see no reason why helping a patient to achieve orgasm—either through traditional psychotherapy, or through training procedures, or both—is not one worthy goal of therapy, among many others. This is especially true if sexual inadequacy is the presenting symptom that brings the patient to therapy, or if it turns out to be a central factor in the patient's anxiety as the therapy proceeds.

Finally, some lay readers and perhaps even some professionals will reject this form of therapy on the ground that the training procedures I have described often involve masturbation. In fact, there are many patients who will firmly reject any procedure that is or seems to be masturbatory.

Actually there are probably few other human responses as poorly understood as masturbation. In our society it is the most frequently used outlet for the relief of sexual tension when sexual intercourse is not available or possible—especially for men, but for women as well. It is so common that the adult, male or female, who reports that he has never masturbated is exceptional, and may be atypical in other sexual responses as well.

Yet false ideas about masturbation, and old wives' tales concerning the damage it causes, while inherited from past generations are far from eradicated today. Many people still feel that it is morally wrong and even physically or mentally harmful.

The medical profession itself must share a good deal of the responsibility for these fearful attitudes. In the past many well-known physicians, holding professorships in leading medical schools, made statements—based mostly on the unsupported opinion of other eminent but uninformed "authorities" —that masturbation if done at all or if done to "excess" could cause not only many organic diseases but insanity as well. Ignorant of the fact that almost everybody masturbated, they convinced themselves of its harmfulness when they found that insane persons or persons with other diseases masturbated; and they regarded it as an evil to be ruthlessly stamped out. Articles in the older literature even went so far as to advocate the following procedures for correcting female masturbation: amputation or cautery of the clitoris, restraining devices such as straitjackets to make the genitals inaccessible to the hands, miniature chastity belts, sewing the vaginal lips together to put the clitoris out of reach, and even castration by surgical removal of the ovaries.[3]

Today it seems incredible that anyone, particularly a physician, could have been so misguided. The acceptance of such kinds of treatment indicates the strength of the attitude toward masturbation held in those days. Physicians, however, were reflecting the attitude of the times.

Modern studies show that masturbation does not produce physical damage of any kind. The old ideas turned out to be false when subjected to scientific scrutiny. Healthy, intelligent, emotionally mature, happily married men and women have just about the same masturbation history as the "horrible examples" cited in earlier literature. (Indeed, Kinsey found that the men and women in his sample who had made the best sexual adjustment in marriage had a history on the average of *more* masturbation than others.)

---

[3] It is of interest to note that there are no references in the medical literature to surgical removal of testicles or amputation of the penis to stop masturbation. One wonders what heroic measures might have been proposed for boys if women instead of men had composed the medical profession of the time.

Nevertheless, echoes of the old fears and taboos are still heard. Most of the men who participated in the Masters-Johnson research program, for example, reported their conviction that "excessive" masturbation is harmful. Each one attributed his own immunity from harm to the fact that "excessive masturbation" must be a little more frequent than his own personal frequency.

Because of these surviving attitudes, some men and women will reject training procedures of the kind I have described if they are offered prematurely or tactlessly. Exploring a patient's attitudes toward masturbation and his or her residual fears should therefore be a preliminary to prescribing training procedures, and the patient's confidence in the therapist should be firmly established. If the resistance is strong, the physician then has his choice between deciding that training procedures are inappropriate in this case, or seeking in the course of psychotherapy to modify the resistance.

PSYCHOTHERAPY AND TRAINING

Though I do not regard training procedures as a panacea for all forms of sexual inadequacy in all patients, still, I see no reason whatever why a firm belief in the psychological *origins* of sexual inadequacy should not go hand in hand with the acceptance of training procedures as a useful form of therapy.[4]

---

[4] The converse is also true, of course. As Dr. Lief points out elsewhere (page 278), Masters and Johnson, for example, use psychotherapy along with their training procedures.

The rationale for such procedures in treating conditions of psychological origin seems to me quite clear. It is identical with the rationale for psychotherapy. The little girl who learned from her mother to reject and draw back from men can learn in psychotherapy to be more accepting. The little boy who learned in his relationship with his mother to be afraid of his own intense emotional responses to respectable women can learn to be afraid no longer. During training procedures, similarly, a woman can learn that the approach of a man is not a threatening occasion for which vaginismus is the appropriate response; or a man who wants to enjoy normal coitus can learn not to ejaculate prematurely. Both psychotherapy and training procedures are in effect learning procedures for the patient, and both have their place as methods of approach for the psychiatrist.

The relief of frigidity or premature ejaculation is a dramatic demonstration to the patient of the effectiveness of the therapeutic relationship, and may thus open the door to psychotherapy. Patients previously inaccessible may become not only accessible to psychotherapeutic procedures but in some cases eager to tackle their other life problems in a therapeutic setting. (Dr. Emily Mudd cites an example on page 243.) Thus training procedures are in some cases a preliminary to psychotherapy, and in others an important stage of psychotherapy itself.

Since a more detailed presentation of the Masters-Johnson therapeutic approach is promised for 1967, we should then be able to judge, on their own merits, the procedures to be described. Do they work? If they do, I see no reason why any psychiatrist, no matter how firmly convinced of the psychological origins of sexual inadequacy, should not make use of them.

If a training procedure merely enabled a man or woman to reach a satisfying orgasm or series of orgasms through masturbation, some physicians might well conclude that the goal was not worth their time and effort. But this is *not* the goal of training therapy. Having once learned to experience orgasm during the training procedure, the patient is freed to integrate it into his or her total response in the sexual relationship, and the relationship is itself thereby enriched and drained of much anxiety. It is not necessary to abandon the emotional rewards of a warm interpersonal relationship, or to sacrifice the values already imbedded in a marriage, or to abandon all the romance that bring a man and woman together in order t embark on a program of training for sexual response. On th contrary, these and other values a man and woman share ca in many cases be transfigured by the addition of this furthe opportunity for sharing.[5]

---

[5] A hallmark of the Masters-Johnson pattern of therapy is the involve ment of four people—a husband-and-wife team of patients plus a male female team of therapists—in a "therapeutic foursome" (see page 209) The use of this pattern in prescribing training procedures as well as in other respects seems sufficiently promising so that we, at the University of Minnesota Department of Psychiatry, are beginning to try it out.

My colleague Dr. Titus Bellville, who has had postgraduate training in both obstetrics and gynecology and in psychiatry, is seeing patients with his wife—who is a college graduate but holds no professional degree.

Dr. Bellville sees many potential advantages to this procedure. It may prove possible to add substantially to the marriage-counseling resources of our country, for example, by giving suitable training to selected wives of medical students. A wife so trained can consult with her physician husband on cases she herself is handling, and the two can see couples jointly as co-therapists where indicated.

It is still too early to say anything about the success or failure of the Bellville study. But it is not too early to suggest that medical and psychiatric centers launch other imaginative small-scale studies along such pioneering lines.

SEX PROBLEMS IN MARRIAGE COUNSELING

Emily H. Mudd, Ph.D.

Editors' note: As a pioneer in marriage counseling, and as director since 1936 of the Marriage Council of Philadelphia, Dr. Mudd here draws on her long experience to consider the role of sexual problems in the total pattern of marital stress.

Dr. Mudd is professor of family study in the Department of Psychiatry, University of Pennsylvania Medical School, a past president of the American Association of Marriage Counselors, and the author or editor of several books on marriage counseling and marital problems, including *Success in Family Living,* written with Howard E. Mitchell and Sara B. Taubin and published in 1965 by Association Press. She was a consulting editor to Dr. Kinsey in the preparation of *Sexual Behavior in the Human Female,* and is a director of the Sex Information and Education Council of the U.S.

The case histories in this chapter were initially pre-

pared for an unpublished paper by Dr. Mudd and the
late Katherine von Minckwitz.

Of what use is sex research? Can it in fact be applied to
help solve the specific problems of married couples? Does the
kind of information secured in the Masters-Johnson laboratory
have any relevance to the day-to-day conflicts of family
life?

The next few years should provide reliable answers. For
every day in the year, countless husbands, wives, and couples
are taking their problems to their friends and relatives, to
their priests, ministers, rabbis, to physicians, clinical psychologists, social workers, lawyers, and other professionals. They
turn for help to members of the American Association of
Marriage Counselors and to the family service agencies that
provide marriage counseling services. Many professional
counselors are already familiar with the Masters-Johnson
findings, and many more will become familiar with them
during the months ahead. Thus the Masters-Johnson research
will encounter direct clinical challenge as counselors draw
on it in the course of their daily work.

What kinds of sex problems do clients bring to marriage
counselors? Classification is difficult, as each client presents
the precipitating problem in a different way. In this chapter,
I shall use six case histories to illustrate the vast range of
problems and then consider the impact of detailed knowledge
of sexual physiology on the masses of cases these six illustrate.

The six cases selected all came from the files of the
Marriage Council of Philadelphia, an agency affiliated with
the Division of Family Study, Department of Psychiatry, at
the University of Pennsylvania. Founded in 1932, it is among
the oldest American counseling agencies. To avoid bias, the
cases have *not* been selected with the Masters-Johnson research in mind. On the contrary, they were selected some
years ago to illustrate sex problems in marriage counseling
generally, and the many ways in which sex problems are
interwoven with other kinds of problems.

An introductory word about the philosophy of marriage
counseling may prove helpful. In nontechnical terms, counseling can be thought of as *the process of helping someone
(hopefully, the engaged or married couple), to come to grips
with any difficult phase of adjustment in their interpersonal
relations*. It is usually fairly *short-term* help. Many clients,

in fact, can obtain what they want in a series of six to t◦
visits. "There is no logic," Franz Alexander has pointed o◦
"in assuming that only a misfortune can have a permane◦
effect on one's personality. A single, equally intensive, bene◦
cent experience can also leave its mark." [1] A counseli◦
interview is designed to be such an experience. Often a seri◦
of interviews may extend over a period of weeks or montl◦
but rarely over years.

With respect to sexual problems, the counselor's usual g◦
is to help a client recognize his own and his partner's re◦
feelings about sex, their relation to reliable information, a◦
to the sexual capacities of both individuals. Often t◦
involves accommodations by each partner, and an acceptan◦
of the impact of the cultural pattern in which each partn◦
was raised. In addition to encouraging accommodatio◦
acceptance and understanding, however, counseling may al◦
significantly *modify* sexual attitudes and behavior, as t◦
cases below will illustrate.

Dr. Abraham Maslow of Brandeis University has introduc◦
the concept of "self-actualizing people," which I find usef◦
in counseling. Self-actualizing people have both *the power*◦
love and *the ability to be loved*. They can love freely a◦
easily and naturally, without getting wound up in conflic◦
or threats or inhibitions, and they can find intense e◦
joyment in their sexuality. Few of the clients who cor◦
to marriage counselors are self-actualizing in this sens◦
There is evidence that some of them come at least a lit◦
closer to the Maslow concept at the conclusion of couns◦
ing.

The six cases that were selected fall under four maj◦
headings:

(1) *Difficulties in sex adjustment which reflect inadequ◦*
information. Frequently there are couples who are having◦
difficult time early in marriage with respect to sex, or coupl◦
whose marriages were at first so satisfying in other wa◦
that they are just now beginning to feel that their sexual l◦
is not all it should be, or older couples who have failed◦
understand the natural changes in sex needs felt by both m◦
and women as they age physiologically. In many such cas◦
where the overall relationship between husband and wife◦
sound, additional information may, by affecting sexual at◦
tudes, profoundly affect marital satisfactions.

---

[1] For complete bibliographical reference, see page 250.

Mr. and Mrs. A are a case in point. Mrs. A reported to a Marriage Council of Philadelphia counselor, after her initial application interview, that she had been "very happy in every way" except that she "didn't react normally to sex no matter how patient and careful her cooperative husband was." Both partners had as a result become highly apprehensive and disturbed, feeling that Mrs. A was "one of these frigid women you hear so much about in the books."

A few questions from the counselor and answers from Mrs. A revealed that she was easily capable of experiencing full and complete orgasm following digital stimulation of her clitoris. Both she and Mr. A, however, felt that this was *abnormal*. Her orgasm, they felt, *should* take place in the "right" position (man above, woman on back with legs straight). And they felt that Mr. A's ejaculation should "end the intercourse."

An explanation from the counselor of the physiology of orgasm indicated clearly to Mrs. A that clitoral stimulation by some means was almost always essential to attain full female orgasmic response. Authorities were cited who stated that a wide variety of methods of stimulation were in common use and within the "normal" range. Present teachings, she was told, indicate that any method acceptable and helpful to both partners is suitable to them. This mention of variation made it possible to explain easily that a number of positions are used by many couples, and that attitudes of experimentation, spontaneity, and playfulness produce variety and refreshment. It was stressed that sexual sharing can be fun and relaxing—a spiritual as well as physically creative act.

Mrs. A was astonished. Relieved from unnecessary guilt and literally bursting with new ideas, she could hardly wait to tell her husband. She made another appointment for two weeks ahead "because you have helped me so much." A letter received before appointment time told the counselor it would not be necessary for her to come in again as "everything was simply wonderful and all it should be. We feel as if we had entered a new world and that we owe it to you."

(2) *Sex difficulties as part of a total marital difficulty.* Frequently couples with sexual problems come to the Marriage Council with questions about divorce or separation. It is only when they begin to consider what they might do to make a go of their marriage that the sexual component of their problem is brought up for discussion.

Mrs. B, for example, was referred to the Marriage Council by her physician because of her complaint that she had not had sexual satisfaction during the twelve years of her marriage and now no longer had "any use for it." As Mrs. B and the counselor talked about her situation it developed that Mrs. B had sought help in the sexual area because her husband had told her he would have legal grounds for divorcing her and gaining custody of their three children if she continued to refuse his sexual demands. Mrs. B's feelings about sex were further complicated by the fact that her marriage had been entered into in the first place only because she was pregnant and thought she had no alternative.

As Mrs. B and the counselor explored these areas together, Mrs. B began to see her situation more clearly. The focus of her need for help changed; she now wanted help around a decision about a divorce.

Mrs. B came in for a second interview, during which she decided that she had long since passed the point where she was able to put anything more into any area of her marriage. Divorce, she decided, was the solution she wished to consider. In additional interviews Mr. B also was seen, and the couple was helped to explore as constructively as possible the various steps necessary to begin divorce proceedings. The couple was referred to reliable legal assistance.

Often clients themselves recognize that the sexual part of their marriage is not a thing apart but rather just one area among many which reflect the difficulties they are having in their total marital relationship. In these cases, as the client begins to work out the other difficulties, the sexual difficulties often work out too, without special counseling in the sexual area.

Mrs. C, for example, came to us for help in deciding whether to get a divorce. She did not mention sexual problems until she and her counselor were discussing a printed schedule, used only during interviews, on which a number of questions were asked, including "Do you want help with your sexual adjustment?" She replied quite simply that she did not feel that would be necessary, for if she could work out other matters with her husband, she was sure *that* would take care of itself.

Mrs. C, it later developed, had not had intercourse with her husband for five years, though before that she had always experienced orgasm. Her husband, she reported, was as overbearing in that as in other matters. She had refused to continue intercourse because of the psychic pain that his attitude caused her.

Both partners came in and worked on the general aspects of their relationship; and at the end of a series of interviews there was a shift in their general behavior toward each other. Almost casually, during her last interview, Mrs. C told the counselor that she and her husband were sharing the same bed again, and had been having coitus frequently for several weeks. "Mr. C is much more *friendly* in bed," Mrs. C commented with an air of satisfaction.

(3) *Sexual problems regarded as the focus of marital difficulty.* "Our life is perfect in every other way." Often the marriage counselor hears this comment on sexual maladjustment, but almost always further exploration reveals that it is mistaken. The client has ignored maladjustment in many other areas of the marriage, and has transferred his or her disturbed feelings to the sexual part of the relationship. Sex used in this manner can be the deadliest of all weapons. In many of these cases, the other partner responds in kind—with the result that the marriage becomes in reality a bitter duel.

The D's are an illustration. Mr. D was referred to the Marriage Council of Philadelphia by his physician; he was very much disturbed because he had become increasingly incapable of carrying the sex act to completion. For the last six months, indeed, he had been practically impotent. As a result his wife seemed even more unresponsive and tense; this further enhanced Mr. D's anxiety. He had been treated during this period by two urologists, but his symptoms had remained. His fear that his condition might be permanent was affecting his work as well as his family relationships. "I am badly hit," he reported, "scared to death."

Because Mr. D's fear was so acutely focused on his sexual problem, the early interviews were spent in discussing this and in checking the Marriage Council schedule on sexual adjustment. It soon became apparent that in spite of his college education, Mr. D had a really abysmal ignorance of female sexual anatomy, physiology, and psychology. He had never heard of most of the organs involved in female orgasmic response. He had no notion of how to arouse his wife sexually. As the sexual items on the printed schedule were reviewed, Mr. D came rapidly to the realization of how inept and unimaginative he had been, and he seemed relieved and hopeful at the new possibilities the data sheet opened up. The importance of gaining his wife's cooperation was stressed by the counselor.

Mrs. D came in for her first appointment a few days later. She was very tearful and upset and expressed considerable resentment toward her husband "for not letting her start a baby until after five years of marriage." She complained that his job took them from town to town, and that the repeated moving made her feel isolated and uncongenial. All this had its effect in the sexual area, of course. As she put it, "If you are antagonistic, you can't give yourself."

At his next interview, Mr. D reported he had been able to have intercourse with his wife the night after his last visit. And after his wife's visit to the counselor, "they had had the most beautiful time they had ever had." Mrs. D verified this later. "I didn't let myself go before," she stated, "because I thought there would be no satisfaction and that would only make it harder for me. I now feel so much more relaxed and better. I see it reflected in my child."

Subsequent interviews—six for Mr. D, four for Mrs. D—enabled each of them to discuss former relationships with their parents and with friends, as well as their experiences with and attitudes toward sex as they were growing up. These discussions, which allowed the expression of many and varied feelings, helped them to perceive their own and each other's needs more realistically, and to meet their *present* situation more understandingly and freely. As some of their intense anxiety and fear about their sexual problems waned, they were able to communicate and to work on other aspects of their relationship.

Eleven months after his last counseling interview, Mr. D again sought help. He no longer had sexual problems; indeed, he reported that "our sexual adjustment is excellent." Both partners, it appeared, were achieving complete satisfaction, and Mr. D was particularly pleased that he was able to continue the sex act for fifteen or twenty minutes after entrance. Mrs. D, too, had regained much of her old sparkle. But something else had now come to the surface. During an earlier interview, the counselor had brought up the question of *fear*. Mr. D had not thought much about fear before, but now he felt it was having a definite effect on other things in his life. He had just been offered a challenging new job—and he was afraid. "The whole business of this sexual adjustment," he explained, "has been so amazing to me and so completely successful that it makes me feel like going at this fear question and doing something about it." Mr. D was able to accept psychiatric referral for this help in another field, and to complete a series of eight psychiatric interviews.

(4) *Complex problems.* Often a marital problem is neither purely sexual nor purely nonsexual, but a complex amalgam of disturbed interpersonal relationships, lack of adequate sex information, and ignorance of sexual technique. Once tensions in other areas have been relaxed or resolved to some degree, the client may be freed to ask for and respond to information and suggestions about sexual problems.

Mr. E, a college graduate, had been married over eight years when he came to the Marriage Council because "he had agreed with his wife that he ought to talk to someone." He himself focused his concern on his inability to find a congenial job. He had earnestly tried a number of different fields and was about to change jobs again. His wife had been so upset at his last shift that she had sought psychiatric help for more than six months. A period of military service, including war separation and the uncertainties of his military assignment, had added to the anxieties of both Mr. and Mrs. E.

Over a period of two months Mr. E was seen weekly. He discussed with the counselor his feelings about jobs, his relationship to his father and mother, his difference in background and life philosophy from his wife, his admiration for his wife's abilities, his children, their meaning to him and his wife. He came back throughout to the ways in which he disappointed and irritated his wife. He felt that the "sore spots" which caused the worst family conflicts were his irresponsibility about keeping commitments at the times scheduled, his deep feeling about wasting anything, and his wife's spending what seemed to him excessive amounts on clothing and household effects. In particular, he felt that his passivity and general easy-goingness irritated his wife.

In the sixth interview, Mr. E described a very recent episode in which his wife had completely lost her temper and struck him. He admitted being scared by the intensity of her feeling, but he could not answer her back. In the seventh interview he quoted his wife as saying what bothered her most was his taking her attack "sitting down." He was then able to tell his wife he would "spank her good and hard if she ever hit him again," which made them both laugh. Up to this point, Mr. E had not discussed sexual problems.

When he did come to sex, his presentation reflected his general lack of assurance and aggressiveness, and his wife's control and domination. Mrs. E, he reported, had never achieved orgasm. Her lack of enjoyment, and her rejection and criticism of him had made Mr. E almost unable to perform and hardly able to enjoy intercourse.

Further discussion of this, and of its probable connection with his general relationship with Mrs. E, seemed to have great significance to Mr. E. Instead of repeating his great admiration for his wife's abilities and rehearsing his own shortcomings, he was now able to express a great deal of negative feeling toward her, and fear.

At this stage, too, it appeared that neither Mr. nor Mrs. E understood even the simple fundamentals of female or male sexual physiology or response. He was able to get definite information from the counselor and supplement it by reading pamphlets and books from the Marriage Council circulating library—and to put this new information to constructive use with his wife. He was also able to persuade his wife to come in for an interview with the counselor.

Mrs. E had three interviews, oriented around her "anger" and the couple's sexual problem. She was able to use these interviews to obtain information and to reorient her attitude toward sex and her role as a marriage partner.

Following his wife's first visit, Mr. E reported, in his last interview, happy experimentation with mutual response and satisfaction for both. In his own words, "talking is much more helpful than books. Books give you something, counseling something else. By necessity written material must be general enough to cover a wide range of possibilities whereas individual differences cannot be discussed. On the other hand, a counselor who knows this subject can say where the individual fits into the general picture and help them with their specific problem."

Mrs. E put it this way in her last interview: "It is amazing what a difference the books and the conferences here make. This approach of having a good time in the process of sexual relations is quite new to me. I used to think it just a business to get through with. Actually, I find my feeling against the whole business of sex quite changed by being mentally prepared. All this has released a lot of energy for my husband. His new knowledge gives him confidence. It opens a new world to us both which he is initiating me into. I have had complete orgasm several times and really enjoyed it."

One further example of a complex cluster of problems, sexual and seemingly nonsexual, will round out this review of cases. The F's came to the Marriage Council because of their concern over the deterioration of their sexual relationship. Mr. F wrote initially to inquire about the fee "for diagnosis" of his wife, who he stated was "frigid." He added he did not feel anything could be done to help her. Later Mrs. F came in for an appointment. Her attitude was, "Well, here I am; change me if you can!" She used the printed schedule of sexual items to prove to the counselor that she couldn't do anything the way she was. She complained bitterly about her husband's sexual behavior; but when she was asked if Mr. F acted in the same sort of way in other areas of their life, she tearfully assured the counselor that their marriage was ideal in every other respect.

The counselor, in offering the possibility of another appointment to continue their discussion, shared with Mrs. F her feeling of doubt as to Mrs. F's ability to use the service. So far as the counselor could see, Mrs. F was leaving the interview just about as she was when she came in. "But I've gotten a lot," Mrs. F herself insisted. "I now know that I want to do something about my condition."

Mrs. F then shifted ground. She told the counselor that her problem was actually physical. She said that she had been examined by a doctor a few years previously, and she quoted him as saying that she was so fashioned physically that it would be impossible for her ever to get sexual satisfaction. Though it seemed obvious that a large part of her difficulty was psychological, the counselor accepted Mrs. F's own definition of her problem and agreed it would be foolish for her to come to the Marriage Council if she felt her "frigidity" was due to physical reasons. They finally worked out that Mrs. F should have another physical examination. Since her own physician had died, she was referred to another doctor.

Mrs. F saw him. The examination showed that she was anatomically normal; but her vitality was so depleted that medical treatment seemed indicated. After medical treatment was started Mrs. F began to show a slight interest in sex; and she now persuaded her husband to come to the Marriage Council to discuss *his* sexual behavior.

During the first interview, the counselor helped Mr. F to talk about his other marital difficulties. He described their early married life as reasonably satisfactory in all areas until he was dismissed from a job that not only paid fairly well but also gave his family prestige in the community. This last meant much to Mrs. F because she had come from an underprivileged family herself. Then, as Mr. F's income dwindled with each succeeding job and as their position in the community declined, Mrs. F's interest in sex decreased to the point where any sexual advance from her husband was more than she could bear. They had not had intercourse for over a year now.

After several interviews, Mr. F began to see a possible connection between these two problems! He responded to it as to a fresh revelation and made arrangements to come in for more interviews to see if he could work out his relationship with his wife. Of his own accord he undertook to tell her what he had "learned," and to ask her to come in to discuss the same thing with the counselor.

Mr. F spent most of his subsequent interview time discussing the various jobs he had held during his marriage, his disappointment that Mrs. F was dissatisfied with him, and his deep personal need to feel that his work would improve the world. Then he began to feel that maybe in the long run he could help the world more if he did the most he could do to help his own family.

He now began to have an increasing awareness of the difficulties their meager income made for Mrs. F. He wanted to know, in turn, how he could get his wife to be more understanding of *his* problems. With much encouragement from the counselor Mr. F began to talk over his plans with his wife *while* he was making them rather than after they had been put into effect. Mr. and Mrs. F discussed his salary and decided together that he should ask for a raise—an unusual form of interaction in this family. He did ask, and both of the F's were most pleased at the increase he was given, not only because of the extra money but also because it showed the value his employer placed on his services.

During this time, Mrs. F also came in and with the counselor's help began to accept the fact that her husband would never be more than a modest provider. She also became more sympathetic with his desire to make a contribution to humanity's welfare.

As their attitudes toward one another began to change, there was some discussion of sexual problems. The counselor made suggestions as to technique. They had resumed intercourse after the wife's second interview, and their sex relations steadily improved thereafter. They both felt that their life together was happier than it had been at any time in the eight years they had been married.

Mrs. F had not yet achieved orgasm; but neither she nor

Mr. F was concerned about that since they were both getting much enjoyment from sex. At this point they felt that they were ready to stop coming to the Marriage Council. A report several months later indicated that Mrs. F's health had improved (she had continued her "doctoring"), that her interest in sex had increased, and that she was "very pleased about it."

From this almost random selection of case histories, several generalizations clearly emerge.

First, neither the Masters-Johnson research nor earlier work in this field can provide a panacea for all the problems of modern marriage. Sexual inadequacies are an important part of marital maladjustment, but they are far from the whole story.

Second, there are instances in which sexual information by itself can work a notable improvement. The prudery and misinformation with which our culture has for generations surrounded sex may in these cases prevent an otherwise well-related couple from achieving sexual fulfillment; and knowledge is a cure for ignorance. Because of the increasing availability of such information in books, pamphlets, and in the mass media, more people have more adequate information than a decade ago.

Third, there are cases in which a couple is unable to use sexual information initially because of maladjustment in other areas. As counseling proceeds, however, sexual information—including precise discussion of sexual techniques—may, by relieving anxieties and guilt, prove of enormous significance at the appropriate stage in the counseling process. In this process the attitudes and atmosphere represented by the counselor are of the utmost importance. Often the counselor is perceived by the client as an authority figure in the culture. Here then is another human being, a father or mother substitute, who can empathize with the conflicts and inhibitions of the client, who indicates that it is constructive and permissible to experiment with sexual activity desired but long repressed. This relationship, together with new ideas based on reliable information, makes first steps in new approaches possible and supports their continuation.

Fourth, the above may prove true even in cases where it seems clear that the sexual problem is only incidental, or is secondary to broader disturbances in the marital relationship.

Fifth, an urgent need for the data with which Dr. Masters

and Mrs. Johnson have supplied us is the need *among counselors themselves*. The blind cannot lead the blind. An effective marriage counselor needs much more than knowledge, of course; but he needs all the knowledge he can get. Just as the two major Kinsey reports have proved of enormous value to counselors through the past decade or more, so I am confident that the Masters-Johnson findings, including their clinical research in marital sexual adjustment, will prove of continuous value through the decade ahead in helping counselors to help their clients.

Finally, it is to be hoped that as the Masters-Johnson findings seep down in various ways from the professional to the nonprofessional level they will have a directly beneficial effect on the majority of citizens. There will always be some whose religious or cultural inhibitions and prejudices will motivate them to reject novel approaches to intimate areas of man's behavior. These men and women may be unable to accept the constructive potentials for human welfare resulting from research and study when they find the methods unacceptable. In spite of such attitudes toward the discovery of new facts, exploration into the unknown will, I am confident, continue in all areas of man's behavior. No one who has not engaged in marriage counseling can believe the abysmal ignorance of various aspects of sex which can still be found among certain intelligent, literate people, and the amount of widespread pseudo-sophisticated misinformation which is responsible for much human misery and disintegration. "Books give you something, counseling something else." The Masters-Johnson work should prove helpful at both levels.

BIBLIOGRAPHY

Alexander, F. and French, T. M., *Psychoanalytic Therapy.* New York: Ronald Press, 1946.

Erikson, Erik H., "Identity and the Life Cycle," *Psychological Issues,* Vol. I, No. 1, Monograph 1. New York: International Universities Press, 1959.

Goodwin, H. G. and Mudd, E. H., "Indications for Marriage Counseling, Methods and Goals," *Comprehensive Psychiatry,* August 1966, in press.

Kinsey, A. C., Pomeroy, W. B., and Martin, C. E., *Sexual Behavior in the Human Male.* Philadelphia: W. B. Saunders Company, 1948; Kinsey, Pomeroy, Martin, and Gebhard, P. H., *Sexual Behavior in the Human Female.* Philadelphia: W. B. Saunders Company, 1953.

Maslow, A. H., *Motivation and Personality.* New York: Harper & Row, 1954.

Masters, W. H. and Johnson, V. E., see chapter in present volume, pages 203–219.

Mudd, E. H., Stein, M., and Mitchell, H. E., "Paired Reports of Sexual Behavior of Husbands and Wives in Conflicted Marriages," II, No. 3, June 1961, pp. 149–156.

SEX AFTER FORTY—AND AFTER SEVENTY

Isadore Rubin, Ph.D.

Editors' note: Dr. Rubin speaks with authority on the sexual problems of the aging and aged. He is the author of *Sexual Life After Sixty* (Basic Books, 1965), editor of *Sexology* magazine, treasurer of the Sex Information and Education Council of the U.S., a fellow of the Society for the Scientific Study of Sex, and a member of the American Association of Marriage Counselors, the National Council on Family Relations, and the American Social Health Association.

SMASHING A DANGEROUS STEREOTYPE

One of the major contributions of Dr. William H. Masters and Mrs. Virginia E. Johnson has been their detailed laboratory study of the sexual responses of older persons. Their work helps fill the gaps in medical knowledge and clinical experience. It helps break the conspiracy of silence about

sexuality in the later years. And it helps destroy the stereotype of "sexless old age," which has done such serious harm
to the health and happiness of the aging. Masters and Johnson, it is true, did find important physiological changes in
sex response occurring as the years go by. But their major
conclusions are unequivocal: "There is no time limit drawn
by the advancing years to female sexuality"; and for the male,
too, there is, under favorable physical and emotional conditions, "a capacity for sexual performance that frequently may
extend beyond the eighty-year age level."

These conclusions are supported by the findings of a growing
body of research by other investigators.

In the past, the failure of society to recognize the sexual
needs of older people was serious, but not critical. Today,
when more than twenty-five million of our population have
reached the age of sixty—a figure that is expected to mount
to over thirty-one million by 1975—society can hardly afford
to maintain the false myths about sexlessness in these years.
In the early 1960's, over thirty-five thousand marriages a year
took place in which at least one of the partners was sixty-five
or older.

These myths are not limited to the years after sixty,
although they take much greater hold in these years. For
women who are not emotionally prepared for it, the end of
menstruation may be a traumatic event. For many of them
menstruation has been a badge of femininity and a symbol of
youth. As long as it continues they may feel they are still
young and attractive in spite of the changes that have taken
place over the years. When menstruation ends, writes gynecologist Howard A. Novell, "a woman suddenly has the
mirror of life thrust at her and she takes a long, agonizing
look and begins a period of marked introspection and usually
faulty reappraisal of herself." It is at this vulnerable time in
her life that all the folklore related to the menopause comes
to bear on some women with great force. One idea is that
after the change of life a woman loses her sexual desire
and is less capable of functioning sexually than before.
This myth, of course, has no anatomical or physiological
basis.

Every counselor who deals in any way with sex problems
can report many cases of marriages that were brought to the
point of disaster because one partner had suddenly decided
that the couple was "too old for sex." "I am fifty-eight years
old and my wife is fifty-five," wrote one husband to the physician conducting the question and answer column of *Sexology*

magazine. "Until about three years ago our sexual life was quite normal, but since that time (contrary to my desires) my wife has not permitted intercourse. Her apathy is even greater since her change of life a year and a half ago. She says I am too old to be so 'foolish' concerning sexual relations and that nobody at this age has sexual desires." "My wife and I are over sixty-five years old but we still like to have sexual intercourse very much," another husband wrote. "Please give us advice in this case. What should we do?"

These examples indicate how older people—unsure about their roles in a new stage of life for which they have been little prepared—reflect the popular ignorance about sexuality. Such attitudes require the authority of the physician to correct them and to dispel the guilt that older couples may have about sexual needs and desires. All too often in the past, however, the physician has had the same ignorance about sex in the later years and has reflected the same guilt feelings about sex. In too many cases an older patient who has sought advice from a physician about waning sex ability and responsiveness is greeted merely with evasive laughter—or with the question, "What do you expect at your age?"

If these attitudes affected only the sex life of older persons, they would still be serious enough. However, they go far beyond this to strike at the whole self-image of the older man and woman, complicating and distorting all their interpersonal reactions in marriage. They have serious effects on the diagnosis of many medical and psychological problems and upon the administration of justice to older persons accused of sex offenses. Not least of all, they have unfortunate effects on the relationships of children and parents thinking of remarriage; the reaction of too many children is, "They ought to know better."

Today, with the benefit of the Masters-Johnson research— added to the surveys of behavior in the later years by the Kinsey investigators, by Drs. Gustave Newman and Claude R. Nichols at Duke University, by urologists at the University of California School of Medicine at San Francisco, by Dr. Joseph T. Freeman in Philadelphia, by *Sexology* magazine, and others—there is no longer any reason for anyone to continue to believe that sex, love, and marriage are the exclusive privileges of youth. The research has clearly established that—under the proper physical and emotional conditions— the capacity to enjoy sex is not lost in the later years but simply slows down gradually, along with other physical capacities.

THE RESEARCH EVIDENCE

A number of other investigators have surveyed the sexual behavior of older persons. Masters and Johnson were the first actually to observe the anatomy and physiology of their sexual response under laboratory conditions. Included in this part of the study were sixty-one menopausal and postmenopausal women (ages forty to seventy-eight) and thirty-nine men (ages fifty-one to eighty-nine). Obviously, these numbers were not large enough to provide biological data of statistical significance and further studies will be required, but they furnished important preliminary information.

When the orgasmic cycles of the women of this group were studied, Masters and Johnson found that generally the intensity of physiologic reaction, and the rapidity and duration of anatomic response to sexual stimulation were reduced with advancing years through all phases of the sexual cycle. That is, the sex flush was more limited and restricted in the older women, there was less lubrication, there was delay in reaction of the clitoris to direct stimulation, reduction of duration in orgasm time, etc. However, they emphasized, they did find "significant sexual capacity and effective sexual performance" in these older women. "The aging human female," they concluded, "is fully capable of sexual performance at orgasmic response levels, particularly if she is exposed to regularity of effective sexual stimulation." They added that there seems to be no physiologic reason why the frequency of sexual expression found satisfactory for the younger woman should not be carried over into the years after the menopause, with no time limit drawn by the advancing years.

As in the female, Masters and Johnson found that in men after fifty the intensity and duration of physical responses during the orgasmic cycle are lessened; particularly after sixty, erection takes much longer, ejaculation lacks the same force and duration, the sex flush is markedly reduced, etc. "There is no question," they state, "that the human male's sexual responsiveness wanes as he ages." However, they add, when regularity of sexual expression is maintained in a sexually stimulative climate within the marriage, a healthy male capacity for sexual expression could extend beyond the seventies and the eighty-year age level.

Masters' and Johnson's findings that sexual activity continues—though on a reduced scale—into advanced old age in many persons is well substantiated by other research as is their finding that there is no basis for any physiological effect of menopause on frequency of intercourse for women.

In the Kinsey studies the investigators also found little evidence of any aging in the sexual capacities of women. "Over the years," they reported, "most females become less inhibited and develop an interest in sexual relations which they may then maintain until they are in their fifties or even sixties." In their later years, sexual activity of course depends to a large extent on the desires and capacities of their husbands, who would generally average three or four years older. The responses of the average husband, in contrast to the average wife, drop with age. Thus, many of the younger women reported that they did not wish to have intercourse as often as their husbands, but in the later years of marriage many of the women expressed the desire to have intercourse more often than their husbands.

As far as males were concerned, the Kinsey investigators did find evidence of a weakening of sexual response with age. Morning erections, for example, which had averaged 4.9 per week in the early years, had dropped to an average of 1.8 at sixty-five and to 0.9 per week at age seventy-five. However, for most males they found that there was no point at which old age suddenly enters the picture. One white male was still averaging seven ejaculations each week at the age of seventy, and an eighty-eight-year-old man and his ninety-year-old wife still continued their sexual life.

In 1959 a group of urologists at the University of California Medical Center at San Francisco reported on their study of 101 men who had come as patients to their outpatient clinics. There was a general decline with age, but sixty-five percent of the men under seventy were still capable of sexual relations. Of the males over seventy, one third of the number were still potent.

In 1960 a report was made by Drs. Gustave Newman and Claude R. Nichols of an investigation into the sexual activity of 250 persons living in the Piedmont area of North Carolina ranging in age from sixty to ninety-three years of age. The found, out of the 149 persons still married and living with their husbands or wives, that more than half were still sexually active (54 percent). They concluded that "given the conditions of reasonably good health and partners who are physically healthy, elderly persons continue to be sexually active into their seventh, eighth and ninth decades."

This same general finding was reported by Dr. Joseph T. Freeman, who among other things found that by the age of eighty a number of men studied still reported no cessation of desire and some were still potent. Drs. L. M. Bowers, R. R. Cross, Jr. and F. A. Lloyd, who studied veterans applying for a pension, reached the same conclusion.

One of the largest surveys was conducted by *Sexology* magazine, which mailed questionnaires to men over sixty-five who had attained enough eminence in various fields to be listed in *Who's Who in America*. More than eight hundred men answered the series of questions. Of the married men who still had partners, over 70 percent indicated that they still engaged with some regularity in sexual intercourse, most with general satisfaction. Even in the group of 104 men aged seventy-five to ninety-two, almost one-half reported that intercourse was still satisfactory, and six engaged in coitus on the average of about eight times a month.

One interesting survey on the attitudes of women toward the menopause was conducted by Dr. Bernice L. Neugarten and her colleagues of the Committee on Human Development at the University of Chicago. They found that among the women who had not yet gone through the menopause there was a great deal of uncertainty about how the menopause would affect their sex lives, with the youngest group disagreeing most with the view that menopausal women may experience an upsurge of sexual impulse. "I was afraid we couldn't have sexual relations after the menopause," said one woman, "and my husband thought so, too." However, in the group of women who were between the ages of fifty-five and sixty-five, 21 percent of them felt that "after the menopause, a woman is more interested in sex than before."

It should be noted that none of these studies involved a sufficiently large or sufficiently representative group of men or women for the figures to be typical of the average older man or woman. However, all of them do confirm the Masters and Johnson findings that there is no particular stage of life or age that represents a cut-off point for sexual desire, response or ability, even though age does reduce the strength of sexual response.

THE IMPORTANCE OF REGULARITY

One of the points that Masters and Johnson keep emphasizing in their discussion of the factors necessary for maintaining sexual capacity and effective sexual performance is regularity of sexual performance. This, they say, is essential for both males and females.

As a result of lowered hormone production in the female in the later years, thinning of the vaginal walls and reduced lubrication make intercourse uncomfortable and even painful. However, three women past sixty years of age were repeatedly observed to expand and lubricate the vagina effectively despite obvious senile thinning of the vaginal walls and shrinking of the major labia. These women had maintained regular intercourse once or twice a week for their entire adult lives. On the other hand, women, five to ten years after the end of menstruation, who had intercourse infrequently (once a month or less) and who did not masturbate with regularity had difficulty in accommodating the penis during their rare exposures to intercourse.

Regularity of sexual expression is also the key to sexual responsiveness for the aging male, say Masters and Johnson. With loss of sexual outlet, many aging males report rapid loss of sexual tension and potency. Regularity is important, apparently, not only in the later years but in the earlier years as well.

"The most important factor in the maintenance of effective sexuality for the aging male is consistency of active sexual expression," Masters and Johnson assert. "When the male is stimulated to high sexual output during his formative years and a similar tenor of activity is established for the 31–40-year range, his middle-aged and involutional years usually are marked by constantly recurring physiologic evidence of maintained sexuality. Certainly it is true for the male geriatric sample that those men currently interested in relatively high levels of sexual expression report similar activity levels from their formative years. It does not appear to matter what manner of sexual expression has been employed, as long as high levels of activity were maintained."

This finding, which indicates that there is a close correlation between activity levels in the earlier years and those in the later years, is supported by the findings of the Kinsey research. It does not, of course, prove a cause-and-effect relationship, since it may merely indicate that those with the strongest sex drives had greater sex activity both in the early and later years. But it does effectively demolish one of the great myths about sexual activity that has persisted from ancient days down to the very present—the idea that one can use oneself up sexually and that it is necessary to save oneself for the later years. This myth is connected with the belief that the emission of semen through any kind of sexual activity weakens and debilitates. Many people still believe that each drop of semen emitted in ejaculation is equivalent to the loss of forty drops of blood. Such beliefs are hard to overcome since they go back thousands of years to ancient Chinese, Greek, and Hindu views.

"My husband," writes a woman to a doctor, "has reached the age of sixty-five. He has decided that, in order to ensure a longer life and health, he will no longer engage in sex activity. He is convinced that intercourse and the emission of semen are quite debilitating, particularly in his years." The feeling of this man is not unusual. Dr. Morton M. Golden reported that many of his patients had the distorted notion that males have a limited number of sperm and were convinced that masturbation had used up their supply of sperm cells and energy. "I have seen patients," he wrote, "who deliberately began a program of abstinence in the fourth decade to postpone the inevitable 'catastrophe of old age.'"

Actually, it is well recognized today that the emission of semen is no more of a loss than the expectoration of saliva. Both are quickly replaced by the body.

The notion that one can prolong sex life by being inactive in the earlier years and less active in the older years is particularly contradicted by the findings of the Kinsey group. They found that at age fifty all of the males who had been sexually active in their early adolescence were still sexually capable, with a frequency about 20 percent higher than the males who had begun activity later. "Nearly forty years of maximum activity," they say, "have not yet worn them out physically, physiologically, or psychologically. On the other hand, some of the males (not many), who were late adolescent and who have had five years less of sexual activity, are beginning to drop completely out of the picture; and the rates of this group are definitely lower in these older age periods."

There is no question that other leading sexologists agree with Masters and Johnson on the importance of regularity and consistency in maintaining effective sexual functioning. Professor Tadeusz Bilikiewicz of the Medical Academy of Gdansk, Poland, points out that "the most effective way to secure the longest possible functioning of organs is by letting them work continuously and systematically." Hence, far from advising abstinence for those who wish to preserve sexual life, he concludes that the best advice that specialists in aging can give is: "Try to maintain your intellectual and sexual activities as long as possible."

Dr. John F. Oliven, an authority on sexual functioning, has also emphasized regularity of intercourse. Very often in the older years, the sexual life of a couple is disrupted by a more or less prolonged period of abstinence because of surgery or some health reason. Prolonging the period of abstinence longer than is necessary invites certain dangers to the marriage, Dr. Oliven notes. He suggests to doctors that as a general rule, the greatest possible sexual freedom at the earliest possible time compatible with the remedial program should be allowed, or even encouraged.

Thus, authorities are in agreement with Masters' and Johnson's emphasis on the importance of regular sexual performance in helping maintain effective sexual capacity for both men and women.

THE POSTMENOPAUSAL YEARS

One of the problems faced by women in their postmenopausal years is the loss of estrogen brought about as the ovaries reduce their production of hormones. This loss generally begins to manifest itself about five years after the end of menstruation and is quite evident in most of the women who have reached sixty years of age, although there are many individual exceptions. Masters and Johnson note that, as the woman moves through her postmenopausal years, the lining of the vagina becomes very thin and atrophic. Instead of having the thick, ridged pattern characteristic of the vagina when it is receiving considerable estrogen stimulation, the walls of the vagina become tissue-paper-thin and, therefore, cannot protect the structures lying next to the vagina—the urethra and bladder—by absorbing the mechanical irritation of active intercourse. There is also a shortening of both vaginal length and width and a shrinking of the major labia, leading to constriction of the opening of the vagina.

In addition, once the woman is about five years past the menopause, the rate and amount of lubrication production diminish to an obvious degree. This is not true for all women, since Masters and Johnson observed three women over sixty, one as old as seventy-three, who consistently responded to sexual stimulation with rapid production of lubrication typical of women under thirty. All three of these women had very active sex lives throughout their mature years.

Another result of steroid imbalance is that contractions of the uterus, which take place during orgasm at all age levels, now become painful. For some women these contractions are so painful that they seek to avoid orgasm and even intercourse itself.

As a result of these changes, intercourse during the post-menopausal years may be painful in many ways. Some women find penetration and the friction of intercourse painful. Some complain of a burning on urination, which develops from mechanical irritation of the urethra and bladder because of the thrusting movement of the penis. It is not unusual for many to have an urgent need to urinate immediately after intercourse.

Fortunately, today, it is easily possible to make up for any lack of hormone production in the body with adequate hormone-replacement therapy. In some cases, local application of a simple lubricant between the lips of the vulva will relieve the discomfort entirely. If the tissues are very thin and tender, estrogen creams or suppositories applied locally to the vulva and vagina may restore the tissues to normal layers and cure the discomfort within a week or two. In addition, more and more women are being given general replacement therapy to make up for the loss of hormone production by the ovaries.

However, as Masters and Johnson point out, the effect of

hormone imbalance on sexual adjustment after the menopause is not the major factor. Sexual performance in many cases depends far more on opportunity for regular intercourse and on numerous emotional factors than it does on hormone balance. Many women develop renewed interest in their husbands and have described a "second honeymoon" during the early fifties as a result of the ending of any fear of pregnancy. In addition, women beyond the years of fifty have resolved most of the problems connected with raising a family, and frequently there is a significant increase in their sexual activity. On the other hand, one must not overlook the fact that many women who have never been too happy about sex during most of their lives find in the menopause or in their advancing years a respectable reason for ending a duty that has always been onerous or distasteful to them.

MAINTAINING MALE RESPONSIVENESS

In their clinical work with older males, Masters and Johnson found six general categories of factors which were responsible for loss of sexual responsiveness during the later years: (1) monotony of a repetitious sexual relationship (usually translated into boredom with the wife); (2) preoccupation with career or economic pursuits; (3) mental or physical fatigue; (4) overindulgence in food or drink; (5) physical and mental infirmities of either the man or his wife; and (6) the "fear of failure."

The problem of monotony, which is probably the single most important factor in the loss of an aging male's sexual interest and responsiveness, has been noted by many others besides Masters and Johnson. Kinsey and his colleagues described it as "psychologic fatigue"—the fact that there is just not as much psychological stimulation in an experience that is repeated without too much novelty or variation with the same partner over an extended period of time.

One factor contributing to this boredom may be the occurrence of many physical and psychological changes—some of them due to slovenly habits developed by a wife as she grows older—which may inhibit or destroy sexual interest or response. This was clearly shown by a study made by Dr. A. L. Wolbarst in the middle 1940's when he studied one hundred consecutive cases of older patients who had come for treatment for "impotence." Dr. Wolbarst found that many of the older patients who considered themselves totally impotent reported that they were not impotent with other women, only with their wives. In some of these cases, the husbands were repelled by physical characteristics, some of which could be corrected by diet, plastic surgery, or other means.

Sexual boredom is more likely to take place if the couple—like most persons in our society—have restricted themselves to a mechanical and repetitious sex life, without variety or novelty to bring new stimulation to it; many have done so because of the no longer accepted view that only certain methods of lovemaking are right and proper, while other methods are degrading and illegitimate.

The practical lesson for married couples that want to maintain their sex lives is an obvious one. "From middle age onward," suggests Maxine Davis, "a wife had better take steps to jolt her husband out of his rut, to use her imagination and experience to bring surprise into their sexual activity. . . . Even though she has been content enough to let the sexual relationship rock agreeably along in a uniform pattern for years, it is never too late—or too soon—to open new doors to adventure and romance."

Of course, it would be wrong to place all the responsibility for weakening sexual response on the wife. In many cases, Masters and Johnson reported, men were so preoccupied with their careers that outside interests were all-consuming, becoming a major deterrent to sexual activity in the home, particularly when communication between husband and wife was poor. For some men over fifty strenuous weekend activity, to which they are generally not accustomed, is enough to reduce their sexual responsiveness. More important is mental exhaustion, perhaps resulting from "a bad day at the office" or from occupational, financial, or personal emergencies.

Excessive consumption of either food or drink also has a tendency to repress sexual feelings; Masters and Johnson found that secondary impotence developing in the late forties or early fifties has a greater connection with excessive drinking than with any other single factor.

It is clear that as men age, they have an increasing number of minor, or in some cases major, physical disabilities, each of which may in some way lower sexual responsiveness. When the wife is affected, it may restrict opportunities for sexual intercourse for the husband, often putting an end to sexual life altogether. With the loss of sexual outlet, as we have seen, many aging males report a rapid loss of sexual responsiveness and ability.

Obviously, any acute illness is accepted without question by both husband and wife. However, there are many cases where couples are given inadequate advice by their physicians and as a result unnecessarily abstain from sexual relations out of ignorance or fear. This was dramatically shown by a report given by three heart specialists at the 1964 annual convention of the American College of Cardiology. These physicians questioned a number of men who had had heart attacks, asking them about their sexual activity after the attacks. The heart attacks had occurred from one to nine years before the interviews. The physicians found that only about a third of these men resumed their normal pattern of sexual activity, and that 10 percent had become completely impotent.

The most significant thing about these results is this: the pattern of sexual activity following the heart attack had *no relation* either to the age of the men or to the severity of the attack. It depended entirely on the attitudes of the men involved. Practically none of the men had received from his physician any detailed and specific advice about sexual activity. One third of the men reported that their doctors had given them only vague advice about sexual intercourse. The other two thirds had received no guidance at all. As a result, each patient had to make his own decision.

Today, heart specialists recognize that, under their advice, men may engage in sexual intercourse under carefully regulated conditions after heart attacks, and that the tension generated by sexual frustration may be more harmful than the tension generated by sedate and relaxed intercourse. In their laboratory research, Masters and Johnson checked heart, blood pressure, and pulse rates of males and females during intercourse, and hope to provide in the near future more complete data to guide physicians in their treatment of heart patients.

Dr. Alex L. Finkle and his colleagues at the University of California Medical Center at San Francisco have also pointed to the responsibility of the physician in contributing to the impotence of males who have undergone prostate surgery in the older years. After most types of prostate surgery, sexual ability is present in many of those males who were capable prior to the surgery. Sometimes, however, the attitude of the physician may help suppress sexual activity, or the physician may even cause impotence by predicting it.

Few factors play as important a part in bringing about impotence as does the fear of failure. A temporary loss of desire or a temporary failure of potency may occur at any age. In the earlier years, however, a temporary failure may be taken more or less in stride, although even here it may strike quite a blow at the male ego. When it occurs in the later years, when a certain decline has already occurred, it may convince the male that "this is it"—that he has reached the end of his sex life. When he embarks on subsequent sexual trials—determined to succeed, but beginning to doubt whether he can—the atmosphere is not conducive to success. Often, after a period of this uncertainty and fear, he may stop attempting intercourse at all because he "knows" he will fail. He often comes to regard himself as totally impotent, feeling that his situation is next to hopeless. Yet it has been demonstrated that once the fear has been overcome, the situation is far from hopeless.

Invariably, the attention of men who consider themselves impotent turns to such possible solutions as hormones, aphrodisiacs, and, as a final resort, artificial devices to satisfy their wives.

It is still a controversial question as to whether or not males go through a physiological readjustment comparable with the female climacteric, or menopause, when there is a sharp decline in the production of hormones. The output of the male hormone (androgen) declines steadily but very slowly in most men until they reach the age of sixty, and remains relatively constant thereafter. Even among octogenarians, individuals with urinary excretion of hormones within the normal range of young adults have been found.

However, some men do show signs and symptoms so similar to the female's that they have been regarded by many physicians as experiencing a climacteric, usually about ten to fifteen years later than in women. One of the symptoms of this may be a sudden *increase* in sexuality—caused by the fear of a loss of potency and the need of the male to demonstrate to himself that he is "still the man he once was."

Where androgen deficiency exists in aging males, administration of sex hormone may help to restore sexual interest and ability. However, Masters and Johnson note their clinical impression that the obvious elevation of eroticism that may occur after the administration of hormones is not a direct effect of steroid replacement, but rather a secondary result of the obvious improvement in total body economy and of a renewed sense of well-being.

Also, one cannot discount the effect of the power of suggestion, as is clearly demonstrated by this story. When the synthetic male sex hormone testosterone was first introduced at the Johns Hopkins Hospital in Baltimore, a fifty-five-year-old technician observed the remarkable improvement that often seemed to occur and asked the doctors to give him an injection in order to help him revive his waning sexual power. After he got the injection, he reported to the hospital in high spirits convinced that his youthful vigor had been restored. Each time he requested an injection thereafter, he was given one of sterile oil, taken from a bottle labeled "testosterone." On each occasion, the technician happily reported that the results of the later injections were just as effective as the first.

This power of suggestion operates in the case of many foods and drinks that have traditionally been described as aphrodisiacs. Their effect is purely psychological, but since sexual functioning has so great a psychological component, they all seem to be quite effective.

There is another group of so-called aphrodisiacs that operate in a different manner. Some of them—like herbs and spices—may irritate the lining of the genital and urinary tract as they are being voided; the irritation may produce sensations resembling sexual arousal, bringing about a vague genital urge and a reflex erection. Some substances—like the famous irritant *cantharides*, known popularly as "Spanish fly"—are powerful corrosive poisons, which can cause serious destruction of tissue and sometimes death.

According to the Kinsey investigators, "good health, sufficient exercise, and plenty of sleep still remain the most effective of the aphrodisiacs known to man."

Judging from the requests that many doctors doing sex counseling receive, there is a wide demand for mechanical

evices to aid the aging and impotent male. These devices
ake many forms, including extensions, splints, suction de-
ices, and clasps. Unfortunately, so little attention has been
aid to these devices by the medical profession that few
octors have enough experience to offer a well-qualified opin-
on. Those who have had experience report that in a few
ases reasonable satisfaction has been obtained, but that in
ost cases the device was soon discarded because the male
ad so little sensation from it and the wife so often found
unromantic or ridiculed it. One leading marriage coun-
elor has pointed out that a simple rubber band placed around
ne base of the penis has helped maintain an erection and has
een less objectionable than expensive devices.

One final word should be said about the man or woman
who does not have an available partner but still has sexual
eeds. Most persons are accustomed to think of masturbation
s a childish activity which is outgrown once the individual
eaches adulthood. Actually, every study of older people has
hown that large numbers of them engage in masturbation
s an alternative method of gaining release from sexual ten-
ion, though some of them feel disturbed because they feel
nere is something wrong for persons of their age to engage
a this practice. "It is to be hoped," said Lester W. Dearborn,
pioneering marriage counselor, "that those interested in the
eld of geriatrics will take into consideration the sexual needs
f the aging and encourage them to accept masturbation as a
erfectly valid outlet when there is a need and other means of
ratification are not available."

SEX EDUCATION FOR YOUNG PEOPLE—
AND FOR THEIR PARENTS
AND TEACHERS

Mary S. Calderone, M.D.

Editors' note: After serving for eleven years as medical director of Planned Parenthood–World Population, Dr. Calderone in May 1964 joined with five colleagues to found the Sex Information and Education Council of the U.S. (SIECUS) and become its executive director. The SIECUS purpose is "to establish man's sexuality as a health entity." Its board now includes representatives from the fields of public health, religion, family life education, sociology, psychiatry, obstetrics, education, law, home economics, and communications, and it is concerned with sex education from the preschool through the graduate school and in adult life. The following chapter by Dr. Calderone was drawn in part from a talk she gave at the Second North American Conference on Church and Family, called by the National and Canadian Councils of Churches of Christ, held at McMaster University, Hamilton, Ontario, Canada, in June 1966.

The Masters-Johnson report on human sexual response

poses a fresh problem to those of us concerned with sex education: Should this significant new information be incorporated into our total sex education program? If so, how should it be done?

Before answering in specific terms, let me outline briefly some of the points I think a sex education program should include.

First, I agree wholeheartedly with Father John L. Thomas, S.J., a member of the board of SIECUS, when he states:

> There seems to be an emerging consensus that we need to develop a more adequate understanding of man's sexuality in its human wholeness and totality. Sex is indeed such a fundamental dimension of human existence, by reason of its connection both with man's desire for personal fulfillment and happiness and his consequent need to establish satisfactory relationships with others, that we cannot long avoid clarifying our stance in its regard. . . . The quality of being "sexed" has profound implications for men and women. It is one element in this totality and the social environment within which the individual develops.

Next, I believe that sex education should be a part of *all* education—in the home, in the school, and in the churches and synagogues, from the nursery-school level through college and adult education programs. It is never too early to begin, and it is never too late to fill the gaps and correct the errors left by earlier miseducation or lack of education.

Sex education, as a matter of fact, begins long before nursery school—in the first warm mother-infant contacts following birth. Professor Harry F. Harlow of the University of Wisconsin has described what happens to infant monkeys in their later sexual development if they are deprived of these first essential learning experiences. Harlow brought up monkeys in total isolation from their mothers and from other monkeys. As "mother substitutes" they had only wire frames with nursing nipples attached. At maturity these monkeys were utterly disorganized sexually—unable to engage in intercourse or even to assume coital positions. Their behavior might be described as schizophrenic.

However, if the wire frames were covered with some soft material, such as fur or terry cloth, to which the infant monkeys could cling and against which they could cuddle, their subsequent sexual disorganization as adults was somewhat less severe. If, in addition, the baby monkeys were allowed to play and cuddle with one another, then, though far from normal, they could at least mate in the normal way. Since all the monkeys were nourished by bottle in exactly the same way, it seems clear that the difference lay in the need of infant monkeys for body-to-body contact in the critical early stages of life. Their sex education literally began at birth.

The real sex education of the human infant also begins almost at birth. The different ways the child is held by the mother and father, his association with maleness or femaleness through the feel of their muscles, the touch of their skin, their characteristic body odor and the sound of their voices speaking to each other and to him in love and tenderness or rejection and hostility—all these have a powerful effect on the child's sexual conditioning and later sexual feelings and behavior. A parent cannot choose whether to give or not to give sex education; he is giving it involuntarily from moment to moment. Communication may be nonverbal—but the child reads the message loud and clear.

The second stage of sex education, too, begins before nursery school. Dr. John H. Gagnon of the Kinsey Institute at Indiana University has called our attention to this second stage in a brilliant paper entitled "Sexuality and Sexual Learning in the Child," published in *Psychiatry*, August 1965. Dr. Gagnon writes:

> The shock for adults of Freud's discoveries was not that children might be involved in sexual activity, but that this activity was not confined to a few evil children and was, in fact, an essential precursor and component of the development of the character structure of the adult.

Just as depriving a monkey or human infant of normal bodily contact may impair its adult sexual responsiveness, so interference with the normal sexuality of young children during this second stage may have its unfortunate consequences. Yet, as Dr. Gagnon also points out:

> During the 19th century the popular method of dealing with childhood sexuality when it intruded upon adults was either to suppress the behavior or to deny its existence, and to avoid thinking about it at all as long as it was not a public

issue. These methods are to this day the most popular ways of dealing not only with the sexuality of children but also with that of adults.

In other words, we have been very busy pretending that the sexuality of children does not exist when in actuality it is our relegation of it to nonexistence that is the cause of distortions and difficulties in later sexuality.

As with the infant, our preschool and elementary-school children also receive an abundant education in sex without our even knowing it. This education consists of the multitude of impressions and attitudes which the child gleans from the adults around him—and from his contact with radio, television, and the pictures in newspapers and magazines. The lifted eyebrow, the strained look, the slap on the hand when the tiny child touches his genitals, the hushed voices when certain subjects are mentioned, the snickers over sexual jokes—these constitute what many children in our culture have to rely on as they strain to understand this most important part of man's life and their future role in it.

This distorted and inadequate background of sexual understanding is hardly counterbalanced by the one-time effort many parents have to force themselves to make to tell their children "the facts of life." Nor are early misimpressions counterbalanced by the books and phonograph records, supposed to reveal the facts of life painlessly, which so many parents shove at their children—a substitute for flesh-and-blood communication between parents and children that reminds one of Harlow's infant monkeys and their wire-frame "mother substitutes."

The problem throughout this early period, of course, is that *parents have not accepted and understood their own sexuality*.

It is here, I think, that the Masters-Johnson research can have its first beneficial effect on sex education. As their findings become a part of our common culture, parents may thereby become more understanding, and therefore more comfortable in their own sexuality and may thus be able to do a better job during the early formative years of their children's sexuality.

Some teen-agers themselves, interestingly enough, see this point quite clearly. "We should educate the adults for sure," one adolescent boy remarked at a public forum. "It seems to be what they need to be happier. And—face it!—it will speed up the progress of what can be done on the teen-age level."

Next, let us consider what these days is ordinarily called "sex education" in the schools—essentially a little information about where babies come from, plus a little on menstruation for girls, on venereal disease for boys, and perhaps a few related details. Here again, the message we think we are implanting is overwhelmed by all the other messages that get through to the teen-ager and preteen-ager—the blatant use of sex in advertising, for example, and in the tabloid newspapers, magazines, comics, and phonograph records. The result is erotic stimulation unbalanced by sound information.

A report made in 1965 by the Public Health Committee of the New York Academy of Medicine, based on the Bronfman School Health Education Study, makes this point clear:

> Adolescents have received little authentic, useful, and practical information about sex. What little . . . has been available to them has consisted mainly of depersonalized accounts of the physiology of sex and a combination of exhortation and admonition. . . . This gap in sex education is not just on the biological side. Probably no previous generation of adolescents has had such an enormous wealth of scientific information made available to them, yet probably none has been left so ignorant and undisciplined in the ethical essentials.

To close this gap, health educators should accept the obligation to present without further ado the basic factual materials that have to do with human reproduction and human sexual behavior—within a context that clearly delineates at all ages what should be obvious but is in practice little understood by adults themselves: *sexual morality is exactly the same as the morality that should apply in any other human relationship*. There is no need to muddle this issue: morality is a question of how one human being deals responsibly with another human being—whether the two are of the same or different age, sex, religion, race, or nationality. This idea of responsibility can and must be taught in schools.

But *what* should be taught? A program from the first grade through high school should certainly culminate in the mastery by adolescents of such factual components of reproductive biology as the anatomy, physiology, and endocrinology of reproduction, including ovulation and spermatogenesis, fertilization, conception, pregnancy, childbirth, and infertility. The biological basis of fertility control should also be included. In view of religious problems, the details of contraception need not perhaps be included—although young people can certainly read the details almost daily in the public press—unless parents specifically request it.

Genetics and human embryology should lead into the highly important study of child development and nurture, including consideration of the destructive effects of early emotional deprivation. Why shouldn't Harlow's work with unmothered monkeys be a part of every high-school curriculum, when within a few years most of these teen-agers will be parents themselves?

Sexual and mating behavior of animals and humans should also be discussed, including the difficult areas of masturbation, homosexuality, and the psychology and physiology of sexual response. The institution of marriage in society should be thoroughly presented and discussed, and the various factors that currently threaten the family should be identified—including urbanization, depersonalization, social and economic mobility, industrialization, overcrowding, prostitution, abortion, venereal disease, and many more.

If our high-school young people had good grounding along these lines and were helped to discuss these topics openly and objectively, they would not be so devastatingly unready to meet the challenges and freedoms of college and employment, or the problems of service in the armed forces. They would be armed with knowledge and attitudes adequate for sound sexual decision-making. Certainly if we want responsible parenthood we must first teach responsible attitudes toward sex.

But here we come to a major obstacle to a sound program of sex education. Just as few parents are comfortable enough in their own sexuality to play their full role, so few teachers are comfortable enough to teach about sexuality without fear and without embarrassment.

The second major way in which the Masters-Johnson research can be useful is precisely at this point. Dr. Mudd has pointed out in another chapter (see page 249) that the Masters-Johnson report can be of great help to marriage counselors, who themselves must have the facts because "the blind cannot lead the blind." Dr. Lief has similarly pointed out (see page 278) that the report can be helpful to medical students and physicians, making them more comfortable as well as more effective in their diagnostic and therapeutic roles. One hopes that as the Masters-Johnson findings become a part of our common culture, they will also affect the attitudes of our teachers, increasing their confidence and thereby their ability to present sex education clearly, simply, and within its ethical context.

The story is told of a German headmaster named Sprengel who published in 1787 an essay entitled "The Newly Revealed Mystery of Nature in the Structure and Fertilization of Flowers." In it he described quite precisely the sexual nature of reproduction in the higher plants. So shocking was this to his contemporaries that he was dismissed from his teaching post and his book was withdrawn from circulation.

We have come a little way since 1787. Teachers can now talk of stamens and pistils and pollen in the classroom without too much embarrassment or criticism from the public. The Masters-Johnson research, I am convinced, can help society take a giant step toward the day when human sexuality, too, can be openly and freely taught—to the children and young people who need such insight so desperately, and to their parents who need it even more.

TEACHING DOCTORS ABOUT SEX

Harold I. Lief, M.D.

Editors' note: **Dr. Lief** is the author of a number of studies showing (a) that American physicians were inadequately trained in the past to treat patients with sexual problems; and (b) that the physicians of the future are still being inadequately trained by most medical schools today. He has been a leader in the movement to correct this shortcoming in medical education—a movement that is meeting with increasing success as more and more medical schools add sex education to their curricula.

A certified psychoanalyst, Dr. Lief is professor of psychiatry at the Tulane University School of Medicine in New Orleans, and director of the Hutchinson Memorial Psychiatric Clinic there. He was one of the founders of the Sex Information and Education Council of the U.S., and is an active leader in The Academy of Psychoanalysis.

The publication of the Masters-Johnson report on human sexual response marks a turning point in the history of sex research. It will no doubt have many consequences; among the most important may be a notable long-run improvement in the ability of the American physician to help solve the sexual problems of his patients.

For several years I have shared with a growing number of my medical colleagues a concern that the medical profession as a whole is not being adequately trained to deal with sexual problems. We know that almost every conceivable difficulty concerning sexuality is being brought by patients to the physician's office and to clinics—questions concerning the sex education of children and adolescents; questions about masturbation, premarital intercourse, homosexuality; problems raised by out-of-wedlock pregnancies; problems of infertility and contraception; questions asked by the parents of babies born with major or minor sexual anomalies; and, most frequent of all, the problems of sexual inadequacy and sexual incompatibility in marriage. Husbands, wives, and couples bring these and countless other problems to their physicians because they assume that the doctor is an expert.

All too often, he isn't.

To be sure, most physicians know more about the gross anatomy and physiology of the sexual and reproductive organs than the patients who come to them for help. But few know enough—and fewer still have been adequately trained in the practical, clinical management of sexual problems. Worst of all, too many physicians still share with their patients the very misconceptions and misplaced inhibitions that give rise to sexual problems in the first place.[1]

An example will illustrate the point. Among the most firmly established principles in the entire sexual area is the finding that *guilt feelings* about masturbation rather than the *act* of masturbation lead to emotional distress. Yet as late as 1959, a study of medical students graduating from five Philadelphia medical schools revealed that half of them still

---

[1] "Perhaps one reason many physicians have abdicated their role in providing sexual advice is recognition that their knowledge is deficient. Part of the deficiency stems from almost universally inadequate teaching at medical schools, but much of the remainder is a simple acknowledgement of the fact that no one really knew physiological details of what happened to normal men and women during intercourse. How, then, could patients be advised whether or not they were normal?" Editorial, *Journal of the American Medical Association*, July 18, 1966.

thought—after three or four years in medical school—that masturbation itself is a frequent cause of mental illness. Worse yet, a fifth of the medical school faculty members shared the same misconception.

It is hard to see what good can be accomplished when a patient in need of reassurance consults a physician who shares his groundless anxieties.

Aware that something must be done, several medical schools —including my own at Tulane—have introduced courses or lectures on sex problems for medical students. But we quickly discovered that the problem was far more complicated than we initially supposed.

We learned, for example, that applicants for admission to medical school are a select group from the point of view of sexual attitudes, and that those admitted are even more select. The most frequent personality description of medical students given by faculty members goes something like this: "He is a hard worker, extremely conscientious, a little shy and retiring, doesn't let go of his feelings, is somewhat hard to draw out." He is, in short, altogether different from the hero of the usual TV program about young doctors and interns. Often he has had little personal coital experience. He tends to solve his personal sexual problems by methods of "over-control."

In medical school, moreover, most students put aside personal concerns to concentrate on their enormously heavy workload. They carry with them the image of the "good doctor," and try to model themselves on it. This further limits in most cases the direct gratification of their own sexual drives. Many marry in medical school, yet continue to place their training above their marital and parental interests. All this tends to cut them off from the experiences their patients have been having during these same years. None of it prepares them for acting the role of the wise and tolerant counselor when they enter the practice of medicine. Nor are a few lectures on sexual anatomy and physiology enough.

Techniques for improving the preparation of physicians in the sexual area are currently being explored at a number of medical schools. Psychiatric counseling for medical students, interns, residents, and their wives is proving to be one helpful approach. Courses in which small groups of students can explore with a psychiatrist, a gynecologist, and a urologist sexual problems that interest or concern them is another. In such ways as these, student *attitudes* are affected, along with the inculcation of knowledge. Some of us have set as a goal the introduction of such approaches at every medical school in the country by 1970. But progress has been delayed by three major gaps in our facilities.

When other branches of medicine are being taught, a progression from normal physiology to pathology has proved the most effective sequence. Students learn first how the normal heart functions, and then the many ways in which it can malfunction. In the area of sexual response, however, we have had no sure framework of normal anatomy and physiology to present. Now that gap is being plugged. The Masters-Johnson studies are beginning to provide precisely the framework against which sexual variations can be identified and understood by the physician.

A second gap in our medical education programs has been lack of a technique for making young physicians in training as comfortable in the sexual area as in other areas of medicine. If a physician is uncomfortable about sex—if he is even embarrassed, for example, when taking a sexual history—the patient invariably knows it, and the possibility of fruitful therapy or counseling is diminished. Here, too, it seems to me, the Masters-Johnson research is precisely what we have been waiting for. By performing sex research in precisely the spirit in which research on the heart, the lungs, or the kidneys is performed, Masters and Johnson have made it easier for the physician to face sexual problems with the same spirit of "objective concern" he applies to other problems. They have shown that the intimate facts of sexual response can be discussed openly and frankly between doctor and patient, with dignity as well as candor. This is an invaluable lesson for both the medical student and the practitioner.

Finally, those of us concerned with medical education have needed a therapeutic model—an example of how a clinic or a physician in private practice can successfully diagnose and treat the common forms of sexual inadequacy, sexual incompatibility, and sexual frustration.

Since 1959 Masters and Johnson have been engaged in the treatment of patients complaining of these conditions. One novel feature of their approach is that they as a male-female team of therapists treat husband and wife as a patient team. A second feature is their use of retraining procedures—the actual training of husband and wife to use techniques described in detail for achieving mutual sexual satisfaction (see pages 216–218). But, in addition, let me stress that Masters and Johnson simultaneously provide psychotherapy for their patients even if it is not structured and formalized in traditional ways. By their own confidence and openness they reduce their patients' anxiety and shyness. This makes it possible for a husband and wife to talk freely about their problems with the therapists and with each other, and then to do something about them. Once patients feel they have made even a little progress as the result of this combination of psychotherapy and training, they feel encouraged to continue further training. Thus, the underlying psychological factors are of great importance in the total approach of Masters and Johnson, and other physicians as well, to the treatment of sexual inadequacies.

How successful have they been? Here, we must wait for their clinical statistics. Masters and Johnson quite conservatively take the position that therapeutic results cannot be fully evaluated until the effect on patients has been followed up for at least five years.

They now have two-year follow-ups on a substantial number of patients, and five-year results are being accumulated. A further report is promised for 1967. They have presented at medical meetings some preliminary figures, however, and it is fair to say that their record to date is enviable. Their next report, let us hope, will supply the nation's medical schools with the third new implement we need: a concrete example of how, both in private practice and in a clinical setting, the physician can successfully treat the common forms of sexual inadequacy and incompatibility.

Part IV

SEX RESEARCH AND

OUR CULTURE

CURRENT SEXUAL
BEHAVIOR AND ATTITUDES

John Corry

Editors' note: Has American sexual behavior changed since the first two Kinsey reports of 1948 and 1953? Shockingly little is known on this subject. The Kinsey Institute itself is currently concerned with other questions, and the few studies that have been made elsewhere since 1953 are small in scale and mostly concerned with college students or college graduates. This article assembles what little information there is. It is reprinted from *The New York Times* of July 11, 1966, and strongly suggests the need for further studies on a larger scale and with a broader base. Mr. Corry, a member of the *Times* staff, held a Nieman Foundation journalism fellowship at Harvard, 1964–5.

Americans talk more about sex than they did before, but there is little to indicate that they are actually behaving much differently than they did, say thirty-five years ago. For instance, Dr. Alfred C. Kinsey and his associates, who began collecting their information in 1938, said in 1948 that perhaps 20 percent of college girls were not virgins. Subsequent studies indicate that this is still a true figure.

They also indicate that Americans are not experiencing sexual relations at an earlier age than before, that promiscuity is still a high-school, not a college, problem, and that the 1920's, not the 1960's, was the time of the great leap forward in permissive sexual behavior. Nonetheless, there is sexual change, and it deals with attitudes, not behavior. Change is not the Sexual Freedom League, which sells buttons on college campuses that say: "Go Naked." But it is the Sex Information and Education Council of the United States, which says that sexuality involves mental health.

Change is also the proposal by the National Association of Independent Schools that its 760 members give priority to sex education, and it is the courses on marriage and the family that are offered in more than seven hundred colleges. It is the lectures to student doctors that are now given in twenty-nine medical schools, and it is the suggestion by the Minnesota Department of Health that pupils in primary grades learn about the function of fathers and mothers in reproduction. At its most thoughtful, this change deals with sexual activity as a part of sexuality and sexuality as an expression of personality. The new sex education, for example, deals with more than the question of where babies come from.

A member of the board of directors of SIECUS, the sex information council, puts it this way: "Sex education in the best sense today means training people emotionally and intellectually to be able to make intelligent and well-informed choices among an array of competing alternatives."

SIECUS was founded in 1964 because, another director said, "It was time to deal with this sex mess." There are forty-one directors at SIECUS, and they are almost all eminent in medical science, education, religion, or marriage counseling.

In a year, SIECUS had 2,819 requests for aid and information. They were from, among other places, 460 schools, 223 colleges, 298 doctors, 156 church organizations, 254 professional groups, and 95 branches of government. SIECUS answered with reprints, letters, discussion guides and outlines for community sex education programs. Yet, its executive director, Dr. Mary S. Calderone, says: "We, none of us, know[s] enough about sex." John H. Gagnon, a senior trustee at the

Institute for Sex Research at Indiana University, agrees. He deplores the paucity of research about sexual behavior and says that the "image of sexuality today is one of crisis and change." Perhaps there really is crisis, he says, but he is not so sure about change. "We have just discovered statistics," he says, "and now we are discovering ourselves." He also says that the rules on speaking about sex have changed and that because Americans talk more about it they conclude that there is more of it.

"A doctor with a dirty mind, who fits a young woman with a diaphragm, can convince himself that there is a sexual explosion," he says. "He talks to the press in the role of marriage counselor, and then everyone else thinks so, too."

Mr. Gagnon says that the three most written about aspects of sexuality today are premarital relations, homosexuality, and the female orgasm. In his studies, Dr. Kinsey emphasized the orgasm. So do most marriage manuals. Because of this, says Dr. Robert R. Bell of Temple University, author of *Marriage and Family Interaction* and *Premarital Sex in a Changing Society,* too many brides are troubled when they are not carried away in a delirium of joy by one. "They expect the world to observe thirty seconds of silence when it first happens to them," he says.

Mrs. Ethel Nash, president of the American Association of Marriage Counselors, notes the emphasis on the female orgasm this way:

> Twenty-five years ago, married couples visited marriage counselors and talked over their problems, which may or may not have been sexual. Later, wives came and said their husbands were sex maniacs, and what could they do about it? Now husbands come to talk about their wives' inability to have orgasms.

Mrs. Nash says that the question is no longer will she or won't she, but can she or can't she?

Dr. Catherine Chilman of the Department of Health, Education and Welfare says there is a "free-floating anxiety" about sexual perplexities and that "Americans are enchanted with finding new problems." Americans now imagine that there has been a sudden collapse of virtue, Dr. Chilman says. She disagrees with this, and the research supports her.

In *Factors in the Sex Life of Twenty-two Hundred Women,* which was published in 1929, Katherine B. Davis studied women who were in college in the early 1900's and concluded that only 7 per cent had had premarital relations. The real change, sociologists say, came in the 1920's. In particular, it was the generation born between 1900 and 1910 that revolutionized American sexual behavior.

In *Psychological Factors in Marital Happiness,* published in 1938, Lewis M. Terman questioned a sample of 104 women born in the decade before 1890 and found that 86.5 percent were virgins when they were married. For 277 women born between 1890 and 1899 the figure was 74 percent, and for 336 women born between 1900 and 1909 it was 51.2 percent. Mr. Terman concluded from this that the virgin bride would disappear by 1960. He was wrong.

In *Premarital Dating Behavior* in 1959, Winston W. Ehrman said that only 13 percent of a sample of girls eighteen to twenty-two years old at a large coeducational university were not virgins. However, the presence of a larger number of the younger girls in the sample may have lowered the percentage.

The objection that is usually made to surveys of sexual behavior such as these is that it is only the middle class that is being surveyed, usually by middle-class professors. No one is ever quite sure what the very poor are doing, although most studies indicate that there is more permissiveness among them. However, there is also evidence that, as more youths attend college and as affluence spreads, middle-class morality becomes more pervasive.

In the *Merrill-Palmer Quarterly* last year, Mervin B. Freedman, who is now chairman of the psychology department at San Francisco State College, reported on a study at an Eastern women's college. The college, which was not identified, is generally considered advanced. Eighty of its freshmen were selected at random and then periodically were interviewed while they remained in college by four psychologists, a sociologist, and an anthropologist.

Most of the girls were from the upper middle class and about half were from the Middle Atlantic states. Some 70 percent were Protestant, 20 percent were Jewish, and 10 percent were Catholic. Twenty-nine of the girls left in the normal attrition of college years and two of those who remained refused to answer some of the questions they were asked. (The questions concerned family income, not sex. Similarly, some hygiene teachers say they can discuss sex, but not acne, with their students; pimples are too personal.) Of the forty-nine girls remaining in the study, eleven had had sexual relations by the time they were graduated. Eight of the eleven were involved in serious emotional relationships with their partners; three were not. Two of these three girls had relations with two men. None of the eleven expressed remorse.

The survey is consistent with the few other studies of sex and the student: they all say that great guilt does not accompany most premarital relationships, and they all put non-virginity among college women at 20 percent or less. Indeed, the question may be why, amidst otherwise sweeping social change, has the pattern of sexual activity apparently remained intact?

William Simon, another senior trustee at the Institute for Sex Research, suggests that perhaps American youth cannot afford the emotional investment that sex demands. However, Professor Freedman wrote:

> Despite an appearance of worldliness and sophistication, it seems that conservatism, inhibition of impulse, cautiousness and willingness to defer gratification are part and parcel of American middle-class character.

A fair consensus of the psychologists, sociologists, marriage counselors, and other professionals in the field would show a feeling that Americans are developing new sex ethics, but little agreement on what those ethics might be. A few believe that Americans will someday accept what they call permissiveness without affection, which means that sexual relations will be acceptable among consenting adults even when there is no great emotional attachment. More, however, believe that America is moving toward an acceptance of what they call permissiveness with affection, which means that sex will be respectable among unmarried partners when there is mutual affection. They note that a pattern that may be developing among the young is engagement, followed by coitus, followed by marriage. Virtually every study that has been made of sexual behavior says that about half of all engaged couples are having relations. If there is a rise in any category of sexual activity, it is thought to be here.

The sociologists, psychologists, and marriage counselors also say that few youths can express an ethical argument either for or against premarital relations with any great conviction. This does not mean that promiscuity is likely to become rampant. In one survey of 253 unmarried sociology students in Iowa, only 59 percent of those who approved of a premarital relationship actually had experienced one.

In 1960, in *Premarital Sexual Standards in America*, Dr. Ira L. Reiss of the University of Iowa predicted that "the next 50 years, like the last 50 years, will witness an increasing acceptance of person-centered coitus and petting." Increasingly, he said, Americans will accept permissiveness with affection. Dr. Reiss has not changed his views on this. He notes that abstinence has lost its traditional supports, that the risk of pregnancy and venereal disease has lessened and that social condemnation and even guilt feelings are different now. Dr. Kinsey, for example, said that almost 90 percent of the women he interviewed had no real remorse about their premarital sexual behavior.

If a new sex ethic does develop, it may not be restricted by social class. Dr. Kinsey and his associates tended to consider each educational group a separate social class, and they said that less educated girls had intercourse five or six years earlier than girls with high-school or college educations. They also said that, at the age of twenty-five, only 10 percent of the unmarried men with eighth-grade educations had not had relations. For high-school graduates, they said, the figure was 16 percent and for college graduates it was 36 percent.

Dr. Kinsey was studying behavior, not attitudes, but the implication was that a drop-out was likely to feel less restrained about sex than an astrophysicist. However, Dr. Reiss, who has studied attitudes, not behavior, disagrees. In the *American Sociological Review*, he describes a survey of 903 single students and 1,515 adults. The students were from two high schools and three colleges in New York and Virginia. The adults, 80 percent of them unmarried, were chosen by the National Opinion Research Center and represent a national sample.

Dr. Reiss concluded that "people who share generally liberal or conservative attitudes are more likely to share similar attitudes toward sex than are people who merely earn the same salary or have gone to school the same number of years." It is the style of life that determines sexual attitudes, according to Dr. Reiss. What matters is being a fundamentalist or a Unitarian, preferring W. C. Fields to Jerry Lewis, or maybe Garbo to Elizabeth Taylor. "Social class," he writes, "seemed to have no real effect on permissiveness." This is particularly true, he says, in the upper social and economic reaches, "where permissiveness represents an underlying set of attitudes that vary independently of conventional indices of status."

For some, the fact that sex is being analyzed and discussed, that it is, in effect, going public, will rob it of enchantment. This is an area where poets and prudes can be agitated together, and perhaps nothing will agitate them as much as the recently published *Human Sexual Response*, by Dr. William H. Masters, a gynecologist, and Virginia E. Johnson, a psychologist. Before them, medical science had made few attempts to explore the physiology of sex. Freud and even Dr. Kinsey had to rely largely on what their subjects told them, and since the work of Dr. Robert Latou Dickinson, whose *Human Sex Anatomy* first appeared in 1933, little has appeared on the subject.

Mrs. Nash, who is an assistant professor at the Bowman Gray School of Medicine in Winston-Salem, N.C., as well as a marriage counselor, says that one great virtue of the Masters-Johnson research is that it can be used in counseling

> to give people a real feeling of what is happening to them during intercourse. You can tell people they're not abnormal, that here is something they can look for. You can also tell them something about the difference in the frequency desires between men and women when things don't work out. For the merely naive, the book can be used to provide a primer on their own responses.

Dr. Masters and Mrs. Johnson, who are working at the Reproductive Biology Research Foundation in St. Louis, began a clinical program on the treatment of sexual inadequacy in 1959. They have not disclosed their results yet, but they say they are working on it together, using a team approach. They say that, in a marriage where there are problems of sexual inadequacy, both partners are involved, and they insist on complete cooperation from both of them. They coach the wife of the sexually inadequate husband in the physiologic and psychologic aspects of her husband's sexual response and then invite her to join the team. Similarly, a husband with an inadequate wife would be told about the female cycle of response, and then he would join.

This attempt to train someone in coitus is the last word in sexual therapy, and it is certain to be both hailed as the final sexual emancipation and excoriated as the final indignity. It is probably neither one nor the other, and its acceptance or rejection will tell a good deal about American sexual attitudes.

"I'M SORRY, DEAR"

Leslie H. Farber, M.D.

Editors' note: Several attacks on the Masters-Johnson research have appeared. The attack by Dr. Farber reprinted here presents the major accusations voiced by other critics as well: the charge that Masters and Johnson have mechanized and dehumanized sex, that their research volunteers were atypical, that they ignored the psychological components of the sexual experience, that they overemphasize the importance of the female orgasm, and so on. All of these topics are treated from other points of view elsewhere in this volume.

Dr. Farber is a practicing psychoanalyst, a training analyst for the Washington Psychoanalytic Institute, and chairman of the Association of Existential Psychology and Psychiatry of New York. He was formerly chairman of the Washington School of Psychiatry and vice-president of the William Alanson White Psychiatric Foundation. The following chapter is from his book, *The Ways of the Will;* it also appeared in a slightly different version in *Commentary* for November 1964.

And the eyes of them both were opened, and they knew that they were naked; and they sewed fig leaves together, and made themselves aprons.

—Genesis

Lust is more abstract than logic; it seeks (hope triumphing over experience) for some purely sexual, hence purely imaginary, conjunction of an impossible maleness with an impossible femaleness.

—C. S. Lewis[1]

The modern dialogue which furnishes me my title is practiced throughout the Western world. As a theme with only a limited number of variations, it cannot sustain much repetition: familiarity breeds silence; although never really abandoned, the script quickly becomes implicit. When reduced to a dumb show—or perhaps to no more than a monosyllabic token—it still remains faithful to its pathetic premise. However, for the purposes of introduction I shall try to represent its essence in a wholly explicit manner. The man speaks first.

"Did you?"

"Did *you*? You *did*, didn't you?"

"Yes, I'm afraid I—Oh, I'm sorry! I *am* sorry. I know how it makes you feel."

"Oh, don't worry about it. I'm sure I'll quiet down after a while."

"I'm *so* sorry, dearest. Let me help you."

"I'd rather you didn't."

"But, I . . ."

"What good is it when you're just—when you don't really want to? You know perfectly well, if you don't *really* want to, it doesn't work."

"But I *do really* want to! I *want* to! Believe me. It *will* work, you'll see. Only let me!"

"Please, couldn't we just forget it? For now the thing is done, finished. Besides, it's not really that important. My tension always wears off eventually. And anyhow—maybe next time it'll be different."

"Oh, it *will*, I *know* it will. Next time I won't be so tired or so eager. I'll make sure of that. Next time it's going to be *fine!* . . . But about tonight—I'm sorry, dear."

Unhappily, no end to talking and trying for our pathetic lovers. To deaden self-consciousness they may turn to alcohol or sedatives, seeking the animal indifference that is unencumbered with hesitations, reservations, grievances—in short, all those human tangles that create the sexual abyss they will themselves to bridge. To delay his moment, to quicken hers, they may try to assist the chemicals by thinking of other matters—football games and cocktail parties—in order finally to arrive at that mutual consummation which, hopefully, will prove their sufficiency unto each other, if not their love. All the strategies and prescriptions of sexology that have often failed them in the past are not cast aside but stubbornly returned to, if only because in such an impasse there is nothing else. Instead of alcohol or drugs or irrelevant reveries they may—in solitude or mutuality—resort to sex itself as their sedative, intending the first try to spend their energies just enough to dull self-consciousness and thicken their passion to the "spontaneity" necessary for their second and final attempt.

Although normally truthful people, our lovers are continually tempted by deception and simulation: he may try to conceal his moment, she to simulate hers—as they stalk their equalitarian ideal. It can happen that they will achieve simultaneity by means of one or several or none of these devices. But their success—in the midst of their congratulations—will be as dispiriting as their failures. For one thing, the joy the lovers sought in this manner will be either absent or too fictitious to be believed. Furthermore, once the moment has subsided they must reckon with the extraordinary efforts that brought it about—efforts that appear too extraordinary for ordinary day-to-day existence. Thus does it happen that success may bring as much as or more pathos than failure. And always lying between them will be the premise borrowed from romanticism: if they *really* loved each other it would work. Small wonder, then, as self-pity and bitterness accumulate, that their musings—if not their actions—turn to adultery: a heightened situation, which promises freedom from the impingements of ordinary sexual life. Or, pushed gradually past heightening, past hope, they may even come to abstinence, which can seem—with some irony—the least dishonorable course.

My conviction is that over the last fifty years sex has for the most part lost its viability as a human experience. I do not mean there is any danger it will cease to be practiced—that it will be put aside like other Victorian bric-a-brac. The hunger will remain, perhaps even increase, and human beings will continue to couple with as much fervor as they can provoke, even as the human possibilities of sex grow ever more elusive. Such couplings will be poultices after the fact: they will further extend the degradation of sex that has resulted from its ever-increasing bondage to the modern will. To those first pioneers at the turn of the century—sexologists, psychoanalysts, political champions of woman's suffrage—"sexual emancipation" seemed a stirring and optimistic cause. Who could have imagined then, as the battle was just beginning, how ironic victory would be: sex was emancipated, true, but emancipated from all of life—except the will—and subsequently exalted as the measure of existence.

At this point I think it only fair that I commit myself, even if briefly, on how sex was, is, or could be a viable human experience. My view is not that of St. Augustine—that man, by reason of the Fall, is necessarily subject to the lust of concupiscence. Nor can I subscribe, at the other extreme, to the position of the Church of England, as reported at the Lambeth Conference in 1958: "The new freedom of sexuality in our time . . . a gate to a new depth and joy in personal relationship between husband and wife."[2] Of the erotic life Martin Buber has remarked that in no other realm are dialogue and monologue so mingled and opposed. I would agree that any attempt to offer a normative description would have to include precisely such mingling and opposition.

Even if we place it optimally within an ongoing domestic world of affection, in which sex bears some relation, however slight, to procreation, our task is still the difficult one of maintaining that sex is both utterly important and utterly trivial. Sex may be a hallowing and renewing experience, but more often it will be distracting, coercive, playful, frivolous, discouraging, dutiful, even boring. On the one hand it tempts man to omnipotence, while on the other it roughly reminds him of his mortality. Over and oven again it mocks rationality, only to be mocked in turn at the very instant it insists its domain is solely within the senses. Though it promises the suspension of time, no other event so sharply advises us of

[2] Dorothea Krook, *Three Traditions of Moral Thought.* Cambridge: Cambridge University Press, 1959, p. 336.

the oppressiveness of time. Sex offers itself as an alternative world, but when the act is over and the immodesty of this offering is exposed, it is the sheer worldliness of the world we briefly relinquished and must now re-enter that has to be confronted anew. Residing no longer in the same room that first enclosed us, we now lie in another room with another topography—a room whose surfaces, textures, corners, knobs have an otherness as absolute and formidable as the duties and promises that nag us with their temporal claims. What began as relief from worldly concern ends by returning us to the world with a metaphysical, if unsettling, clarity.

Though sex often seems to be morality's adversary, it more often brings sharply in its wake moral discriminations that previously had not been possible. Because the pleasure of sex is always vulnerable to splitting into *pleasuring* and *being pleasured*, the nature of pleasure itself, as well as the relation between pleasure and power, are called into question. If pleasuring is the overpowering concern, intimations of the actual and immediate experience of slavery or peonage will appear. On the other hand, if being pleasured is most compelling, tyranny and oppression will invade experience with some urgency. And finally, should the lovers will equality between these two concerns, in their effort to heal the split, they will personally suffer the problematic character of democratic forms. To some extent our political past influences our sexual negotiations, but in equal measure sexual pleasure itself is a source of political practice and theory.

The list of oppositions and minglings could easily be extended, but such an extension would not change the fact that human sex inevitably partakes of human experience, for better or for worse, and through its claim on the body simultaneously asserts its particular difference, for better or for worse.

Its particular difference from everything else in this life lies in the possibility, which sex offers man, for regaining *his own* body through knowing the body of his loved one. And should he fail that *knowing* and *being known*, should he lapse into all those ways of *knowing about*, which he has proudly learned to confuse with knowing—both bodies will again escape him. Increasingly, as D. H. Lawrence understood, man has become separated from his body, which he yearns to inhabit, such yearning understandably bringing sentimental and scientific prescriptions for the reunion eluding him. Yet it is through the brief reconciliation with his own and his loved one's body that he can now grasp—and endure—the bodily estrangement that has always been his lot, without succumbing to the blandishments that would betray the realities of both sides of this duality.

In order to develop more concretely my conviction that sex for the most part has lost its viability as a human experience, I wish to consider the Sex Research Project, directed by Dr. William H. Masters at the Washington University School of Medicine. Through the use of women volunteers Dr. Masters is endeavoring "to separate a few basic anatomic and physiologic truths" about "the human female's response" to what he calls "effective sexual stimulation." The subject, he believes, has been hopelessly beclouded by "literary fiction and fantasy," "pseudoscientific essays and pronouncements," and "an unbelievable hodgepodge of conjecture and falsehood." His debt to Kinsey is clear, though qualified. He acknowledges his "complete awe" for Kinsey's "time-consuming efforts," which have made his own research not only "plausible, but possible." On the other hand he finds that the work of his predecessors, including Kinsey, has unfortunately been "the result of individual introspection, expressed personal opinion, or of limited clinical observation"—rather than "a basic science approach to the sexual response cycle."[3] Therefore, he has done what was indeed inevitable: he has moved the whole investigation into the laboratory.

I should make clear that Dr. Masters' project itself interests me far more than his exact findings. This project strikes me as one of those occasional yet remarkable enterprises that, despite its creator's intentions, quite transcends its original and modest scientific boundaries, so that it becomes a vivid allegory of our present dilemma, containing its own image of man—at the same time that it charts a New Jerusalem for our future. Such an enterprise, when constitutive, is apt to be more relevant and revealing than deliberate art. Because no actual artist is involved, it is not particularly rewarding to ask how this matter acquires its revelatory, even poetic, power. Often its director merely pursues the prevailing inclination in his field. Yet the pursuit is so single-minded, so fanatical

---

[3] These and all subsequent quotations, unless otherwise noted, are from Dr. Masters' article, "The Sexual Response Cycle of the Human Female." *Western Journal of Surgery, Obstetrics, and Gynecology,* January–February, 1960.

and literal, that part of the power of the enterprise as constitutive symbol must be credited to the director's unflagging lack of imagination and his passionate naïveté, which stay undeterred by all the proprieties, traditions, and accumulated wisdom that would only complicate his course.

I shall not linger over the anatomical and physiological detail in Dr. Masters' reports, except to say it concerns the changes observed on the various parts of the bodies of his volunteers as they approach, accomplish, and depart from sexual climax. Of all the mechanical, electrical, and electronic devices at his command in this research, it is movie-making that seems to give Dr. Masters the clearest edge over the subjective distortions of his predecessors.

Since the integrity of human observation of specific detail varies significantly, regardless of the observer's training or good intent, colored motion-picture photography has been used to record in absolute detail all phases of the human sexual response cycle. The movie is a silent one. Wisely, I think, the director has omitted a sound track, for the tiny events of the flesh he wishes to depict are not audible. Moreover, had there been sound equipment, all one would have heard would have been those adventitious rustlings of any well-equipped laboratory, and perhaps the quickened breathing and gasping of the subjects.

The movie opens quite abruptly with a middle-distance shot of a naked woman, standing, her head and lower legs deliberately outside the movie frame. One arm hangs at her side, the other is stretched toward her genitals in an Eve-like posture, except that it is immediately apparent she is caressing, rather than covering, her parts. More in the service of decorum than science, there are no close-ups of her hand. This opening scene of a faceless woman silently playing with herself against a neutral antiseptic laboratory background quickly sets the tone for what is to follow. The naked, yet faceless, body informs us this is a "human female" we are observing. The other bodies that will subsequently appear in the film will also be faceless; the viewer may momentarily wonder, as cuts are made from one body to another, if it is the same body he is looking at, until he becomes used to distinguishing one body from another by differences in shape of breasts, distribution of pubic hair and the like. At no time do any scientists or technicians appear; they may be presumed to be standing fully clothed behind the camera. In any large dramatic sense, the arm manipulating the body's private parts furnishes the only real movement and cinematically asserts, even when not in view, that it will continue to fondle during the photographing of more microscopic and glandular events. Since what is to follow will focus on relatively small and minute areas of flesh that ordinarily would not be cinematic, the first shot of the moving hand heightens the dramatic effect of the oozings, engorgements, and contractions this flesh will undergo as climax approaches.

Following this middle-distance shot that is extended a bit in time to give the illusion of mounting excitement, the camera moves in on the skin of the abdomen and back, so that the film can record the fine rash beginning to appear over the lower body.

Through the use of cuts, several bodies exhibit their rashes until the phenomenon is safely established. Now the camera moves to the breasts to portray distension, venous engorgement, and changes in the nipples. As these changes are repeated on a number of breasts, we must remind ourselves that the initial arm or arms are continuing their work, although it is obvious that views of such action must be suspended from time to time to allow for certain close-ups. Up to this point, all that occurs in the movie could take place on that lonely, upright body that appeared in the opening scene. Now, quite suddenly and without preparation, that body is no longer upright but supine, and the scene is a brilliantly lit close-up of the opening of the vagina. At this point, something of an operating-room atmosphere intrudes, largely because a speculum spreads the lips of the vagina apart to permit an unobstructed view of all that will occur during orgasm.

It is obvious from this portion of the movie that the source of vaginal lubrication is of special interest to the project, as evidenced by a series of ingenious shots of the wall of the vagina showing the formation of individual drops of secretion. The movie then proceeds with a rush to the point that has been imminent since the beginning—namely, orgasm—objective orgasm, displayed visually in the contractions around, and the dilations within, the vagina. The film ends, as might be anticipated, with a succession of photographs of other bodies undergoing similar spasms. With some shrewdness, the director has withstood the tempting aesthetic impulse to conclude his movie with a final shot of the upright naked body with both arms now hanging limply down. [Editors' note: The scientific usefulness of the Masters-Johnson films is discussed on pages 80–81.]

This movie is often referred to in Dr. Masters' writings and, I am told, has been exhibited at a number of scientific institutes throughout the country. So fond is he of this medium that there seem to be occasions when his scientific prose seeks, however incompletely, to emulate not only the objectivity but the aesthetic brilliance of his movie sequences:

> If the bright pink of the excitement phase changes to a brilliant primiparous scarlet-red, or the multiparous burgundy color, a satisfactory plateau phase has been achieved.

There is even a point at which the movie medium itself becomes the inventor: like the accidental solution or the contaminated culture, which have heroic roles in older scientific romances, movie-making allows Dr. Masters to uncover "the vascular flush reaction to effective sexual stimulation," which had not been previously described in the scientific literature.

> With the aid of artificially-increased skin surface temperature, such as that necessary for successful motion-picture photography, the wide distribution of this flush becomes quite apparent. . . . With orgasm imminent, this measle-like rash has been observed to spread over the anterior-lateral borders of the thighs, the buttocks and the whole body.

Probably it was this discovery of the "measles-like rash" that inspired a more Pavlovian venture which, if read slowly, will be seen to have quite eerie dimensions:

> One observed subject, undergoing electroencephalographic evaluation, had been trained for 4 months to attain orgasm without producing concomitant muscle tension in order to provide significance for her tracing pattern. Yet, this patient repeatedly showed a marked flush phenomenon over the entire body during plateau and orgasm, and during resolution was completely covered with a filmy, fine perspiration.

If movie-making is Dr. Masters' main laboratory device, "automanipulative technics" constitute his "fundamental investigative approach" to "the sexual response cycle of the

human female." His frankness here is to be commended—
particularly since some scientists might feel that such automanipulation was inadequate to the verisimilitude necessary
for laboratory demonstration. Dr. Masters himself does not
discuss the issue, but his obvious preference for this approach
over "heterosexual activity" does not appear to be ascribable
to decorum. To some degree, I imagine, it was the laboratory
procedures and devices—particularly motion picture photography—which determined the approach, automanipulation being clearly more accessible to scientific inspection than coition.
But more important, there is evidence that Dr. Masters
regards automanipulation to be a more reliable—that is, more
predictable—technique than "heterosexual activity" in the
pursuit of "the more intense, well-developed, orgasmic
response" cycle.

> This type of total pelvic reaction is particularly true for an
> orgasmic phase elicited by manual manipulation, but it also
> occurs, although less frequently, with coition.[4]

Yet even this approach, so admirably suited to laboratory
research, must share part of the blame for Dr. Masters'
inability to measure the "clitoral body" during sexual excitement.

> The attempts to measure increases in clitoral size objectively
> have been generally unsatisfactory due to the marked vari-
> ation in size and positioning of the normal clitoral body, and
> the multiplicity of automanipulative techniques employed by
> the various subjects under observation.

Little is told us about the volunteers in this research.
Apparently the project began with prostitutes. But when
objections were made that such a profession might not yield
the best "normal" sample, subjects were chosen among
medical students and medical students' wives who volunteered
and were paid a modest fee for their activities. Naturally no
studies could be made on those who, for whatever reason,
would not volunteer. And presumably quickly eliminated
were those young women who offered themselves out of their

---

[4] William H. Masters and Virginia E. Johnson, "The Artificial Vagina:
Anatomic, Physiologic, Psychosexual Function," *West. J. Surg., Obst. &
Gynec.*, No. 69, May–June 1961, p. 202.

enthusiastic wish to contribute to science, only to discover they could not sustain their sexual excitement in the setting of the laboratory, the paraphernalia, the cameras, the technicians, the bright lights. And even more quickly eliminated were those women who on initial interview were not sure whether or not they had experienced climax: "Our rule of thumb is if they're not sure about it they probably haven't had it."

Other circumstances surrounding the study can only be guessed at. Like much scientific research, this particular project must have been an orderly affair. It can be assumed that the investigators did not wait on the whim of their volunteers; that is, they were not subject to call day or night whenever the volunteer felt in the mood. No, the women were given regular appointments during the working day when the entire research crew was available. Doubtless, too, the directors of the project considered it scientifically unseemly to encourage sexual titillation in their volunteers—certainly out of the question would have been anything resembling a physical overture. Should suggestive reading matter be required by the research—as it indeed occasionally was—it would have to be offered the volunteers in a spirit of detachment; not even the hint of a smirk could be allowed to disrupt the sobriety of the occasion. On the whole, the erotic basis would have to be provided by the scientific situation itself, in addition to the actual manipulation: that is, the prospect of arriving at the laboratory at 10:00 A.M., disrobing, stretching out on the table, and going to work in a somewhat businesslike manner while being measured and photographed, would have to provide its own peculiar excitement. (Thank you, Miss Brown, see you same time next week. Stop at the cashier's for your fee.) So, back to one's ordinary existence.

If these speculations have any truth, what can be said about the qualities that the ideal subject for such experiments would have? In a general way, her sexuality would have to be autonomous, separate from, and unaffected by her ordinary world. "World" here would have to include not only affection but all those exigencies of human existence that tend to shape our erotic possibilities. Objectively, her sexuality would be mechanically accessible or "on call"—under circumstances which would be, if not intimidating, at least distracting to most bodies. Hers would have to be indifferent to the entire range of experiences, pleasant and unpleasant, whose claim is not only not salacious but makes us forget there is such a thing as sexuality. Her lust would lie to hand, ready to be invoked and consummated, in sickness or in health, in coitus or "automanipulation," in homosexuality or heterosexuality, in exasperation or calm, hesitancy or certainty, playfulness or despair. (This would be the other side of that older, though not unrelated romanticism that just as willfully insisted on soft lights, Brahms, incense, and poetical talk.) In other words, her sexuality would be wholly subject to her will: whenever she determined—or the project determined—that she should have reached a climax, she would willingly begin those gestures that would lead to one. To use the modern idiom, all that would be unavailable to her sexological dexterity would be frigidity. Or, to speak more clearly, all that would be unavailable to her would be a real response to the laboratory situation. Insofar as her sexuality was under her will's dominion, she would resemble those odd creatures on the old television quiz programs—also ideal subjects in their own way—who were led from boarding houses to stand in a hot soundproof isolation booth, and when the fateful question was delivered from the vault, answered correctly and without a tremor how many words there were in *Moby Dick*—answered correctly in a loud clear voice under circumstances in which most of us could not even mumble our name. The popularity of these programs (at least until skullduggery was revealed) suggests the audience looked with envy and/or admiration at this caricature of knowledge—a knowledge equally responsive to its owner's will, regardless of contingency or trapping.

A truly constitutive symbol should embody both an accurate rendering of contemporary life and a clear indication of what life should be. Taking, for the moment, only the ideal contained in my description of the volunteer in these experiments, I would say that she is a latterday Queen of Courtly Love, a veritable Queen Guinevere. For most modern men and women, who grow ever more discouraged by their bodies' stubborn refusal to obey their owners' will, this Lady of the Laboratory has long been the woman of their dreams: men long to channel or claim this creature's prompt and unspecific response for their own specific overtures, while women dream of rivaling her capacity to serve her body's need whenever she so wills.

And what of those self-effacing scientists behind the camera who conceived and guided this research? Do they too reflect who we are and who we would become? We know as little about this research team as we know about the volunteers. How the scientific boundaries were staked out and protected against trespass is not described in the reports. Once again we can only surmise, but that there was difficulty is suggested by a remark Dr. Masters made in one of his lectures—namely, that he preferred to have a woman scientist alongside him in these investigations because she helped to make him or keep him more "objective." I assume he meant that having an actual woman present, fully clad in the white coat of science, reminded him not only of the point of the matter at hand but of the more hazardous life to be lived with women outside the laboratory—of the difference between the ideal and the actual.

It would be a ticklish problem how to maintain the proper detachment to protect the scientists without at the same time inhibiting the volunteers. Here the equipment and rituals of research would help. And very possibly there would be a deliberate effort to eliminate even the ordinary frivolity that sometimes overcomes a surgical team in the midst of the most delicate operations, because frivolity in this sort of research might be only a way station en route to the lubricious. Any falling-away into the most ordinary locker-room talk, in or out of the laboratory, would have to be regarded as a danger signal. I imagine each scientist, with all the resolution at his command, would remind himself continually it was just an ordinary day's work in the laboratory, no different from the work next door with the diabetic rats. At the end of the day, when his wife asked, "How were things at the lab today?" he would reply, "Oh nothing, just the same old grind." And if she pressed him in a jealous fashion, his justifications might resemble those of a young artist explaining his necessity to sketch nude models. Of course, there would be strict rules forbidding dalliance between scientist and volunteer after hours. But should they happen to run into one another in the cafeteria, each would keep his conversation casual, trying not to allude to those more cataclysmic events of a few hours before. Mindful of his professional integrity, the scientist would have to guard against prideful thoughts that he knew her, if not better, at least more microscopically than those nearest her. Most troublesome of his self-appointed tasks, it seems to me, would be his effort to prevent his research from invading his own ordinary erotic life, particularly if it were worried by the usual frustrations. In this regard he would be indeed heroic to withstand the temptation of comparing his mate's response to those unspecific, yet perfectly formed, consummations of the laboratory.

Again, if these imaginings have any truth, how may we characterize the ideal scientist in research of this immediate order? First of all, he would have to *believe*, far more than the volunteers, in a "basic science" approach to sex. This is not to say that he would consider the practice of sex a possible science, even though his practice might eventually be informed by his scientific theories. But it would have to be an article of faith for him that the visible palpable reactions of the organs themselves, regardless of whatever human or inhuman context they might occur in, would speak a clear unambiguous truth to all who cared to heed. In his hierarchy of beliefs, these reactions would take precedence in every sense. The questions we are apt to ask about human affairs, not excluding lust, ordinarily have to do with appropriateness, affection, etc.—in other words, right or wrong, good or bad, judged in human terms. On the other hand, the ideal sexologist, as he presses his eye to his research, finds another variety of drama —inordinately complicated in its comings and goings, crises and resolutions—with its own requirements of right and wrong, good and bad, all writ very small in terms of "droplets" and "engorgements" and "contractions."

The will of the ideal sexologist seems different from the will of the Lady of the Laboratory, but it may be the opposition is more illusory than actual. The latter wills orgasm through physical manipulation. Certainly the sexologist supports and approves her willing—such sexual promptness being ideal for laboratory study. However, while his approval may be invented by his will, it is by no means the most important expression of his will. As a scientist his will must be given to the systematic inspection of the sexual response of the "human female," literally portrayed. To this end he persists in his gadgetry, always at the expense of any imaginative grasp of the occasion.

His will to be a scientist requires his further commitment to any number of willful enterprises; in the present circumstance he finds it necessary to will his own body to be unresponsive—not merely to the events on the laboratory table but to any fictional construction of these events his imagination might contrive, because imagination, at least in this arena, is his opponent in his pursuit of science. On the surface his dilemma may seem a familiar one, being comparable to older ascetic ventures, particularly of the Eastern yoga variety. But the sexologist's task is actually more difficult: asceticism is not his goal—the very nature of his enterprise points in an opposite direction. He wishes indifference, which he can invoke at will: it may be the project that demands his not responding, but—as we shall see later— it may be other moments, unofficial and unscientific, which seem to call forth his willed lack of response. The will not to respond and the will to respond are related possibilities of the will. In this sense, the Lady of the Laboratory and the ideal sexologist are collaborators rather than opponents. Of course, I speak in ideal terms—whether these ideals can be achieved is another matter. But if the Lady of the Laboratory is a latter day Queen of Courtly Love, then our ideal sexologist is the modern Sir Galahad, and together—separately or commingled—they rule our dreams of what should be.

Let us remind ourselves that most of us could not hope to qualify for this research—either as volunteers or as scientists. But this does not mean the differences are great between us and them. True, compared to ours, their lives have an oversized quality, and true, they are in the vanguard. But in a real sense our fleshly home is that laboratory. Whatever room we choose for our lovemaking we shall make into our own poor laboratory, and nothing that is observed or undergone in the real laboratory of science is likely to escape us. At this stage, is there any bit of sexology that is not in the public domain, or at least potentially so for those who can read? Whatever detail the scientific will appropriates about sex rapidly becomes an injunction to be imposed on our bodies. But it is not long before these impositions lose their arbitrary and alien character and begin to change our actual experience of our bodies. Unfortunately our vision of the ideal experience tends to be crudely derived from the failure of our bodies to meet these imperatives.

Our residence in the laboratory is recent: really only since the turn of the century has the act of sex been interviewed, witnessed, probed, measured, timed, taped, photographed, judged. Before the age of sexology, objectifications of the sexual act were to be found in pornography and the brothel, both illicit, both pleasurable in purpose, both suggesting the relatively limited manner in which will—given absolute dominion—could be joined to sexual pleasure. However else the Marquis de Sade may be read, he at least offered the most exhaustive inventory yet seen of techniques for exploiting the pleasure of the body's several parts, if one wholeheartedly put one's will to it. As a moralist he seemed to say, Why our particular rules? What if there were no limits? More recently, yet still before sexology, it was possible for shy erotomaniacs, disguised as greengrocers, to visit brothels, there to peek at the antics of the inmates. The bolder ones could join the sport. When the performance reached its final gasp our tradesmen, now satiated, would slink back to the propriety and privacy of their own quarters, convinced their ordinary domestic world was discreetly separate from the world of the peephole which they paid to enter. In fact, or so it seemed, the separateness of these two worlds heightened the erotic possibilities of each. The emancipation which sexology enforced gradually blurred this distinction, making it unclear whether each home had become its own brothel or whether every brothel had become more like home. The truth is that sexology eventually not only blurred the distinction, but by housing us all in laboratories, made both the brothel and pornography less exciting dwellings for our erotic investigations.

When last we left our pathetic lovers I suggested that as their self-pity and bitterness mounted, they might—in desperation—turn to adultery. Yet even for the person who believes himself to be without scruples, adultery—in fact or fantasy—is difficult to arrange, exhausting to maintain. Requiring, as it does, at least two persons and two wills, this illicit encounter risks the danger of further pathos. But if we heed our laboratory drama carefully, we can see there is another possibility preferable to adultery. According to the lesson of the laboratory there is only one perfect orgasm, if by "perfect" we mean one wholly subject to its owner's will, wholly indifferent to human contingency or context. Clearly, the perfect orgasm is the orgasm achieved on one's own. No other consummation offers such certainty and moreover avoids the messiness that attends most human affairs.

The onanist may choose the partner of his dreams, who very probably will be the Lady of the Laboratory, or he may have his orgasm without any imagined partner. In either case, he is both scientist and experimental subject, science and sex now being nicely joined. In his laboratory room he may now abstract his sexual parts from his whole person, inspect their anatomic particularities, and observe and enjoy the small physiologic events he knows best how to control. True, this solitary experience may leave him empty and ashamed. But as a citizen of his times he will try to counter this discomfort by reminding himself that sexology and psychoanalysis have assured him masturbation is a morally indifferent matter. As a true modern he tells himself that it is not as good as what two people have, but that does not make it bad. Superstitious people of other ages thought it drove one crazy, but he knows better; he knows that the real threat to *his* sanity is unrelieved sexual tension. In fact—he may decide—were it not for certain neurotic Victorian traces he has not managed to expunge from his psyche, he could treat the matter as any other bodily event and get on with his business. So we must not be too harsh with our pathetic lovers if they take refuge in solitary pleasures—even if they come to prefer them to the frustrations of sexual life together. Nor should we be too surprised if such solitary pleasure becomes the ideal by which all mutual sex is measured—and found wanting.

Let us now turn to the phenomenon being inspected and celebrated in our laboratory—the phenomenon that contributes most of all to our lovers' impasse. Of all the discoveries sexology has made, the female orgasm remains the most imposing in its consequences. De Tocqeville's prediction of life between the sexes in America[5] might not have been so sanguine, could he have anticipated first, the discovery of sexology and psychoanalysis, and second, their discovery of the female orgasm.

In the second half of the nineteenh century Western man began to see nature in a new and utilitarian way as a variety of energies, hitherto unharnessed, which could now be tamed and transformed into industrial servants, which in turn would fashion never-ending progress and prosperity. The health of the machine, powered by steam and electricity, and the sickness of the machine if those energies were misdirected or obstructed, were obsessive considerations of the period. It was entirely appropriate to regard the human body as still another natural object with many of the vicissitudes of the machine:

[5] ". . . I never observed that the women of America consider conjugal authority as an unfortunate usurpation of their rights, or that they thought themselves degraded by submitting to it. It appeared to me, on the contrary, that they attach a sort of pride to the voluntary surrender of their will. . . . Though their lot is different, they consider both of them as beings of equal value. . . . If I were asked . . . to what the singular prosperity and growing strength of that people ought mainly to be attributed, I should reply: To the superiority of their women." Alexis de Tocqueville, *Democracy in America*.

this had always been medicine's privilege. But for the first time the scientists, in their intoxication, could forget the duality previous centuries knew: namely, that the body is both a natural object and not a natural object. And once it was decided the dominant energy of the human machine was sex, the new science of sexology was born. With the suppression of the second half of the dialectic, sexology and psychoanalysis could—with the assistance of the Romantics— claim the erotic life as their exclusive province, removing it from all the traditional disciplines, such as religion, philosophy, literature, which had always concerned themselves with sex as human experience. Qualities such as modesty, privacy, reticence, abstinence, chastity, fidelity, shame—could now be questioned as rather arbitrary matters that interfered with the health of the sexual parts. And in their place came an increasing assortment of objective terms like *ejaculatio praecox,* foreplay, forepleasure, frigidity—all intended to describe, not human experience, but the behavior of the sexual parts. The quite preposterous situation arose in which the patient sought treatment for *ejaculatio praecox,* or impotence, and the healer sought to find out whether he liked his partner.

If the Victorians found sex unspeakable for the wrong reasons, the Victorian sexologists found it wrongly speakable. (To what extent Victorian prudery was actually modesty or reticence, I cannot say. It has become habitual for us to regard Victorian lovemaking as an obscenity.) Science is usually democratic, and since sex now belonged to science, whatever facts or assumptions were assembled had immediately to be transmitted to the people, there to invade their daily life. Writing on the Kinsey Report, Lionel Trilling finds—correctly, I believe—a democratic motive for the study:

> In speaking of its motives, I have in mind chiefly its impulse toward acceptance and liberation, its broad and generous desire for others that they be not harshly judged. . . . The Report has the intention of habituating its readers to sexuality in all its manifestations; it wants to establish, as it were, a democratic pluralism of sexuality. . . . This generosity of mind . . . goes with a nearly conscious aversion from making intellectual distinctions, almost as if out of the belief that an intellectual distinction must inevitably lead to a social discrimination or exclusion.

If we disregard Kinsey's scientific pretensions, we still must recognize his eminence as arbiter of sexual etiquette. Like the lexicographer who finds his sanction in usage, Kinsey discovers his authority in practice: his democratic message is that we all do—or should do—more or less the same things in bed. And any notion lovers retain from an older tradition that what they have together is private and unique is effectively disproved by his cataloguing of sexual manners, providing they join him in equating behavior with experience. As a fitting disciple of Kinsey, Masters actualizes the "pluralism of sexuality" within the democratic unit of the laboratory and enlarges behavior to include the more minute physiological developments, which, too, should belong to every citizen.

The political clamor for equal rights for woman at the turn of the century could not fail to join with sexology to endow her with an orgasm, equal in every sense to the male orgasm. It was agreed that she was entitled to it just as she was entitled to the vote. Moreover, if she were deprived of such release her perturbation would be as unsettling to her nervous system as similar frustration was thought to be for the man. Equal rights were to be erotically consummated in simultaneous orgasm. On the one hand it was unhealthful for her to be deprived of release and, on the other hand, psychoanalysis decreed that an important sign of her maturity as woman was her ability to achieve it. In other words, without orgasm she was neurotic to begin with or neurotic to end with.

Though simultaneous orgasm seemed to be a necessary consequence of equal rights, the problem remained that in matters of lust more than a decree or amendment was required for such an achievement. True, the sexologists were most generous with instruction, but each citizen has had to discover over and over again the degree to which he is caught in the futile struggle to will what could not be willed—at the same time that he senses the real absurdity of the whole willful enterprise. The lover learns, as his indocrination progesses, to observe uneasily and even resist his rush of pleasure if it seems he is to be premature. When no amount of resolution can force his pleasure to recede, he learns to suffer his release and then quickly prod himself to an activity his body's exhaustion opposes. In other words, he learns to take his moment in stride, so to speak, omitting the deference these moments usually call forth and then without breaking stride get to his self-appointed and often fatiguing task of tinkering with his mate—always hopeful that his ministrations will have the appearance of affection. While she is not likely to be deceived by such dutiful exercises, she nevertheless wishes for both their sakes that her body at least will be deluded into fulfilling its franchise.

As far as I know, little attention was paid to the female orgasm before the era of sexology. Where did the sexologists find it? Did they discover it or invent it? Or both? I realize it may seem absurd to raise such questions about events as unmistakable as those witnessed in our laboratory, but I cannot believe that previous centuries were not up to our modern delights; nor can I believe it was the censorship imposed by religion which suppressed the supreme importance of the female orgasm. My guess, which is not subject to laboratory proof, is that the female orgasm was always an occasional, though not essential, part of woman's whole sexual experience. I also suspect that it appeared with regularity or predictability only during masturbation, when the more human qualities of her life with her mate were absent. Further, her perturbation was unremarkable and certainly bearable when orgasm did not arrive, for our lovers had not yet been enlightened as to the disturbances resulting from the obstruction or distortion of sexual energies. At this stage her orgasm had not yet been abstracted and isolated from the totality of her pleasures, and enshrined as the meaning and measure of her erotic life. She was content with the mystery and variety of her difference from man, and in fact would not have had it otherwise.

Much that I have said, if we leave aside the erotomanias, which have always been with us, applies to the male of previous centuries. For him, too, the moment of orgasm was not abstracted in its objective form from the whole of his erotic life and then idealized. And he too preferred the mystery of difference, the impact of human contingency, becoming obsessed with the sheer anatomy and mechanics of orgasm only when all else was missing, as in masturbation.

Theological parallelism is a treacherous hobby, especially when we deal with movements flagrantly secular. Nevertheless, the manner in which lovers now pursue their careers as copulating mammals—adopting whatever new refinements sexology devises, covering their faces yet exposing their genitals—may remind us of older heresies which, through chastity or libertinism, have pressed toward similar goals; one heretical cult went so far as to worship the serpent in the Garden of

Eden. But the difference between these older heresies and modern science—and there is a large one—must be attributed to the nature of science itself, which—if we accept such evidence as the Lambeth Conference—by means of its claims to objectivity can invade religion and ultimately all of life to a degree denied the older heresies. So, with the abstraction, objectification, and idealization of the female orgasm we have come to the last and perhaps most important clause of the contract that binds our lovers to their laboratory home, there to will the perfection on earth that cannot be willed, there to suffer the pathos that follows all such strivings toward heaven on earth.

BIBLIOGRAPHY OF
DR. WILLIAM H. MASTERS
AND HIS ASSOCIATES

Masters, W. H. and Allen, W. M., "Female Sex Hormone Replacement in the Aged Woman." *J. Gerontol.*, 3:183–190, 1948.

Masters, W. H., "Caudal Analgesia." *J.M.S.M.A.*, 45:592–597, 1948.

Masters, W. H., "Continuous Caudal Analgesia (A Report of 1,500 Cases)." *Am. J. Obst. & Gynec.*, 56:756–761, 1948.

Masters, W. H., "The Advantages of Conduction Anesthesia in Premature Labor and Delivery," in Lull and Hingson, eds., *Control of Pain in Childbirth*, 3rd ed., Philadelphia: J. B. Lippincott Co., 1948, pp. 473–476.

Masters, W. H., "Ectopic Pregnancy." *J.M.S.M.A.*, 46:405–410, 1949.

Masters, W. H. and Allen, W. M., "Investigation of Sexual Regeneration in Elderly Women." *Conference on Problems of Aging.* Transactions of the Tenth and Eleventh Conferences, February 1948 and April 1949. New York: Josiah Macy Jr. Foundation, pp. 21–29.

Masters, W. H. and Ross, R. W., "Conduction Anesthesia (Protection Afforded the Premature Infant.)" *J.A.M.A.*, 141:909–912, 1949.

Masters, W. H. and Magallon, D. T., "Androgen Administration in the Postmenopausal Woman." *J. Clin. Endocrinol.*, 10:348–358, 1950.

Masters, W. H. and Magallon, D. T., "Hormone Replacement Therapy in the Aged Female—Estrogen Bioassay." *Proceedings of the Soc. for Exp. Biol. and Med.*, 73:672–676, 1950.

Masters, W. H. and Magallon, D. T., "The Experimental Production of Irregular Shedding of the Endometrium." *Am. J. Obst. & Gynec.*, 59:970–978, 1950.

Magallon, D. T. and Masters, W. H., "Basal Temperature Studies in the Aged Female: Influence of Estrogen, Progesterone and Androgen." *J. Clin. Endocrinol.*, 10:511–518, 1950.

Masters, W. H., "The Rationale and Technique of Sex Hormone Replacement in the Aged Female and a Preliminary Result Report." *S. Dakota J.*, 4:296–300, 1951.

Masters, W. H., "The Female Reproductive System," in Cowdry's *Problems of Aging*, 3rd ed., Baltimore: The Williams and Wilkins Co., 1952, pp. 651–685.

Masters, W. H., Grody, M. H., and Robinson, D. W., "Management and Treatment of Infertility." *J.M.S.M.A.*, 49:327–337, 1952.

Grody, M. H., Robinson, D. W., and Masters, W. H., "The Cervical Cap: An Adjunct in the Treatment of Male Infertility." *J.A.M.A.*, 149:427–431, 1952.

Masters, W. H., Magallon, D. T., and Grody, M. H., "Gonadotrophin Titer in the Adult Human Male: The Effect of Ejaculation." *J. Urol.*, 67:1028–1036, 1952.

Goldhar, A., Grody, M. H., and Masters, W. H., "The Vaginal Smear as an Ovulatory Index." *Fertil. & Steril.*, 3:376–392, 1952.

Masters, W. H., Grody, M. H., and Magallon, D. T., "Progesterone in Aqueous Crystalline Suspension vs. Progesterone in Oil: Comparable Withdrawal Bleeding Experiments in the Human Female." *J. Clin. Endocrinol. & Metabol.*, 12:1445–1453, 1952.

Masters, W. H., "Long Range Sex Steroid Replacement—Target Organ Regeneration." *J. Gerontol.*, 8:33–39, 1953.

Lamb, W. M., Ulett, G. A., Masters, W. H., and Robinson, D. W., "Premenstrual Tension: EEG, Hormonal, and Psychiatric Evaluation." *Am. J. Psychiat.*, 109:840–848, 1953.

Grody, M. H., Lampe, E. H., and Masters, W. H., "Estrogen-Androgen Substitution Therapy in the Aged Female: I.

Uterine Bioassay Report." *Obst. & Gynec.*, 2:36–45, 1953.

Masters, W. H. and Grody, M. H., "Estrogen-Androgen Substitution Therapy in the Aged Female: II. Clinical Response." *Obst. & Gynec.*, 2:139–147, 1953.

Goldhar, A. and Masters, W. H., "Continuous Caudal Analgesia—Housestaff Management of 5,000 Consecutive Cases." *Miss. V. Med. J.*, 75:1953.

Masters, W. H., "The Abdominal Approach to Cystourethrocele Repair." *Am J. Obst. & Gynec.*, 67:85–91, 1954.

Ballew, J. W. and Masters, W. H., "Mumps: A Cause of Infertility. I. Present Considerations." *Fertil. & Steril.*, 5:536–543, 1954.

Masters, W. H. and Ballew, J. W., "The Third Sex." *Geriatrics*, 10:1–4, 1955.

Masters, W. H. and Ballew, J. W., "The Third Sex." Proceedings of the 3rd International Congress of Gerontology, *Old Age in the Modern World*. London: E. & S. Livingstone Ltd., 1955.

Masters, W. H., "Sex Life of the Aging Female," in *Sex in Our Culture*. New York: Emerson Books, Inc., 1955.

Masters, W. H., "Rationale of Sex Steroid Replacement in the 'Neutral Gender.'" *J. Geriatrics*, 3:389–395, 1955.

Allen, W. M. and Masters, W. H., "Traumatic Laceration of Uterine Support. The Clinical Syndrome and the Operative Treatment." *Am. J. Obst. & Gynec.*, 70:500–513, 1955.

Masters, W. H., "Sex Steroid Replacement in the Aging Individual," in *Hormones and the Aging Process*. New York: Academic Press Inc., 1956, pp. 241–251.

Lampe, E. H. and Masters, W. H., "Problems of Male Fertility. II. Effect of Frequent Ejaculation." *Fertil. & Steril.*, 7:123–127, 1956.

Riley, F. J. and Masters, W. H., "Problems of Male Fertility. III. Bacteriology of Human Semen." *Fertil. & Steril.*, 7:128–132, 1956.

Masters, W. H., "Endocrine Therapy in the Aging Individual." *Obst. & Gynec.*, 8:61–67, 1956.

Masters, W. H., "The Present Status of the Estrogen-Androgen Replacement Experiments." *J. Miss. V. Med.*, 78:177–178, 1956.

Masters, W. H., "The Infertile Couple. A Basic Evaluation Technique." *J. Okla. S.M.A.*, 49:517–521, 1956.

Masters, W. H., "The Surgeon's Role in Geriatric Female Endocrinology." *J. Int. Col. Surg.*, 27:189–192, 1957.

Masters, W. H., Maze, L. E., and Gilpatrick, T. S., "Etiological Approach to Habitual Abortion." *Am. J. Obst. & Gynec.*, 73:1022–1032, 1957.

Masters, W. H., "Sex Steroid Influence on the Aging Process." *Am. J. Obst. & Gynec.*, 74:733–746, 1957.

Masters, W. H., "Infertility—A Family Unit Problem." *Minn. Med.*, 40:842–846, 1957.

Masters, W. H., "Amenorrhea," in H. F. Conn, ed., *Current Therapy*. Philadelphia: W. B. Saunders Co., 1958, pp. 679–682.

Masters, W. H., "Menopause and Thereafter." *Minn. Med.*, 41:1–4, 1958.

Masters, W. H., "Infertility—A Family Unit Problem." *Medical Times*, 86:825–832, 1958.

Masters, W. H., "The Infertile Male—An Obstetrical Problem." *S. Dakota J. Med. & Pharm.*, 12:131–134, 1959.

Masters, W. H., "The Sexual Response Cycle of the Human Female: Vaginal Lubrication." *Ann. N.Y. Acad. Sci.*, 83:301–317, 1959.

Dunnihoo, D. R. and Masters, W. H., "Ectopic Pregnancy: A Report of 219 Cases." *Minn. Med.*, 42:1768–1772, 1959.

Masters, W. H. and Johnson, V. E., "The Human Female: Anatomy of Sexual Response." *Minn. Med.*, 43:31–36, 1960.

Masters, W. H., "The Sexual Response Cycle of the Human Female: I. Gross Anatomic Considerations." *West. J. Surg., Obst. & Gynec.*, 68:57–72, 1960.

Masters, W. H., "Influence of Male Ejaculate on Vaginal Acidity." *Endocrine Dysfunction and Infertility* (Report of the Thirty-fifth Ross Conference on Pediatric Research), 1960, pp. 76–78.

Masters, W. H. and Johnson, V. E., "Orgasm, Anatomy of the Female," in A. Ellis and A. Abarbanel, eds., *The Encyclopedia of Sexual Behavior*, Vol. II. New York: Hawthorn Books, Inc., 1961, pp. 788–793.

Masters, W. H. and Johnson, V. E., "The Physiology of the Vaginal Reproductive Function." *West. J. Surg., Obst. & Gynec.*, 69:105–120, 1961.

Holmes, D. R. and Masters, W. H., "Ectopic Pregnancy." *Clin. Med.*, 8:899–903, 1961.

Masters, W. H. and Johnson, V. E., "The Artificial Vagina: Anatomic, Physiologic, Psychosexual Function." *West. J. Surg., Obst. & Gynec.*, 69:192–212, 1961.

Johnson, V. E. and Masters, W. H., "Treatment of the Sexually Incompatible Family Unit." *Minn. Med.*, 44:466–471, 1961.

Masters, W. H. and Johnson, V. E., "Intravaginal Environment. I. A Lethal Factor." *Fertil. & Steril.*, 12:560–580, 1961.

Johnson, V. E. and Masters, W. H., "Intravaginal Contraceptive Study. Phase I. Anatomy." *West. J. Surg., Obst. & Gynec.*, 70:202–207, 1962.

Masters, W. H. and Johnson, V. E., "The Sexual Response Cycle of the Human Female. III. The Clitoris: Anatomic and Clinical Considerations." *West. J. Surg., Obst. & Gynec.*, 70:248–257, 1962.

Masters, W. H. and Johnson, V. E., "The Sexual Response Cycle of the Human Male: I. Gross Anatomic Considerations." *West. J. Surg., Obst. & Gynec.*, 71:85–95, 1963.

Johnson, V. E. and Masters, W. H., "Intravaginal Contraceptive Study. Phase II. Physiology (A Direct Test for Protective Potential)." *West. J. Surg., Obst. & Gynec.*, 71:144–153, 1963.

Masters, W. H. and Johnson, V. E., "The Clitoris: An Anatomic Baseline for Behavioral Investigation," in G. W. Winokur, ed., *Determinants of Human Sexual Behavior.* Springfield, Illinois: Charles C Thomas, 1963, pp. 44–51.

Johnson, V. E., Masters, W. H., and Lewis, K. C., "The Physiology of Intravaginal Contraceptive Failure," in M. E. Calderone, ed., *Manual of Contraceptive Practice.* Baltimore: Williams & Wilkins, 1964, pp. 138–150.

Masters, W. H. and Johnson, V. E., "Sexual Response: Part II. Anatomy and Physiology," in C. W. Lloyd, ed., *Human Reproduction and Sexual Behavior.* Philadelphia: Lea & Febiger, 1964, pp. 460–472.

Johnson, V. E. and Masters, W. H., "Sexual Incompatibility: Diagnosis and Treatment," in C. W. Lloyd, ed., *Human Reproduction and Sexual Behavior.* Philadelphia: Lea & Febiger, 1964, pp. 474–489.

Johnson, V. E. and Masters, W. H., "A Team Approach to the Rapid Diagnosis and Treatment of Sexual Incompatibility." *Pac. Med. & Surg.*, 72:371–375, 1964.

Masters, W. H. and Johnson, V. E., "Counseling with Sexually Incompatible Marriage Partners," in R. H. Klemer, ed., *Counseling in Marital and Sexual Problems* (A Physician's Handbook). Baltimore: Williams & Wilkins, 1965, pp. 126–137.

Masters, W. H. and Johnson, V. E., "The Sexual Response Cycle of the Human Female: I. Gross Anatomic Considerations," in J. Money, ed., *Sex Research—New Developments.* New York: Holt, Rinehart & Winston, Inc., 1965, pp. 53–89.

Masters, W. H. and Johnson, V. E., "The Sexual Response
    Cycle of the Human Female: II. The Clitoris: Anatomic
    and Clinical Considerations," in J. Money., ed., *Sex
    Research—New Developments.* New York: Holt, Rinehart
    & Winston, Inc., 1965, pp. 90–112.
Johnson, V. E. and Masters, W. H., "A Product of Dual
    Import: Intravaginal Infection Control and Conception
    Control." *Pac. Med. & Surg.,* 73:267–271, 1965.
Masters, W. H. and Ballew, J. W., "The Third Sex," in
    C. G. Vedder, ed., *Problems of the Middle-Aged.* Spring-
    field, Illinois: Charles C Thomas, 1965, pp. 134–140.
Masters, W. H. and Johnson, V. E., "The Sexual Response
    Cycles of the Human Male and Female: Comparative
    Anatomy and Physiology," in F. A. Beach, ed., *Sex &
    Behavior.* New York: John Wiley & Sons, Inc., 1965,
    pp. 512–534.

Other SIGNET Books of Special Interest

☐ **LOVE AND ORGASM by Alexander Lowen, M.D.** A distinguished psychiatrist examines the physical and psychic conditions and effects of complete sexual satisfaction, presenting a revolutionary view of the role of love in sex. (#Y4645—$1.25)

☐ **COMPLETE SEXUAL FULFILLMENT by Barbara Bross and Jay Gilbey.** In a revolutionary guide to sexual fulfillment in the light of today's changing morality, two experts in the field discuss all facets of the sexual relationship, sweeping away the long-standing clichés and replacing them with practical suggestions designed to add vigor and gratification to any sexual relationship. (#Y4438—$1.25)

☐ **THE SEXUALLY FULFILLED WOMAN: A Step-by-Step Guide to the Power of Positive Sex for Women by Rachel Copelan.** Unless you are that rare one woman in ten who has never had any sexual difficulty, this book has been written for you. By following the Seven Steps to Sexual Satisfaction you too can cure yourself of emotional inhibitions and achieve the ultimate in sexual satisfaction. (#W5676—$1.25)

☐ **THE SEXUALLY FULFILLED MAN: A Step-by-Step Guide to the Power of Positive Sex for Men by Rachel Copelan.** The most erotic part of anyone's body is his or her mind. Now Rachel Copelan reveals how through the use of exercise, Creative Meditation and Auto-suggestion you can become a sexually fulfilled man. (#W5675—$1.25)

SIGNET Titles of Related Interest

☐ **THE ART OF EROTIC MASSAGE by Stanley Whelan, Ph.D. & Rachel Cochran.** Touching a person's body is the most intimate form of human contact. It is pleasant, relaxing, reassuring, and, if properly done, sexually stimulating. But touching a body in a sensually stimulating way is nothing less than an art. Complete with diagrams and easy-to-follow instructions, this book shows you how the key to new vistas of pleasure is right at your fingertips! (#Y6401—$1.25)

☐ **AN ABZ OF LOVE by Inge and Stan Hegeler.** A Connoisseur Guide to Lovemaking more revealing than **The Joy of Sex**, presenting the fine art of lovemaking in words and pictures that describe, with complete candor, all the many deliciously stimulating things a couple can do with each other to make their sex life richer and more varied. (#W5872—$1.50)

☐ **DR. KINSEY AND THE INSTITUTE FOR SEX RESEARCH by Dr. Wardell B. Pomeroy.** Find out about the man who shattered all those sacred myths about your sexual behavior—the cool researcher who described a nymphomaniac as "a person who has more sex than you do." **The New York Times** calls this book "vivid . . . provocative and humane." (#J5354—$1.95)

☐ **THE ENJOYMENT OF LOVE IN MARRIAGE by LeMon Clark, M.D.** An honest guide to sexual harmony—illustrated with line drawings demonstrating positions in intercourse. (#T3886—75¢)

THE NEW AMERICAN LIBRARY, INC.,
P.O. Box 999, Bergenfield, New Jersey 07621

Please send me the SIGNET BOOKS I have checked above. I am enclosing $_____(check or money order—no currency or C.O.D.'s). Please include the list price plus 25¢ a copy to cover handling and mailing costs. (Prices and numbers are subject to change without notice.)

Name_____

Address_____

City_____State_____Zip Code_____

Allow at least 3 weeks for delivery